KU-342-825

SALTERS HORNERS ADVANCED PHYSICS

AS level

Student book

Heinemann Educational Publishers
Halley Court, Jordan Hill, Oxford OX2 8EJ
A division of Reed Educational and Professional Publishing Ltd
Heinemann is a registered trademark of Reed Educational & Professional Publishing Ltd

OXFORD MELBOURNE AUCKLAND
JOHANNESBURG BLANTYRE GABARONE
IBADAN PORTSMOUTH NH (USA) CHICAGO

© Science Education Group, University of York, 2000

Copyright notice
All rights reserved. No part of this publication may be reproduced, stored in a
retrieval system, or transmitted in any form or by any means, electronic,
mechanical, photocopying, recording, or otherwise without either the prior
written permission of the Publishers or a licence permitting restricted
copying in the United Kingdom issued by the Copyright Licensing Agency Ltd,
90 Tottenham Court Road, London W1P 0LP.

First published 2000
Published as trial edition 1998

ISBN 0 435 628909

04 03 02 01 00
10 9 8 7 6 5 4 3 2 1

Typeset and Illustrated by Tech Set Ltd, Gateshead

Printed and bound in Spain by Edelvives

Acknowledgements

The authors and publishers would like to thank the following for permission to use photographs:

P2 f1a,b,c Colorsport. P4 f2 Colorsport. P18 f17a,b,c JohnCleare Mountain Camera Picture Library. P23 f27 John Cleare Mountain Camera Picture Library. P29 f33a Colorsport b Roger Scruton. P29 f34a,b,c Colorsport. P30 f35 G Lewis. P33 f38 Allsport/Mike Hewitt. P35 f41 Colorsport. P36 f42 Authors. P40 f46 Albrecht G Schaeler/Corbis. P43 f52 Colorsport. P64 f1 SPL/NASA. P66 f2 Rutherford Appleton Laboratory, f3 Rutherford Appleton Laboratory. P67 f4 Rutherford Appleton Laboratory f5 Surrey Satellite Technology Ltd., Centre for Satellite Engineering Research, Univ. of Surrey. P68 f6 NASA. P72 f11 Chris Butlin. P75 f14 NASA. P88 f29 NASA. P90 f32 Daimler-Benz, Stuttgart. P93 f33 example from "Ciel et Espace" magazine, June 1996 p.23, AFA Paris. P96 f37 SPL. P100 f40 Science and Society Picture Library. P101 f41 European Space Agency/IAL Space, University of Liege, Belgium. P102 f43 Rutherford Appleton Laboratory. P102 f44 NASA. P103 f45 NASA. P104 f46 NASA. P106 f47 Chris Butlin. P120 f1 G Lewis. P126 f7 SPL/Eadwaeard Muybridge Collection/Kingston Museum. P135 f23 Picture Viewer. P138 f27 Picture Viewer. P140 f30 David J Rubio. P141 f32 Picture Viewer. P148 f41 G Lewis. P149 f42a SPL/Dr Jeremy Burgess b SPL. P164 f61 SPL. P182 f1a,b,c Ancient Art & Architecture Collection. P186 f4 Author. P198 f19a SPL/Alexander Tsiaras b Roger Scruton. P198 f20 Prof. Ian Isherwood, University of Manchester. P199 f21 English Heritage. P199 f22, 23 York Archaeological Trust. P200 f24, 25 York Archaeological Trust. P202 f27 AKG, London. P204 f30 York Archaeological Trust. P205 f32 Authors. P207 f34a,b,c Authors. P210 f40, 41 SPL. P214 f42 Ancient Art and Architecture Collection. P221 f48 Ancient Art and Architecture Collection. P236 f6 CSC Scientific Company, Fairfax, Virginia f8 Chris Butlin. P244 f22 Science Photo Library. P248 f27 Science Photo Library. P249 f29 Authors. P250 f30, 31 Science Photo Library. P251 f34 Stable Micro Systems. P252 f35 Stable Micro Systems. P253 f41 Science and Society Picture Library. P254 f42 Instron Corporation. P257 f46 Corbis/Julia Waterlow. P258 f48 Chris Butlin. P259 f50 Science Photo Library. P261 f53 Chris Butlin. P264 f54 NASA. P279 f5,6 Colorific/Alfred Wolf. P287 f14 Perplas Medical Ltd. P288 f15a,b Chris Butlin. P293 f23a,b Author. P294 f25 Author. P298 f30 Science and Society SPL/Andrew Mcclenaghan. P313 f45 Ardea. P314 f46 SPL. P317 f50 SPL/David Campione. P318 f51,52 SPL

The publishers have made every effort to trace the copyright holders, but if they have inadvertently overlooked any, they will be pleased to make the necessary arrangements at the first opportunity.

Contributors

Many people from schools, colleges, universities, industries and the professions have contributed to the Salters Horners Advanced Physics project.

Central team

Andy Butlin, York College (technical support)
Chris Butlin
Nancy Newton (Secretary)

Elizabeth Swinbank (Director and General Editor)
David Waddington

Advisory committee

Prof. Frank Close — CERN, Geneva
Prof. Cyril Hilsum F.R.S. — Unilever and University College, London
Prof. Sir Derek Roberts F.R.S. (Chair) — University College, London
Prof. Robin Millar — University of York

Sponsors

AEA Technology	British Nuclear Fuels	British Steel	British Telecom
Esso UK	The Horners Company	Pilkington	The Salters Company
Smiths Industries	The UK Steel Industry Education Group	The University of York	Urenco

AS authors

Chris Butlin	University of York	Steve Cobb	Tadcaster Grammar School
Tony Connell	Wilberforce College, Hull	Howard Darwin	John Leggott College, Scunthorpe
Nick Fisher	Rugby School	Bob Kibble	University of Edinburgh
Maureen Maybank	Argyll	Averil Macdonald	University of Reading
David Neal	John Leggott College, Scunthorpe	David Sang	Bognor Regis
Tony Sherborne	Sheffield Hallam University	Richard Skelding	Epic Multimedia Group Plc
Elizabeth Swinbank	University of York	Carol Tear	York
Nigel Wallis	York		

We would also like to thank the following for their advice and assistance with the development of the AS materials:

Peter Addyman	York Archaeological Trust	Ian Bailiff	University of Durham
Cathy Batt	University of Bradford	Stephen Beckett	Nestlé, York
David Bolton	Tesco Technical Services	Suzanne Bolton	Nestlé, York
Roger Boyle	York District Hospital	Richard Crisp	Nestlé, York
Jeremy Curtis	Rutherford Appleton Laboratory	David Glover	Cambridge Science Media
Gil Graham	Cambridge Science Media	Rex Godby	University of York
Neil Hubbard	Perplas Medical, Bacup	Colin Humphreys	University of Cambridge
Maxine Keeping	Nestlé, York	Andy Kurzfeld	Rutherford Appleton Laboratory
Peter Main	University of York	Vince Martin	formerly Nestlé, York
John North	Nestlé, York	John Sproston	University of Liverpool
John Szymanski	University of York	Alun Vaughan	University of Reading
Clive Wallis	Shefford	Peter Weeks	Bristol General Hospital
Sarah Wilson	Nestlé, York	Jeff Winston	Mechanical Testing Lab., Nike US

Contents

How to use this book   vi

Unit 1
Physics at Work, Rest and Play

Higher, Faster, Stronger   1

1. Running   4
2. Rock climbing   18
3. Working out work   27
4. Stretching and springing   39
5. Jumping and throwing   45
6. Last lap   53

Answers   57

Technology in Space   63

1. Satellites in space   66
2. Solar cells and electric circuits   71
3. Energy transfer and control   87
4. Mission accomplished   109

Answers   115

The Sound of Music   119

1. Making sounds   122
2. The compact disc player   148
3. Encore   170

Answers   175

Unit 2
Physics for Life

Digging Up the Past   181

1. The secrets of resistance   184
2. The inside story   197
3. The dating game   207
4. Reconstruction   222

Answers   227

Good Enough to Eat   229

1. Physics in the food industry   232
2. Going with the flow   234
3. Testing, testing …   248
4. Sweetness and light   257
5. Wrapping up   263

Answers   268

Spare Part Surgery   273

1. Spare parts   276
2. Boning up   276
3. A sight better   297
4. Heartbeat   316
5. Recovery   329

Answers   333

Maths Notes   339

How to use this book

Context-led study

Welcome to the AS part of the Salters Horners Advanced
Physics course.

Each teaching unit in the course starts by looking at particular
situations in which physics is used or studied, and then develops the
physics you need to learn to explore this 'context'.

We have tried to select contexts to give you some idea of how
physics can help improve people's lives, how physics is used in
engineering and technology, and how physics research extends our
understanding of the physical world at a fundamental level. These will
show you just some of the many physics-related careers and further
study that might be open to you in the future.

Within each teaching unit, you will develop your knowledge and
understanding on one or more areas of physics. In later units, you will
meet many of these ideas again – in a completely different context –
and develop them further. In this way, you will gradually build up your
knowledge and understanding of physics and learn to apply key
principles of physics to a variety of contexts.

About this book

Each teaching unit includes the following features:

Main text

This presents the context of each teaching unit and explains the
relevant physics as you need it.

Within the main text, some words are printed in **bold**. These are
key terms relating to the physics. We suggest that you make your own
summary of the these terms (and others if you wish) as you go along.
Then you can refer back to it when you revisit a similar area of physics
later in the course and when you revise for exams.

Activities

The text refers to many *Activities*. These include practical work, the use
of information technology (e.g. CD-ROMs and the Internet),
reading, writing, data handling and discussion. Some activities are best
carried out with one or more other students, others are intended for
you to do on your own. For some activities, there are handout sheets
giving further information, details about apparatus and so on.

There is an introductory activity you can do to help you decide how
you will make your summary of key terms. Ask your teacher for the
activity sheet.

Questions

You will find plenty of *Questions* in this book. Some are to do as you go
along and at the end of each main section. The answers to these
questions are given at the end of each teaching unit.

Once you have had a go at a question, check your answer.
If you have gone wrong, use the answer (and the relevant part of the
book chapter) to help you sort out your ideas. Working in this way is
not cheating! Rather, it helps you to learn.

Maths notes

Maths references in the main text will direct you to the *Maths notes*, which are to help you with the maths needed in physics. This may involve calculations, rearranging equations, plotting graphs, and so on. You will probably have covered most of what's needed at GCSE, but you may not be used to using it in physics.

The *Maths notes* at the end of the book summarise the key maths ideas that you need in the AS course, and show how to apply them to situations in physics.

Study notes

These notes in the margin are intended to help you to get to grips with the physics – for example, they indicate links with other parts of the course.

Further investigations

If you continue into the second year of this course, you will spend two weeks on a practical project exploring a topic of your own choice as part of your coursework. You will be asked to research some background information on your chosen topic, plan and carry out your laboratory work, and write a report. As you proceed through the first-year teaching units, keep a note of any areas you might like to pursue further. We have included some suggestions under the heading *Further investigations*, but any unanswered question that intrigues you could form the basis of a future investigation.

Achievements

At the end of each teaching unit you will find a list of *Achievements*. This is a summary of the key points that you have covered in that unit, and shows what you can expect to be tested on in the exams. (It is copied from the Exam Specification.) Look through the *Achievements* when you check back over your work after finishing a unit. If there is anything that looks unfamiliar, or that you think you have not properly understood, consult your teacher and the explanations in this book.

HIGHER, FASTER, STRONGER

Figure 1 *Highest, fastest, strongest*

Why a unit called Higher, Faster, Stronger?

'Unthinkable' they said. 'Surely no-one will ever run a mile in under four minutes.' Not only were the commentators proved wrong, but in the fifty years since then, 15 seconds have been lopped off the world mile record. More impressive still, a full six minutes have been hacked off the women's 5000 metre record. Off the track, the story is the same. Before the authorities stepped in and changed the design of the javelin, javelin throws were beginning to endanger the crowd at the other end of the stadium.

What's going on? Are we becoming a more powerful species? The place to search for an explanation of this record-breaking frenzy is in the laboratory. With physiology, psychology and physics, science has revolutionised sport, giving us a better understanding of bodily and mental processes with which to train winners (Figure 1).

The new scientific discipline of sports science has emerged to help build tomorrow's champions. Using tools such as computer-linked video, researchers can now analyse the movements involved in sporting activity in minute detail. This allows trainers to correct even tiny errors in an athlete's performance. Advances in the science of materials have brought equally dramatic changes, with almost every conceivable property of an athlete's clothing and footwear optimised for performance. And with so much resting on winning, measurement technology now enables races to be decided on differences of just a few milliseconds.

Higher, Faster, Stronger is (loosely) the Olympic motto. In this unit, you will see how many basic physics concepts can be applied to sports, ranging from sprinting to bungee jumping, to help athletes go 'higher, faster, stronger'.

Overview of physics principles and techniques

In this unit, you will study the physics of motion, force and energy. You may be familiar with some of the ideas from GCSE. In this unit you will deepen your understanding of these concepts by applying them to solve real problems. Many of the concepts, like force and energy, are fundamental to the whole of physics, and you will meet them in almost every unit of the course.

You will have many opportunities for practical work, investigations and computer data-logging. You will learn how graphs can be used not only to display data but also to extract additional information from a set of measurements, and you will also use computer software to analyse various sporting activities, just as sports science researchers do.

In later units you will do further work on

- vectors in *Probing the Heart of Matter*;
- graphs in *Digging Up the Past*, *The Medium is the Message* and *Probing the Heart of Matter*;
- kinematics and dynamics in *Good Enough to Eat* and *Transport on Track*;
- kinetic energy and work in *Transport on Track*, *Probing the Heart of Matter* and *Reach for the Stars*;
- properties of materials in *Good Enough to Eat*, *Spare Part Surgery* and *Build or Bust?*.

1 Running

1.1 Biomechanics

By studying physics, you are following in the footsteps of one of the world's best athletes. Durham physics graduate Jonathan Edwards (Figure 2) became the world record holder in the triple jump in the summer of 1995 at the World Athletics Championships in Gothenburg, Sweden. He leapt his way into the record books by jumping in excess of 18 m. In the space of a couple of months he became an MBE and BBC Sports Personality for 1995. He won the silver medal in the Olympics in Atlanta the following year.

To be a good jumper, Jonathan Edwards had to train to be a very fast sprinter. He also had to develop very careful timing in his jumping techniques. The science of biomechanics is devoted to trying to help sports people get the best possible results by helping them to improve their technique. Biomechanics concerns itself with the forces on a human body and sports equipment, and the effects of these forces. Much work has been conducted at Loughborough University (where former world record holder Sebastian Coe studied and trained) to help training methods and improve performance.

External forces (such as those exerted by a cyclist on a pedal) are measured using transducers to convert the force into an electrical signal. Internal forces exerted by the muscles and applied to the bones and joints in the human body are harder to measure directly (transducers would have to be implanted), but they can be calculated indirectly by a technique known as inverse dynamics. If the mass of each part of the human body is known and the accelerated motion measured, then forces can be calculated. Position–time data from video can be used to calculate accelerations of each segment of the body. We will look at some examples of inverse dynamics later on in this part of the unit. First we will see how motion can be recorded and analysed.

Figure 2 *Jonathan Edwards jumping the triple jump*

1.2 Describing motion

The performance of an athlete in a running event is usually recorded simply as the time taken to complete the distance. Table 1 lists some times for the men's and women's 10 000 metre world record. It has been suggested that women will soon be running faster than men.

ACTIVITY 1 Record times

Plot the data from Table 1 on a single set of axes. Choose a sensible scale for your graph and label it clearly.

Continue (extrapolate) each graph forward in time and discuss (with reasons) whether you think women will one day beat the men in the 10 000 m event.

Year	Time/minutes	
	Women	**Men**
1970	35.30	27.39
1975	34.01	27.30
1980	31.45	27.22
1985	30.59	27.13
1990	30.13	27.08
1995	29.31	26.43
1999	29.31	26.23

Table 1 *World record times for the 10 000 m event*

Speed

Data such as those in Table 1 allow us to calculate the average speed of an athlete:

$$\text{average speed} = \text{distance travelled} \div \text{time taken} \qquad (1)$$

Expressed in the symbols that are normally used, equation (1) becomes

$$v = \frac{\Delta s}{\Delta t} \qquad (1a)$$

Maths reference

The symbol Δ

See Maths note 0.2

The symbol Δ is the Greek capital letter delta, and is used to mean 'change in' or 'difference in'. So if s represents the athlete's position, then Δs means 'change in position', i.e. the distance travelled; Δt represents the time interval. Notice that Δ is *not* a number multiplying s or t.

In the right direction

An orienteer runs from post A a distance of 300 m, then 500 m, then 400 m, finally reaching post B. How far is she from the first post A? Figure 3 shows some possibilities. You do not know how far she is from A, because the directions were not specified. An orienteer would use a compass to get her bearings and find out which direction to travel in. She would need to specify the distance to be travelled in a given direction.

When we mean 'distance in a specified direction' we use the word **displacement**. Similarly, speed in a specified direction is called **velocity.** Physical quantities *where direction is as important as size* are called **vector quantities**. (The size of a vector is often called its **magnitude**.) A quantity where there is no question of a direction being involved is called a **scalar**. A good example of a scalar quantity is *temperature*: 5 °C south-east hardly makes sense. When measuring vector quantities we need to pay attention to how the measuring instrument is directed: as a rather trivial example you can hardly measure an object's weight with a horizontal spring balance. But if a patient's temperature is being taken, it does not matter in which direction the thermometer is pointing out of their mouth!

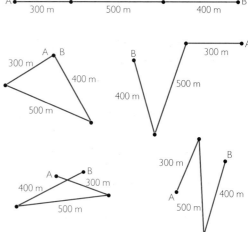

Figure 3 *Some possible locations of post B if directions are not specified*

Study note

In a maths course you may have come across the term 'vector' as a directed line – what we are looking at here is an extension of the same idea to other types of quantity.

ACTIVITY 2 Vectors and scalars

Write down a list of as many physical quantities as you can (not just mechanical – you could try electrical as well). Also write the SI unit by the side of each.

Draw up two columns headed 'Vector' and 'Scalar' and allocate each quantity to its correct column. You can start with displacement (metre) and temperature (kelvin). Remember that the question you have to ask of each is 'Does direction matter?' (It seems quite straightforward but there are one or two deceptive ones – work? energy?)

In part 1 of this unit we will be concerned only with motion in one dimension (back and forth along a straight line), and we will use positive and negative signs to denote the direction.

Acceleration

When we just say that something is moving, we are not giving much information away. Is an athlete travelling at constant speed? Is she changing direction? Is she speeding up or slowing down? In other words, we are interested in how the velocity changes:

$$\text{change in velocity} = \text{final velocity} - \text{initial velocity} \qquad (2)$$

Conventionally, u represents the initial velocity and v the final velocity, and Δv the change in velocity. We can write equation (2) as

$$\Delta v = v - u \qquad (2a)$$

This leads to a definition of **acceleration** as

$$\text{acceleration} = \text{change in velocity} \div \text{time taken} \qquad (3)$$

In symbols

$$a = \frac{\Delta v}{\Delta t} \qquad \text{or} \qquad a = \frac{(v - u)}{\Delta t} \qquad (3a)$$

Another useful version of equation (3) is

$$v = u + a\Delta t \qquad (3b)$$

Notice that change of velocity is used and not change in speed. Acceleration is a vector quantity, having both magnitude and direction. Equation (3) can only be used in situations with **uniform acceleration** as in Table 2, which shows motion with an acceleration of $2\,\mathrm{m\,s^{-2}}$, i.e. the velocity is increasing by $2\,\mathrm{m\,s^{-1}}$ every second.

An important example of uniform acceleration is that of an object in **free fall**, i.e. moving only under the influence of gravity. In the initial part of a parachute jump or a bungee jump, you are in free fall, accelerating vertically downwards with the **acceleration due to gravity**, symbolised g, which (close to the Earth's surface) is always $9.8\,\mathrm{m\,s^{-2}}$.

Study note

In part 2 of this unit you will see how to deal with vectors in two dimensions.

Time	Velocity
0 s	$1.5\,\mathrm{m\,s^{-1}}$
1 s	$1.5\,\mathrm{m\,s^{-1}} + 2\,\mathrm{m\,s^{-1}}$ $= 3.5\,\mathrm{m\,s^{-1}}$
2 s	$3.5\,\mathrm{m\,s^{-1}} + 2\,\mathrm{m\,s^{-1}}$ $= 5.5\,\mathrm{m\,s^{-1}}$
3 s	$5.5\,\mathrm{m\,s^{-1}} + 2\,\mathrm{m\,s^{-1}}$ $= 7.5\,\mathrm{m\,s^{-1}}$

Table 2 *Changing velocity*

Maths reference

Index notation and powers of 10
See Maths note 1.1

Index notation and units
See Maths note 2.2

ACTIVITY 3 **Free fall**

Carry our some simple activities to illustrate the constant acceleration of objects falling under gravity.

QUESTIONS

1 A jogger who is initially running at $2.0\,\mathrm{m\,s^{-1}}$ accelerates uniformly at a rate of $1.5\,\mathrm{m\,s^{-2}}$ for $3.0\,\mathrm{s}$. Calculate the final velocity.

2 How fast will a bungee jumper be moving after he has been in free fall for $2.5\,\mathrm{s}$?

3 A squash ball travelling at 9.0 m s^{-1} horizontally to the right is hit by a racket which stops it in 0.003 s. Calculate the acceleration.

4 A tennis ball moving to the right at a velocity of 5.0 m s^{-1} is struck by a tennis racket and accelerated to the left, leaving the tennis racket at a speed of 25 m s^{-1} to the left. If the contact time is 0.012 s, calculate the average acceleration.

1.3 Motion graphs

Graphs are often used to represent motion. Not only do they give a visual record but they also enable us to extract additional information about the motion. Figure 4 shows two **displacement–time graphs**. In Figure 4(a), the velocity is constant: the graph is a straight line, and dividing any given displacement Δs by the corresponding time interval Δt gives the same answer for the velocity – the velocity is equal to the **gradient** of the displacement–time graph.

Maths reference
....
Gradient of a linear graph
See Maths note 5.3
....

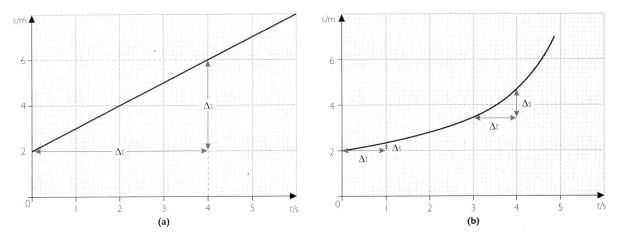

Figure 4 *Displacement–time graphs for motion with (a) uniform velocity and (b) non-uniform velocity*

In Figure 4(b) you can tell that the velocity is non-uniform, because the graph does not show equal displacements in equal time intervals – the graph is not straight. A calculation of $\Delta s/\Delta t$ gives the average velocity in a given time interval Δt.

Figure 5 shows three **velocity–time graphs**. In Figure 5(a) the velocity does not change – the acceleration is zero. Figure 5(b) is a plot of the data in Table 2: the acceleration is uniform (the velocity changes by equal amounts in equal time intervals) so the graph is a straight line, and dividing any given change in velocity Δv by the corresponding time interval Δt gives the same answer – the acceleration is the gradient of the velocity–time graph. In Figure 5(c) the graph is not straight, because the acceleration is not uniform – the velocity does not change by equal amounts in equal time intervals.

In everyday language, 'accelerate' just means 'get faster', and 'decelerate' means 'get slower'. In physics we tend always to use the term 'accelerate' and use appropriate signs to indicate its direction. A negative acceleration is *not* necessarily a slowing down – if something that is already moving in the negative direction experiences an acceleration in the same direction it will get faster!

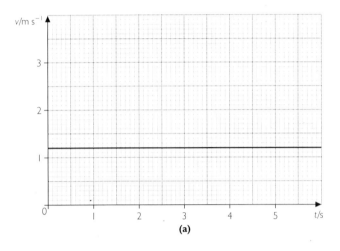

(a)

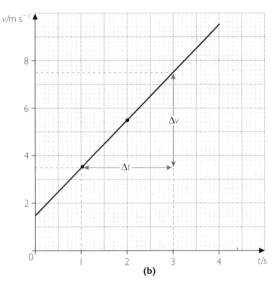

(b)

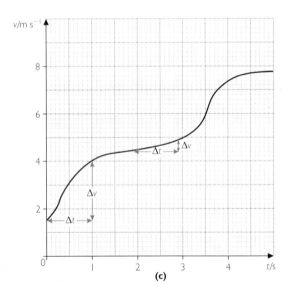

(c)

Figure 5 *Velocity–time graphs for motion with (a) zero acceleration, (b) uniform (non-zero) acceleration and (c) non-uniform acceleration*

QUESTIONS

5 Find the velocity of the motion shown in Figure 4(a) by (**a**) using the values of Δs and Δt shown and (**b**) drawing another triangle on a copy of Figure 4(a) that has a different Δs and Δt.

6 How would you interpret (**a**) a displacement–time graph that sloped more steeply than Figure 4(a) and (**b**) a displacement–time graph that sloped downward from left to right?

7 Calculate the acceleration of the motion shown in Figure 5(b).

8 How would you show a negative acceleration on a velocity–time graph?

Small changes

Athletes such as sprinters, hurdlers, triple jumpers and so on improve their technique by observing their motion on a video playback frame by frame, or in a strobe photograph. This allows them to study their motion in detail and then work with a coach to develop ways of improving their technique. In Activities 4 and 5 you will do something similar, analysing motion in some detail.

In most real-life examples of motion, the velocity is not uniform. Usually there is some acceleration from rest, and often the velocity changes before the final deceleration to rest. Acceleration, too, is not usually uniform. It can change because of wind resistance or changing muscle effort, or running on a slope. It is still possible to use equation (2), however, if you split the motion into small time intervals where the velocity is *nearly* uniform (as in Figure 4b). Likewise, acceleration can be calculated using equation (3) for a small time interval where it is *nearly* uniform as in Figure 5(c).

ACTIVITY 4 **Non-uniform motion**

Use ticker-tape or a stop-frame video to record your own motion when sprinting from a crouched start and plot a graph of your displacement against time.

Calculate your velocity in each small interval between dots or between frames, and hence also calculate your acceleration in each small time interval.

If you have many very small time intervals, you need to perform lots of calculation. This can be very boring and so a computer program is usually used. The CD-ROM package *Multimedia Motion* contains a catalogue of video clips that can be played back frame by frame, and the motion can be analysed to find displacement, velocity and acceleration.

ACTIVITY 5 **Producing graphs of motion**

Use *Multimedia Motion* to produce graphs showing the displacement, velocity and acceleration for one or more of the following (see Figure 7): sprint start; squash; soccer; tennis. Alternatively, use a motion sensor to generate graphs of your own motion. Keep a copy of your graphs for use in later activities.

In Activity 4 you found the **instantaneous velocity** by dividing a small change in displacement by a small change in time. If you are working directly from a curved displacement–time graph, it is difficult to read values that are very close together. It is better to

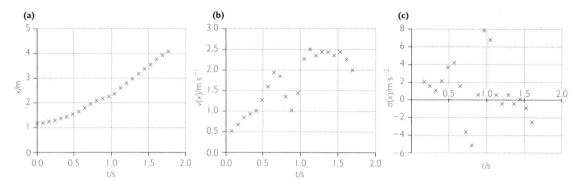

Figure 7 *The motion of a sprinter shown as graphs of (a) displacement–time, (b) velocity–time and (c) acceleration–time*

draw a **tangent** (a straight line touching the curve) at the required point as shown in Figure 8 and then work out its gradient. Likewise, you can find the **instantaneous acceleration** by drawing a tangent to a velocity–time graph and working out its gradient.

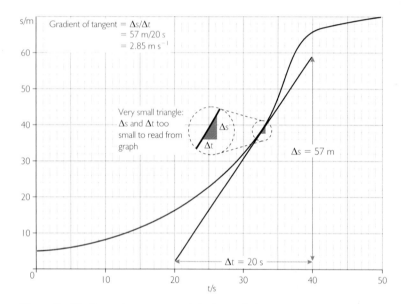

Figure 8 *Working out instantaneous velocity from a displacement–time graph*

ACTIVITY 6 Tangents and gradients

By drawing tangents on a displacement–time graph from Activity 5, find the velocity at two different times. Compare your answers with the velocities at those times calculated by the *Multimedia Motion* software. Similarly, find the acceleration at two times by drawing tangents on a velocity–time graph.

Going the distance

You have seen how a record of displacement can be used to deduce an athlete's velocity, and how velocity data can, in turn, be used to find acceleration. But can the same thing be done in reverse? Can a record of velocity be used to deduce displacement?

In Figure 9(a) the displacement in the first 4 s is

$$1.5 \text{ m s}^{-1} \times 4.0 \text{ s} = 6.0 \text{ m}$$

This displacement is equal to the area of the shaded portion of the graph. In Figure 9(b) the velocity is not uniform, but if we choose a time interval small enough that the velocity v is *nearly* uniform, then the displacement in that small time interval Δt is given by

$$\Delta s = v \Delta t$$

which is equal to the area of the narrow shaded strip. The total displacement in a longer time interval can be found by adding up all the areas of the narrow strips (each with a different height). In other words, displacement can be found from the **area under a velocity–time graph**.

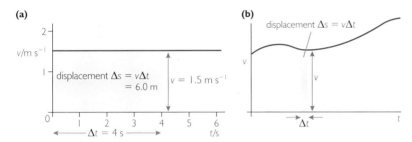

Figure 9   *Working out displacement from a velocity–time graph (a) with uniform velocity and (b) with non-uniform velocity*

Uniform acceleration

If the acceleration is uniform, then the velocity–time graph is a straight line, as in Figure 10, and the displacement can be found by adding together the areas of the rectangle and the triangle as shown.

Expressing the areas of the rectangle and triangle in symbols leads to another useful equation for uniformly accelerated motion, which lets us calculate displacement directly without going via a graph:

$$\Delta s = u \Delta t + \tfrac{1}{2} a (\Delta t)^2 \tag{4}$$

Usually you will see equation (4) written using just t (not Δt) to represent the overall time taken and s to represent the overall displacement:

$$s = ut + \tfrac{1}{2} a t^2 \tag{4a}$$

Equations (3b) and (4a) can be combined to produce another useful relationship that relates change of velocity directly to the displacement:

$$v^2 = u^2 + 2as \tag{5}$$

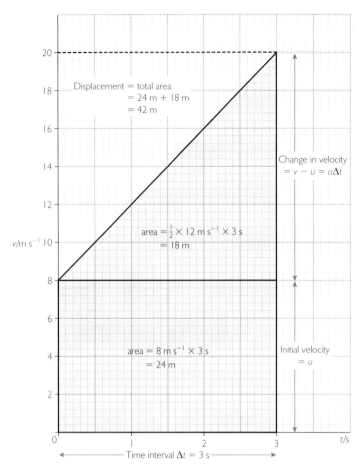

Figure 10 *The area under a straight velocity–time graph*

You can derive equation (5) by squaring equation (3b) (and dropping the Δ):

$$v^2 = (u + at)^2 = u^2 + 2aut + a^2t^2$$

and multiplying equation (4a) by $2a$:

$$2as = 2aut + a^2t^2$$

Comparing the right-hand sides leads to equation (5).

Maths reference

Algebra and elimination

See Maths note 3.4

ACTIVITY 7 Free fall again

Carry out some explorations of freely falling objects that show how the time of fall is related to the distance fallen.

Non-uniform acceleration

If the velocity–time graph is curved, then the area can be found by using a computer program to work out and add together the areas of many very narrow strips, or by counting squares on the graph paper.

When you are counting squares, the vertical axis must start at zero otherwise the height of each strip does not represent the velocity. Also, be careful to use the scales of the graph and not the actual sizes of the squares.

QUESTIONS

9 A sprinter is running at a uniform speed of 8.00 m s^{-1} as she approaches the finish, then she puts on a spurt to overtake her rival and accelerates at 0.70 m s^{-2} for 3.00 s before crossing the line. What is her final velocity, and what distance does she cover in the final three seconds of her sprint?

10 Figure 11 shows velocity–time graphs for two athletes in a race. After 30 seconds, who is ahead and by approximately how much?

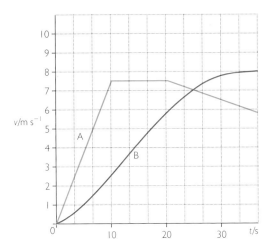

Figure 11   *Velocity–time graphs for question 10*

1.4 *Force and acceleration*

You have seen how acceleration can be deduced from measurements of velocity or displacement. Sports scientists often find it useful to go one stage further and use so-called inverse dynamics to work out the forces that provide the accelerations, using the relationship

$$F = ma \qquad\qquad (6)$$

where m is the mass of the accelerated object and F the net force acting on it. Like acceleration, force is a vector, and when dealing with one-dimensional motion we can use positive and negative signs to indicate the direction of a force. It is sometimes useful to combine equations (3a) and (6) to give

$$F = ma = \frac{m\Delta v}{\Delta t} \qquad\qquad (6a)$$

Equation (6) expresses **Newton's second law of motion.**

   Newton's first law of motion states that an object moves at constant velocity or remains at rest unless an unbalanced force acts on it, while the second law relates the size of the unbalanced force to the change that it causes.

QUESTIONS

11 When starting a race, a sprinter of mass 65 kg accelerates forwards at 2.0 m s^{-2} (Figure 12). What must be the net forward force acting on her body?

12 A tennis ball of mass 120 g approaches a racket at 5.0 m s^{-1} and is hit back in the opposite direction at 25 m s^{-1} (Figure 13). If the contact time with the racket is 0.015 s, what is the average force exerted on the ball by the racket?

Figure 12 *A sprint start*

Figure 13 *A tennis ball in contact with a racket*

ACTIVITY 8 **Inverse dynamics**

Using your results from Activity 5, estimate the net force acting to accelerate the person or object that you studied. You might need to estimate the mass of the sprinter, or of the squash, tennis or soccer ball.

ACTIVITY 9 **Measuring forces directly**

Use a force sensor with graphing software, or bathroom scales calibrated in newtons, to measure the forces involved in various activities such as jumping, throwing and catching.

In Activity 9 you probably took it for granted that the bathroom scales or force sensor register a non-zero vertical force even when you are standing still. But how does this tie in with Newton's first and second laws of motion, and equation (6)? The explanation involves some careful thinking about forces – and another of Newton's laws of motion.

Weight and gravitational field

The relationship between force, mass and acceleration (equation 6) gives us another way of looking at free fall. Close to the Earth's surface, *any* object in free fall has an acceleration of 9.8 m s^{-2}. The gravitational force responsible for the acceleration must therefore depend on the object's mass – an object of mass 1 kg must experience a force of 9.8 N, a 2 kg object must experience a force of 2×9.8 N, and so on. We can express this by saying that, close to its surface, the Earth's **gravitational field strength**, symbolised g, is 9.8 N kg^{-1}.

The gravitational force acting on an object is called its **weight**. This can be confusing, because in everyday language the word 'weight' is used to mean the same thing as mass. Weight is measured in newtons and is a vector (it acts downwards). The weight W of an object of mass m is given by a special case of equation (6):

$$W = mg \qquad (7)$$

QUESTION

13 Estimate your own weight.

If gravity is the only force acting, a downward acceleration will result, so, if you are standing still, your weight must be balanced by an upward force. How does this come about?

Pairs of forces

The sprinter in question 11 exerts a 'backwards' force on the starting block, but she accelerates because the block (and the Earth to which it is attached) exerts a 'forwards' force on her. This is an example of **Newton's third law of motion**, which can be stated as 'all forces involve the interaction between two objects' or 'all forces come in pairs'. The two forces are always equal in size but opposite in direction, and always involve two *different* objects exerting forces on one another. In the example of the sprinter, she pushes backwards on the starting-block-plus-Earth with a force of 130 N, and the block pushes her forwards also with a force of 130 N (Figure 14). A force of 130 N on a 65 kg person gives her a significant acceleration, but the same size force acting on the block-plus-Earth produces such a minute acceleration that it is not detectable.

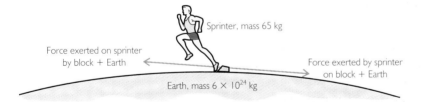

Sprinter, mass 65 kg

Force exerted on sprinter by block + Earth

Force exerted by sprinter on block + Earth

Earth, mass 6×10^{24} kg

Figure 14 *Forces involved in the interaction between sprinter and starting block*

Consider another example: when a bungee jumper is in free fall, there is a pair of gravitational forces acting between him and the Earth. The downward force on the bungee jumper (his weight) produces an acceleration of 9.8 m s^{-2}, but an upward force of the same size acting on the Earth produces no noticeable effect (Figure 15).

If you stand on the floor, there is still a pair of gravitational forces acting between you and the Earth. But now you exert a downward force on the floor (equal to your weight) and the compressed material in the floor exerts an equal force upwards on you – you and the floor are interacting according to Newton's third law. In

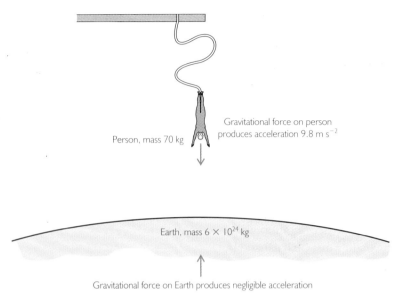

Figure 15   *Forces involved in the interaction between bungee jumper and Earth*

Activity 9, you recorded the force exerted by the scales (or a force sensor): you and the scales interact via a pair of forces and, in turn, the scales and the floor also interact. If you are at rest, the force registered is equal to your own weight; but if you jump off the scales, you do so by pushing downwards with an additional force and the scales in turn exert a upward force on you to produce an upward acceleration.

The forces involved in the interactions between athletes and their surroundings are not only important in producing the required accelerations. They are also responsible for injuries – if you hit something with a force, you also experience a force of the same size exerted by the object.

QUESTIONS

14 A squash player hits the ball of mass 0.024 kg with her racket. The ball is decelerated at 12 200 m s^{-2}. Calculate the size and direction of the force exerted on the ball, and write down the size and direction of the force exerted by the ball on the racket.

15 (**a**) What are the pairs of 'Newton's third law' forces involved when a (not very good) diver (**i**) is in free fall and then (**ii**) splashes into the water?

(**b**) Explain why splashing awkwardly into the water is painful, whereas a smooth dive is not.

1.5   *Summing up part 1*

In this part of the unit, you have used some key ideas about forces and motion and seen how graphs can be used to display and analyse motion. You will use all these ideas again later in this unit and elsewhere in your study of physics. Activity 10 is intended to help you to review your work so far, and question 16 shows that ideas about motion are relevant to situations other than sport!

ACTIVITY 10 Summing up part 1

Spend a few minutes checking through part 1, making sure that you understand the meanings of all the key terms printed in bold. Then use at least five of those terms to describe the forces involved in sprinting and hence to explain how the 'cushion' in the sole of a running shoe helps prevent damage to a sprinter's feet.

Further investigations

In practice, many falling objects do not fall freely – they are affected by air resistance as well as by gravity. If you have an opportunity, you could investigate some of the records of falling objects (and people) included in *Multimedia Motion* to see to what extent their motion is affected by air resistance.

A shuttlecock is designed to be affected by air resistance. You could investigate how the shape and weight distribution of a cone-shaped object affect its motion in air.

QUESTION

16 An instrument called a dynamometer is used to test the performance of trains. It can measure and record, amongst other factors, a train's speed, acceleration and distance travelled, together with the time at which the measurements were taken. Figure 16 shows a record for a train of mass 200 000 kg until it reached its maximum speed of 35 m s^{-1}.

(**a**) (**i**) Between what times was the train's acceleration uniform?

(**ii**) What was the magnitude of this uniform acceleration?

(**iii**) What was the magnitude of the instantaneous acceleration at $t = 80$ s?

(**b**) Calculate the size of the net force that produced the uniform acceleration.

(**c**) How far had the train travelled during the interval from $t = 0$ s to $t = 40$ s?

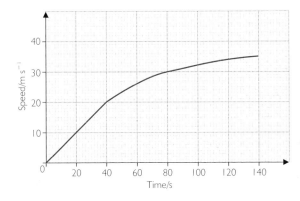

Figure 16 *Dynamometer record for question 16*

2 Rock climbing

Groping with my other gloved hand in the crack, I found a solid fist-jam, my axe hanging from its strap around my wrist. Pulling into the rock and releasing my other axe, I lifted it high above my head and hooked it over a chockstone in the crack. I straightened my arm, and relaxed the muscles, so that I could feel the strain tugging from within my shoulders. I placed the front points of my boot on the original flat ledge, which caused my left hand to rip from the crack. I palmed it against the rock on the left. I was totally absorbed. I stood up on the right foot, first transferring my weight from the left and shivering it from the crack. With my left axe I reached as high as I could into the back of the groove where it opened out like the base of a peapod. I hit only rock beneath powdery snow. 'Shit!' My right calf muscles began to complain. Rather desperately I kicked my left foot back into the crack and pushed up again, leaning into the base of the groove, scratching both my axes across the snow. I found a patch of névé and sank my teeth into it. I exhaled and pulled up into a resting position. ... I gazed up the groove towards the sun and the deep blue sky. 'Brilliant' I said jubilantly. 'This climbing is brilliant!' The drag of fatigue was forgotten.

(a)

In the passage above, climber Andy Fanshawe is describing a climb in the Karakoram mountains. The sport of rock climbing is quite a contrast to athletics. However complicated or contorted the move in rock climbing, all the forces must somehow combine to produce **equilibrium** (i.e. a net force of zero) almost all of the time, unlike athletics where forces and accelerations can be deliberately large. The only occasion when a rock climber is not in equilibrium is when there might be an acceleration in transferring position – or of course when falling!

In this part of the unit we are going to explore the equilibrium of forces and also look at some of the physical properties of materials that help to make the sport of rock climbing safe.

(b)

2.1 Hanging on

The climber in Figure 17(a) is clearly in equilibrium – there are no horizontal forces acting and the upward vertical force exerted by the rock face balances his weight vertically downwards. But so also is the climber in Figure 17(b). Here, though, the situation is a little more complicated – there are three points of contact with the rock which together with his weight (the rope is more or less slack) produce four forces all acting in different directions. Figure 17(c) shows yet another situation (a so-called *Tyrolean traverse*) where forces are acting in different directions.

(c)

Figure 17 *Rock climbers in equilibrium*

ACTIVITY 11 **Forces in different directions**

Can you see any similarities between the equilibrium situations of Figures 17(b) and (c)? (Try to wipe the 'physical context' from the pictures and think just about the directions of forces acting on the climbers.)

Use the arrangement shown in Figure 18 to explore the effect of pulling ropes in different directions but still trying to maintain equilibrium.

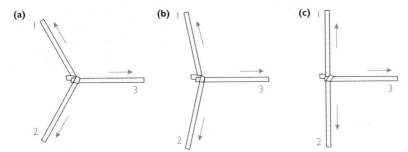

Figure 18 *Diagram for Activity 11*

It should be clear from Activity 11 that, when forces combine with each other, we don't just have to think about how large each one is, but also in which direction it is acting. In Activity 13 you will extend the qualitative ideas of Activity 11 by taking measurements of tension in and angle of a rope. Before you do that, what sort of behaviour might you expect? We can get a clue from considering what is probably the simplest vector quantity of all – displacement.

Combining displacement vectors

You will be familiar with displacement vectors if you have ever done orienteering or any navigation across open country. It is simply an instruction to move from one point to another, and it must contain the *two* pieces of information: how far? which way? (unlike the situation in Figure 3).

Figure 19(a) shows two displacement vectors: $\boldsymbol{d}_1$ is 5 km north (call this direction 0°) and $\boldsymbol{d}_2$ is 3 km in a direction 40° clockwise from north. Let us start from a point O and carry out the displacement $\boldsymbol{d}_1$ first, then $\boldsymbol{d}_2$. This is shown in Figure 19(b) and takes us to point P. Alternatively we could do $\boldsymbol{d}_2$ first, then $\boldsymbol{d}_1$, as in Figure 19(c).

Whichever way we combine the vectors, the net effect is exactly the same. The vector from O to P is the same in both diagrams and is the *single* vector that replaces the two separate ones. Careful measurement on Figure 19(d) shows that it is 7.5 km in a direction 15° from N. This single vector is called the **resultant** vector of $\boldsymbol{d}_1$ and $\boldsymbol{d}_2$: if we denote it by $\boldsymbol{R}$ we write

$$\boldsymbol{R} = \boldsymbol{d}_1 + \boldsymbol{d}_2 \tag{8}$$

Study note

In printed texts vectors are usually in **bold** or ***bold italic*** type. When writing them yourself it is usual to underline them with a wavy line. The magnitude (size) of a vector is a scalar quantity, so is shown in the same way as any other scalar, i.e. in *italic*, non-bold type.

Study note

Note that the '+' sign in equation (8) is not the same as an ordinary arithmetic (scalar) addition, but we borrow the sign to show that we are combining the vectors and we describe the procedure as vector addition. It is obviously not true that $R = d_1 + d_2$ *(scalars, magnitude only)*.

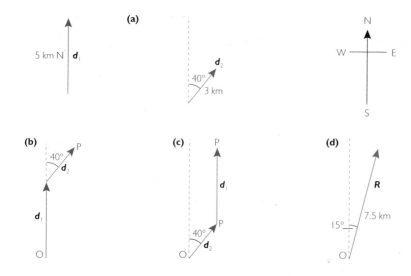

Figure 19 *Combining displacement vectors (1 cm = 2.5 km)*

If we need to combine more than two vectors then we just continue the process of joining them 'head-to-tail', ending up with a **vector polygon** as in Figure 20. The resultant is always found by joining the starting point O to the finishing point P.

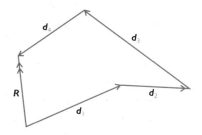

Figure 20 *A vector polygon*

Zero resultant
We can rewrite equation (8) as

$$\boldsymbol{d}_1 + \boldsymbol{d}_2 - \boldsymbol{R} = 0 \qquad (9)$$

which we can interpret as the combination of the vector $-\boldsymbol{R}$ with the sum $(\boldsymbol{d}_1 + \boldsymbol{d}_2)$, giving a resultant of zero. If in Figure 19(b) or (c) we added the vector $-\boldsymbol{R}$ at point P (the minus sign simply means reverse the direction), then it is clear that we end up back at O and the resultant is zero.

ACTIVITY 12 **Vector polygon**

Draw on graph paper a vector polygon similar to Figure 20. It need not be an exact match. Draw up a table of two columns headed 'Magnitude' and 'Direction' and with the help of a ruler and protractor enter the information for each of the vectors.

Now combine the vectors in a variety of different orders. You will get quite different polygons, but you ought to find the resultant is the same in each case.

Combining force vectors by drawing

Figure 21 shows three forces **W**, $\boldsymbol{T}_1$ and $\boldsymbol{T}_2$ that are in equilibrium and so their resultant is zero. Do they combine like displacement vectors? Activity 13 provides the answer.

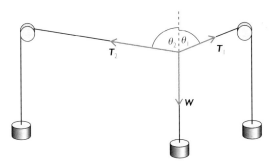

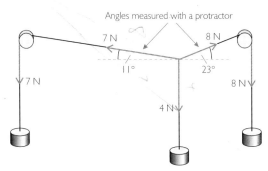

Angles measured with a protractor

Each mass exerts a force equal to its weight

Figure 21 *Three force vectors in equilibrium*

Figure 22 *Apparatus for Activity 13*

ACTIVITY **13** **Forces in equilibrium**

Use the apparatus shown in Figure 22 to investigate whether force vectors combine like displacement vectors. For each equilibrium arrangement, construct a vector addition diagram and see if it is closed – do we end up back where we started? The critical step is to choose a scale so that each force is represented by a line of length proportional to its magnitude, e.g. 2 cm to 1 N.

Careful measurements show that forces do indeed behave as displacement vectors when they combine. This means that when any number of forces are in equilibrium, the vectors form a closed polygon. A common special case is when there are just three forces – here the polygon is a triangle usually called the **triangle of forces**.

QUESTION

17 Figure 23 shows a simplified end-on view of a cable car (looking along the length of the cable) in operation. It is being blown by high wind, which can produce a sideways force of up to 5000 N. The total weight of the car is 2.5×10^4 N. Assume that it is in equilibrium (i.e. not swinging). **T** is the force exerted on the car by the support arm, which is fixed rigidly to the car but can rotate on the cable.

Draw a triangle of forces for this arrangement. Choose a suitable scale, working on graph paper for convenience, and start with a vector whose details you know. (Does it matter which?) As accurately as you can, measure the values of **T** and θ.

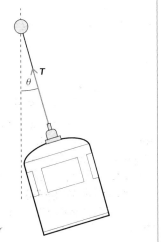

Figure 23 *Forces acting on a cable car*

ACTIVITY **14** **What stops a rock climber falling?**

By tracing the directions of the forces in Figure 17(b), you can deduce an important result about forces in equilibrium.

It is always true that if three **coplanar** non-parallel forces (coplanar means acting in the same plane) are in equilibrium, their lines of action pass through the same point. With a bit of imagination many rather complicated real-life situations can be reduced to three forces in equilibrium, as in Activity 15.

ACTIVITY 15   **Forces acting on a power cable**

Study (from a safe distance!) an overhead power cable. Make a scale drawing of the cable as accurately as you can and use it to estimate the force that the cable is exerting on the pylon if the mass per unit length of the cable is 2 kg m^{-1}.

Combining force vectors by calculation

Since most force situations of interest will involve different directions, it is obviously important, not least from considerations of strength and safety, to be able to deal accurately with them (just think about buildings, bridges or aircraft). Is there any way of doing it apart from scale drawing?

As an introduction, consider the case when two force vectors are acting at a point at right angles to each other (Figure 24a). The vector addition diagram, including the resultant R, is obviously a right angled triangle as in Figure 24(b). (Remember that R *replaces* F_1 and F_2 and is equivalent to the other two acting together – we are *not* introducing a third extra force.) From Pythagoras we can say

$$R^2 = F_1^2 + F_2^2 \qquad \text{or} \qquad R = \sqrt{F_1^2 + F_2^2} \qquad (10)$$

and also

$$\tan \theta = F_2/F_1 \qquad \text{or} \qquad \theta = \tan^{-1}(F_2/F_1) \qquad (11)$$

so in this special case we can find the magnitude and direction of R by calculation alone.

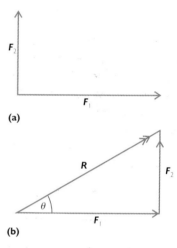

(a)

(b)

Figure 24   *Two forces at right angles*

Maths reference

Sine, cosine and tangent of an angle

See Maths note 6.2

QUESTIONS

18 A sky-diver falling vertically experiences a net vertical force of 500 N. A sideways gust of wind exerts a force of 100 N. What are the magnitude and direction of the resultant force on the sky-diver?

19 Figure 25 shows a climber supported by a rope and 'walking' down a vertical rock face. Sketch the triangle of forces acting on the climber when she is momentarily at rest and hence calculate the magnitudes of the horizontal force exerted by the rock and the tension in the rope.

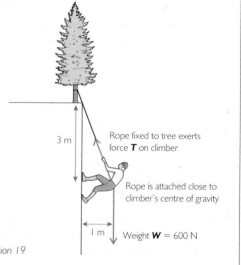

3 m

Rope fixed to tree exerts force T on climber

Rope is attached close to climber's centre of gravity

1 m

Weight W = 600 N

Figure 25   *Diagram for question 19*

Resolving a force into perpendicular components

But what about two vectors that are not at right angles, as in Figure 19 and Activity 14? The trick is to take each force in turn and **resolve** it (split it up) into two perpendicular **components** (parts). For example, the vector d_2 in Figure 19 can be thought of as the resultant of two displacements – one due north (d_N) and one due east (d_E) (Figure 26). These two components form a right angled triangle with d_2 as the hypotenuse, from which we can see that the magnitudes of the components are given by

$$d_N = d_2 \cos 40° \qquad \text{and} \qquad d_E = d_2 \sin 40°$$

The overall displacement $d_1 + d_2$ can then be treated as the sum of two northerly displacements plus an easterly displacement, which together make two sides of a right-angled triangle, so the magnitude and direction of the resultant can be calculated.

This example illustrates a general rule. Any vector P making an angle θ with a particular direction can be resolved into two components, one parallel to the chosen direction and one perpendicular to it:

$$\text{magnitude of parallel component} = P \cos \theta \qquad (12)$$

$$\text{magnitude of perpendicular component} = P \sin \theta \qquad (13)$$

We now have another way of looking at equilibrium of forces. In any direction you choose, all the components of forces in that direction must combine to produce a resultant of zero. Activity 16 illustrates this.

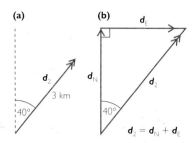

Figure 26 *Resolving a displacement vector into perpendicular components*

Study note

Note that there is nothing special about the directions of the components – provided they are at 90° to each other. In practice they will often be horizontal and vertical, or parallel and perpendicular to a surface.

Think about the two special cases $\theta = 0$ and $\theta = 90°$. What would be the northerly and easterly components of the displacement vector 5 km north?

ACTIVITY 16 **Components of force vectors**

Return to your data for Activity 14. Using your values of tensions, weight and directions, draw up a table of the horizontal and vertical components of each force.

By adding separately the horizontal and vertical components, show to what extent the condition for equilibrium is satisfied experimentally.

Tyrolean traverse

The Tyrolean traverse (Figure 17c) is a technique for crossing a deep chasm suspended on a rope. In the pioneering days of mountaineering the rope was thrown across a chasm and lassoed onto a suitable spike. Figure 27 shows a close-up of how it might work in practice. In question 20 and Activity 17 you are going to use what you have learned about forces to explore the Tyrolean traverse in a bit more detail, and question 21 applies the same ideas to a more complicated situation where the two ends are not on a level.

Figure 27 *Tyrolean traverse*

Suppose for convenience the two parts of the rope each make an angle of 15° with the horizontal and the climber has a weight of 600 N. How can we find the tension in the rope? The actual situation can be cut down to its essentials as in Figure 28. From the symmetry, the tension in the two halves must be the same. (Warning! – only of course true when the two angles are the same.) If we resolve vertically

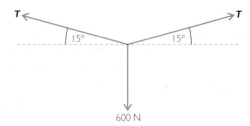

Figure 28   Force vector diagram for a Tyrolean traverse

$$T \cos 75° + T \cos 75° = 600 \text{ N}$$

(or $T \sin 15° + T \sin 15° = 600$ N)

$$2T \cos 75° = 600 \text{ N}$$

$$0.52T = 600 \text{ N}$$

$$T = 1160 \text{ N}$$

i.e. the tension is nearly twice the climber's weight.

QUESTION

20 (**a**) Repeat the calculation in the text for progressively smaller angles with the horizontal. (Hint: call the angle with the horizontal θ and produce a formula for T in terms of θ.) What is your general conclusion?

(**b**) If the rope is designed to take a maximum tension of 15 kN, what is the smallest angle the rope must be allowed to make with the horizontal for this particular weight of climber?

ACTIVITY **17**   **Model of Tyrolean traverse**

Set up the apparatus as in Figure 29 so that the tensions in both sides are *equal* and much bigger than **W**. Gently pull the load across the traverse from one side to the other by lowering one of the side masses, and investigate how the sag y varies with distance from the centre x (Figure 30).

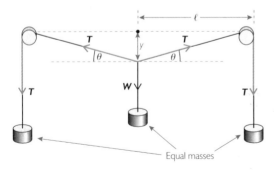

Figure 29   The starting arrangement for Activity 17

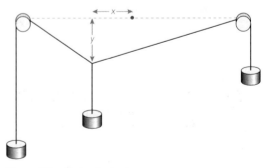

Figure 30   Moving the load

QUESTION

21 The cable car of question 17 is now being pulled up the mountain in calm conditions. The cable above it is at angle of 24° with the horizontal and the cable down to the valley station is at 23°.

(**a**) By resolving horizontally and vertically, form a pair of simultaneous equations containing the tension in each part of the cable. Solve these to find the tensions. (The weight of the car is 1×10^5 N.)

(**b**) Why is it impossible for the two angles to be the same? (Note: this question becomes much more manageable if you first draw a diagram and then write down your working carefully step by step.)

2.2 On the ropes

Climbing ropes obviously have to be **strong** (a large tension is needed to break them). Hanging from a horizontally supported rope can produce tensions several times the hanging weight, and if you fall while climbing, the safety rope must be able to exert large decelerating forces on your body.

Climbing ropes are also **elastic** – they stretch when put under tension, and return (not always completely) to the original length when the load is removed. A useful term to compare different samples is **stiffness**: one rope is stiffer than another if the extension is smaller for the same force. (The opposite to stiffness is **compliance**.)

The stiffness k of a sample is defined as

$$k = \frac{F}{x} \tag{14}$$

where F is the net applied force and x is the resulting extension. The SI units of stiffness are N m^{-1}.

ACTIVITY 18 **Tension and extension**

Use a variety of different 'ropes' (at least, fibres that could be made up into ropes) with the arrangement shown in Figure 31 to produce graphs showing how the extension varies with tension and to find the breaking strength of your sample.

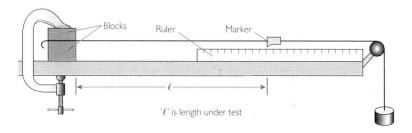

Figure 31 *Diagram for Activity 18*

Hooke's law

In Activity 18 you might have found that some of your samples had a constant stiffness for a range of loads. Samples that behave in this way are said to obey **Hooke's law**. For such a sample

$$\text{tension} \propto \text{extension} \qquad \text{or} \qquad F \propto x \qquad (15)$$

and the stiffness k is constant. In graphical terms, for Hooke's law to hold, the force–extension graph has to be linear *and pass through the origin*. You will probably find that your results show that Hooke's law is not very closely followed. A point where the graph starts to deviate significantly from Hooke's law is called the **limit of proportionality**.

Maths reference

Graphs and proportionality
See Maths note 5.1

Study note

There are some materials (notably metals) that follow Hooke's law quite well for small extensions, and then suddenly deviate from it. You will study this behaviour in the unit *Spare Part Surgery*.

QUESTIONS

22 A certain rope extends by 0.020 m when supporting a load of 800 N and by 0.012 m when supporting a load of 600 N. Does the rope obey Hooke's law? Calculate the stiffness of the rope under each of the loads.

23 Suppose a 2 m length of climbing rope obeys Hooke's law and has a stiffness of 60 kN m^{-1}.

(**a**) If the rope supports the weight of a 650 N climber, by how much does the rope extend?

(**b**) If the same climber was supported by 4 m of the same rope, what would be the extension?

Drop tests

The skill in designing climbing ropes for different tasks is to get the right combination of stiffness and strength. Climbing ropes are subjected to a standard drop test for safety certification: a mass of 80 kg attached to 5 m of the rope is dropped freely and the force exerted on the rope is measured as it brings the mass to rest.

2.3 Summing up part 2

In this part of the unit you have studied two areas of physics, both of which you will revisit shortly. In section 2.1 you have seen how to resolve and combine displacement and force vectors in two dimensions – you will meet these ideas again in parts 3 and 5 of this unit. You have also begun to study elastic properties of materials, which you will meet again in part 4 of this unit and later in this course.

ACTIVITY 19 **Summing up part 2**

Check through part 2 and make sure you know the meaning of all the terms printed in bold. Then discuss the following questions in a small group.

● What can you say (qualitatively) about the stiffness of a rope suitable for a Tyrolean traverse?

- When setting up a Tyrolean traverse, should you aim to get the rope nearly horizontal, or to let it sag?
- Thinking about the design of a rope for rock climbing, what are the consequences for the climber for making it either very stiff or very compliant?
- A climbing rope catalogue states that the standard drop test produces an extension of 7.5% of the original length. What extension(s) do(es) this correspond to for your samples in Activity 18? Would any sample have broken already in trying to reach this extension?
- What can you say about the motion of a falling climber from the instant the rope starts to go under tension?
- Suppose you had rope samples of widely varying stiffness and you subjected them to the standard drop test. Sketch a sequence of graphs (on the same axes of force against time) to show the effect of decreasing stiffness. (Qualitative only – no calculation.)

Maths reference

Fractions and percentages
See Maths note 3.1

Further investigations

For ropes with widely varying stiffnesses, use a force sensor to study how the tension in the rope varies with time during a drop test, and how this variation itself depends upon the stiffness.

The behaviour of many natural fibres is affected by their water content. Investigate how the force–extension graph and the breaking strength of some natural fibres depend on water content.

Activity 17 used a simple model of a Tyrolean traverse. Investigate, and analyse theoretically, a less simple model in which the rope extends. Investigate how the sag varies with load when the load is in the middle, or as a fixed load is moved from the middle to one end.

3 *Working out work*

3.1 *Energy return shoes*

Walk in to a sports shop, looking for a new pair of trainers, and you're confronted with an incredible choice. Gone are the old-style rubber 'plimsolls'; now you can attach space-age technology to your feet, packed with gels, fluids and air bags. Companies spend millions on research each year, with engineers putting new designs and materials through their paces with the help of computer-linked sensors in mechanical testing laboratories. The most significant innovation has been the advances in cushioning. A runner hits the ground with a force up to three times his or her body weight, so athletes have welcomed materials that lessen the impact and the chances of injury.

Cushioning aside, how do you choose between all the varieties? Sales people will often try to blind you with science and technological jargon. In this section we will examine one particular claim – that some shoes can supply you with extra energy, so you can jump higher, and run further. These 'energy return' shoes are supposed to store energy like a spring, in the cushioning material of the sole, when your foot hits the ground, and return it as you move off.

ACTIVITY 20 **Selling science**

Read the article in Figure 32 about the 'Recoil' trainer, a fairly recent one in a line of energy return shoes. Discuss in a group the following questions.

● How does the article use science to try to persuade the reader?
● What scientific claims do the manufacturers make?
● Are the claims supported by any evidence?

THE NEW RECOIL TRAINER FROM Z-TECH

The Z-Tech Recoil Trainer is the most exciting innovation in running shoes since rubber soles. Run in them once, and you'll never want to run in anything else.

THE Z-TECH SPRING...THE ULTIMATE SHOCK ABSORBER

When you run, you hit the ground with a force between 2-4 times your body weight. The majority of this force is transferred into your body immediately upon impact with the ground. This quick rate of impact is one of the main reasons so many runners suffer injuries. That's why we developed the Z-Tech Spring. The Spring offers the greatest impact absorption of any running shoe, significantly reducing impact related injuries.

The graph below illustrates the more gradual rate of impact of the Recoil running shoes vs. the competition. The reduction in impact translates into more effective and safer training.

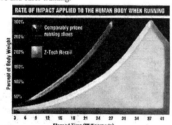

CUSTOMIZED SHOCK ABSORPTION... THREE SPRING TENSIONS

Since no two runners are alike, each Recoil Spring is available in three tensions based on your weight, training pace, and foot strike specifications. The Recoil is the only running shoe giving you customized shock absorption based on your body and running style. Each Spring is easily interchangeable and replaceable.

Research was conducted by the Los Alamos National Laboratory under the auspices of the U.S. Department of Energy. Testing performed compared shock absorption and energy return of the Recoil vs comparably priced running shoes. Testing procedures may not accurately reproduce the biomechanical forces and effects that would be experienced by an actual runner.

THE Z-PLATE... MAXIMIZING STABILITY

To ensure absolute stability on any surface, we've created the revolutionary Z-Plate. Located above the Spring midsole, it stabilizes and supports the heel, arch and center foot, while the Spring works independently.

ENERGY RETURN...

Other running shoes dissipate your precious energy, thus wasting it. The Recoil running shoe returns up to 49% of the impact energy with each step forward. Once compressed, hundreds of pounds of tension are built up and stored in the Z-Tech Spring. Upon release, this built up energy is catapulted back into your legs causing you to be propelled forward with a burst of power.

LEAVING THE COMPETITION IN THE DUST...

They may stare, some may even laugh, but not for long. Not after they realize that the Recoil makes you run more comfortably with less fear of injury. Not after you pass them on the track, or keep going long after they've tired. Especially not after they too, try a pair on. Because it only takes one try to know, right down to your bones, that the Recoil is everything you've ever wanted in a running shoe.

©1997 Z-tech Inc., Inc. All Rights Reserved
info@Ztech-inc.com

Figure 32 *The Recoil trainer*

How well does science imitate nature? Do 'energy return' shoes justify the hype? We will try to find out if there is any truth in the claims, using ideas about energy.

Energy

In your GCSE work you probably learned that there is gravitational potential energy, electrical energy, chemical energy – you may know several others. They are all measured in the same units, joules (J), but do you know what makes, say, gravitational energy different from chemical energy? When energy seems to come in so many varieties, things can start to become confusing. You may be relieved to know that, basically, there are only two 'types' of energy – **kinetic energy** and **potential energy**. All the others are really either kinetic or potential or a combination of the two.

Kinetic energy is the energy an object has because of its movement. Figure 33 shows two examples of kinetic energy: the sprinter clearly has kinetic energy, but so does a hot drink because its molecules are in rapid motion.

Figure 33 *Two examples illustrating kinetic energy*

Potential energy is the energy a body has due to its position or the arrangement of its parts. Look at the examples of potential energy in Figure 34.

Figure 34 *Three examples illustrating potential energy*

Gravitational energy, due to a body being raised up, is such a common example of potential energy, you can be forgiven for thinking it is the only one. But 'chemical energy' in the drink is really potential energy, due the arrangement of atoms in sugar molecules. The 'elastic energy' stored in the running-shoe sole is also potential energy because it is due to the rearrangement of molecules as the material is compressed.

You will also have met the idea of **energy conservation**: in any process, energy can be transferred but cannot be created or destroyed. While bearing in mind that all energy is kinetic or potential, it is still sometimes useful to use other terms to 'label' the stages in an energy transfer process in order to keep track of what is happening.

ACTIVITY 21 **Talking energy**

Describe the energy transfers that are shown in Figure 35.
    Can you think of a way of communicating with a friend that does not involve an energy transfer?

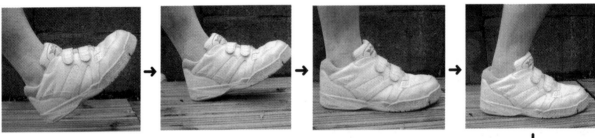

Figure 35   *The stages of a foot strike*

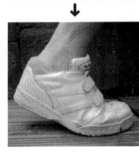

The claim for energy return shoes is that they store significant amounts of the runner's kinetic energy and return it as kinetic energy perhaps, to make you run faster, or jump higher. To investigate this further, we need to be able to measure energy.

Work

We measure the energy an object has by the **work** it can do. 'Work' in physics has a more precise meaning than in everyday life: work is done when something is moved by a force. So a body has energy if it can do work, i.e. move something else with a force. Look back at Figures 33 and 34 and convince yourself that all these examples of energy can do work. Work is defined as follows:

$$\text{work} = \text{force} \times \text{displacement } \textit{in direction of force} \qquad (16)$$

When work is done, energy is transferred, which gives us a useful way of measuring energy:

$$\text{work done} = \text{energy transferred} \qquad (17)$$

In symbols

$$\Delta E = \Delta W = F\Delta s \qquad (17a)$$

For example, at the start of a race, a rower pulls her oars backwards a distance of 0.8 m during a stroke, exerting a constant force of 250 N (Figure 36):

$$\text{work done} = 250\,\text{N} \times 0.8\,\text{m} = 200\,\text{J}$$

Study note

Force and displacement are both vectors, but equation (17a) involves their magnitudes. Work and energy are scalars.

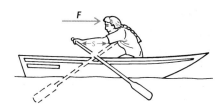

Figure 36 *A rower at the start of a race*

There has been an energy transfer: 200 J of potential energy (stored in her muscles) has been transferred so that she now has 200 J of kinetic energy.

Efficiency

In addition to the 200 J of 'useful' energy transfer, some energy will be 'wasted' in heating – rowing makes you hot! – so rather more than 200 J will have been transferred from her muscles altogether. The **efficiency** of any energy transfer process is defined as

$$\text{efficiency} = \frac{\text{energy usefully transferred}}{\text{total energy transferred}} \qquad (18)$$

Efficiency is often expressed as a percentage. For example, if the rower's muscles are 20% efficient, then 20% (one-fifth) of the energy transferred does work on the oars, while the remaining 80% is wasted in making her hot.

Maths reference

....

Fractions and percentages
See Maths note 3.1

....

Calculating energy return

Using the concept of work to measure energy, it is possible to test the claims about energy return shoes. For an adult male runner, Figure 37 shows the pattern of compressions in the sole of an 'energy return' shoe. As a rough approximation, the average force on the shoe during a running step is about 2.5 times body weight (about 2000 N for a person of mass 80 kg). From such pictures, we can estimate the average compression to be about 5 mm (0.005 m). So

$$\text{work done} = 2000\,\text{N} \times 0.005\,\text{m} = 10\,\text{J}$$

This figure agrees well with what researchers have found. They have also found that only about 6 J of this may be recovered (the rest is 'wasted' in heating the shoe and the surroundings). Could 6 J

(a)

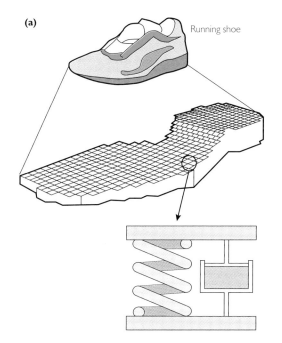

Running shoe

(b)

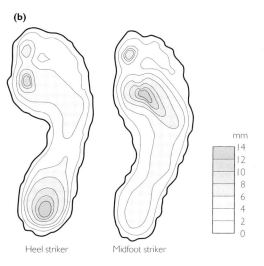

mm
14
12
10
8
6
4
2
0

Heel striker   Midfoot striker

Figure 37 *Computer-generated pictures showing*
(a) a model of how the sole of a shoe is compressed during impact and
(b) peak deflections of a sole caused by two types of runner

enable a basketball player to jump much higher? Can it give you extra speed while you're running? To answer these questions, we need some more formulae.

Kinetic and potential energy

As an object falls, it loses **gravitational potential energy**. If an object of mass m falls through a height Δh then the force acting is just the object's weight, and so

loss of gravitational potential energy = weight × loss of height (19)

If the object is moved upwards, then the process is reversed and it regains its gravitational energy. Using ΔE_{grav} to represent change in gravitational potential energy, and equation (7) to express the object's weight, we get

$$\Delta E_{grav} = mg\Delta h \qquad (19a)$$

Study note

Equation (19a) is often stated as $E_{grav} = mgh$, where h is the height above some zero reference point, e.g. the bench, or floor. But since there is no absolute reference point, you can really only calculate a *change* in potential energy.

ACTIVITY 22 **Gravitational energy in a jump**

Measure the height through which you can jump and hence calculate the change in your gravitational potential energy.

What difference would an additional 6 J from 'energy return' trainers make to the height of your jump?

What about running? How can we calculate kinetic energy? From your earlier work you are probably familiar with the formula for **kinetic energy** E_k of an object of mass m moving at speed v:

$$E_k = \tfrac{1}{2}mv^2 \qquad (20)$$

This expression can be derived using others that you have used in part 1 of this unit. Suppose a force of magnitude F accelerates an object of mass m from rest so that it reaches a speed v after moving through a distance Δs. Putting $u = 0$ in equation (5) we can write

$$v^2 = 2a\Delta s \qquad \text{so} \qquad a\Delta s = \tfrac{1}{2}v^2$$

We can also use equations (6) and (17a) to write

$$\Delta E_k = F\Delta s = ma\Delta s = \tfrac{1}{2}mv^2$$

Maths reference

Algebra and elimination
See Maths note 3.4

ACTIVITY 23 **Kinetic energy in running**

Measure your kinetic energy when running. Try to devise a way to measure your speed as accurately as possible.

What difference would 6 J from 'energy return' trainers make to your speed?

It is likely that you found that the energy returned was too small to give you much extra speed or height, so it looks as if the effect of energy return shoes is minimal. The only published research with real athletes (at the time of writing, 1999) did however find that running in a shoe with a gas-inflated cushioning system reduced the oxygen consumption by 2%, compared to a regular foam-cushioned shoe (although the researchers suggested that this could have been due to factors other than energy return).

Nature has already endowed us with an energy return mechanism, one which, it turns out, is rather more efficient. When your heel strikes the ground, about 70 J of energy are stored and returned by the quadriceps muscle in the lower leg, and another 70 J by the Achilles tendon. Energy return training shoes owe a lot more to marketing than to science.

QUESTIONS

24 Suppose the rower discussed above has an efficiency of 20%. How much energy is transferred from her muscles when she does 200 J of work?

25 Calculate the kinetic energy of a jet boat, mass 200 kg, that can tear across the water at 160 km h^{-1} (44 m s^{-1}).

26 Which do you think has more kinetic energy (don't calculate it), a speed skier at 150 mph or a small car travelling at 50 mph? Use the following typical figures to check whether your guess was right:

mass of car 600 kg	mass of skier 80 kg
speed of car 22 m s^{-1}	speed of skier 66 m s^{-1}

27 Acapulco, Mexico, is the home of high diving championships, where divers jump from a ravine 35 m above the sea.

(**a**) Calculate the loss in gravitational potential energy, and hence the gain in kinetic energy, of a diver of mass 65 kg, and so calculate the speed on hitting the sea.

(**b**) Explain whether a more massive diver would hit the sea at the same speed. (Assume the diver falls freely, i.e. gravity is the only force acting, and use g = 9.8 N kg^{-1} = 9.8 m s^{-2}.)

3.2 Speed skiing

Speed skiing (Figure 38) is the fastest non-motorised sport on Earth. The world record is close to 145 miles per hour – about the top speed of a sports car. Wearing only a rubber suit, and with feet strapped into two 2.4 m long boards, the speed skier hurtles down a steep 'waterfall' of ice.

The speed skier has a huge amount of kinetic energy, which in a collision could easily break every bone in the body, and prove fatal. Because of this the ski authorities limit the speed that the skiers can reach by specifying a maximum length of the acceleration zone (see Figure 39). They can calculate the maximum allowable distance using equations (17) and (19). But can you see a problem? Equation (17) says that we must use the displacement in the direction of the force, but the skier's motion is not parallel to the vertical force of gravity.

Figure 38 Speed skier

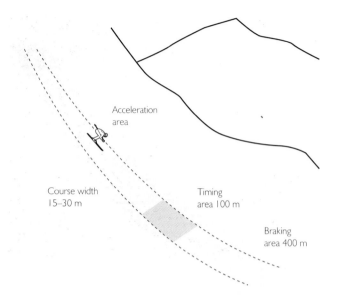

Acceleration area

Course width 15–30 m

Timing area 100 m

Braking area 400 m

Figure 39 *The RTS speed skiing course at Willamette Pass, Oregon, is one of three sanctioned courses in the USA and 10 in the world. One section has a 52° slope*

From Figure 40 you can see that, while the skier travels a distance Δs along the slope, the displacement *in the direction of the force* is the change in vertical height Δh. Using the trigonometric rules for a right angled triangle:

$$\Delta h = \Delta s \cos \theta$$

In other words, Δh is the vertical component of the skier's displacement vector. It is the component of the displacement parallel to the direction of the force, as described by equation (12) in part 2 of this unit. We can modify equation (17) to take account of the angle θ between force and displacement:

$$\Delta E = \Delta W = F\Delta s \cos \theta \qquad (21)$$

You can also arrive at equation (21) by considering the component of the force that acts along the slope, $F \cos \theta$, and multiplying by the overall displacement Δs.

(a)

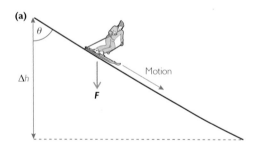

θ

Motion

Δh

F

(b)

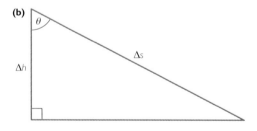

θ

Δs

Δh

Figure 40 *Skiing down a slope*

QUESTION

28 Calculate the maximum length of an acceleration zone at 50° to the horizontal if skiers are not to exceed 66 m s^{-1} (about 150 mph). (Hint: look at your answers to questions 26 and 27.)

3.3 Pumping iron

It's not just circus strong men and weight-lifters who pump iron. These days, gyms are full of people who build 'resistance training' into their workouts (Figure 41). Even if you don't play sport competitively, lifting weights can benefit your health. Stronger muscles are less prone to injury, and it is believed that building muscle can help you 'burn' your food more quickly.

Figure 41 *Pumping iron*

Power

Weight-training simply means increasing the resistance to a muscle's movement. Making the muscles work harder stimulates their growth. But for most athletes it's not strength itself that is the main objective, it's **power**. Loosely speaking, power is 'fast strength'. Whether it's in the legs, back, arms, or shoulders, power is important for almost every sport. If you look in a sports training manual, you might see power defined as:

$$\text{power} = \text{force} \times \text{velocity} \tag{22}$$

But if you consult a physics textbook you will find it is defined as 'the rate of doing work' or 'the rate of energy transfer':

$$\text{power} = \frac{\text{work done or energy transferred}}{\text{time taken}} \tag{23}$$

or

$$P = \frac{\Delta W}{\Delta t} \qquad \text{or} \qquad P = \frac{\Delta E}{\Delta t} \tag{23a}$$

The SI units of power are watts (W) or $J\,s^{-1}$; $1\,W = 1\,J\,s^{-1}$.

Both the physics and the sports definition of power involve force and time, but are they really the same thing?

Using equations (17) and (23)

$$P = \frac{(F\Delta s)}{\Delta t} = F\left(\frac{\Delta s}{\Delta t}\right)$$

From equation (1), $\Delta s/\Delta t = v$, and so we have

$$P = Fv \tag{22a}$$

So the two meanings are equivalent – they are both useful in different circumstances. (Remember, though: just as Δs is the displacement in the direction of the force, so v is the component of velocity in the direction of the force.)

Worked examples

Q   A woman training on a stepping machine 'climbs' 150 m in 2 minutes. If her mass is 60 kg, calculate her power.

A   Using equations (7), (17) and (23):

$$\text{work done against gravity} = F\Delta s = mg\Delta s$$

$$\text{power} = mg\frac{\Delta s}{\Delta t}$$

$$= \frac{60\,\text{kg} \times 9.8\,\text{N kg}^{-1} \times 150\,\text{m}}{120\,\text{s}} = 736\,\text{W}$$

Q   A Formula 1 racing car travelling at its top speed of 95 m s⁻¹ has an engine power of 15 kW. Calculate the thrust of the engine (i.e. the force it produces in the car).

A   Rearranging equation (22):

$$F = \frac{P}{v} = \frac{1.5 \times 10^4\,\text{W}}{95\,\text{m s}^{-1}} = 158\,\text{N}$$

In the second example, you might wonder why the engine needs to provide a thrust if the car is not accelerating. The thrust from the engine is balanced by an equal and opposite force from air resistance and friction with the road, and the car moves at constant velocity.

QUESTIONS

29 An athlete is working out, doing 'bench presses'. Each lift raises 60 kg through a distance of 60 cm. If he wants to generate 150 W of power, how quick does each lift have to be?

30 A sprinter, mass 60 kg, accelerates to her top speed of 10 m s⁻¹ in 3 s. Calculate her average power while accelerating.

Measuring power

Which type of sport are you better at: 'explosive' sports like sprinting, or activities that require more endurance? One reason why people often fall into one or other category is the composition of their muscles. There are two distinct types of muscle fibre (Figure 42), called slow twitch (ST) and fast twitch (FT). FT fibres produce more force and power but they can only operate over a short period. We all have different compositions of FT and ST muscle fibres. People who have a high percentage of ST muscle may have an advantage in prolonged endurance, whereas those with predominantly FT fibres are often better suited to short-term explosive activities. With world-class athletes the contrast is striking. Marathon champions, for instance, have over 90% ST fibres, whereas sprinters' muscles contain 75% FT fibres.

Every time you need a short burst of maximum power, you're relying on your FT fibres. Unlike ST fibres, which need oxygen to break down fuel, your FT fibres can work without it – anaerobically –

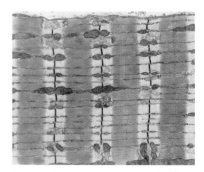

Figure 42   *A micrograph of human muscle*

but at a cost. If you continue to work at high power, a substance called lactic acid builds up in your muscles, making them hurt and eventually forcing you to stop or slow down.

ACTIVITY 24 Anaerobic power

In a laboratory or a gym, devise experiments to measure your power while running up stairs, cycling, jumping or sprinting. Compare your results with the averages shown in Figure 43.

ACTIVITY 25 The power of an athlete

Use *Multimedia Motion* to estimate the power produced by a weight-lifter, or by the Space Shuttle as it takes off.

Activity	Input power/W kg^{-1}
resting, lying down	1.2
sitting	1.2
standing	1.2
eating	1.2
dressing/undressing	2.3
showering	4.1
typing at a computer	2.3
walking (5.5 km h^{-1})	6.4
cycling (15 km h^{-1})	5.8
jogging (8 km h^{-1})	9.4
fast running (6 min mile)	18
swimming (fast crawl)	18
playing musical instrument	2.9
playing cricket	4.7
playing table tennis	5.3
playing tennis	7.1
skiing	9.4
dancing (energetically)	7.6
playing football	11
gymnastics	12

Table 3 *Some activities and their input power demands*

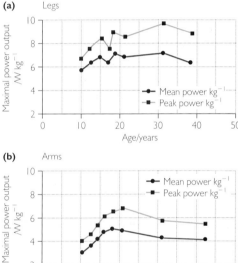

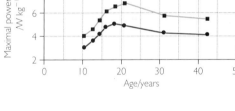

Figure 43 *Graphs of maximum power output per kg of body mass against age*

In any physical activity, the output power that you measure (as in Activities 24 and 25) is less than the overall input power from your muscles, because the process is never 100% efficient and you have not measured the energy wasted in heating. Table 3 lists some typical input powers for various activities. You might like like to compare them with your output power measured in Activity 24.

Event	Typical power
click beetle leaping into the air	0.5 W
TV when switched on	50 W
leaping red deer	2 kW
sports car	150 kW

Table 4 *Power ratings. Where do you fit in?*

ACTIVITY 26 **Aerobic power**

Find out what athletes mean by 'VO$_2$ max', and how this relates to oxygen uptake and aerobic power. Find out how you can measure your own aerobic power in a 'shuttle run'. Compare your own measurements with the data in Table 4.

ACTIVITY 27 **Energy demands**

Use the data in Table 3 to estimate how much energy you need to take in (from food) in a typical day.

A *Fuse* bar supplies about 1000 kJ. Use Table 3 to estimate how many *Fuse* bars you would 'burn off' during a sporting activity.

In discussion or by exchanging notes, compare your results with someone else's.

QUESTIONS

31 A sports car can generate a maximum 60 kW of power. If it has a mass of 800 kg, what is the minimum time in which the car could accelerate from rest to 30 m s^{-1}?

32 Your 'basal metabolic rate', the amount of power you generate while resting (pumping blood, breathing and keeping warm), is about 90 W. Calculate the amount of energy you need a day for simply existing.

33 A new 'kinetic' watch needs no battery. A tiny weight is set in motion by the slightest movements of your arm and, according to the manufacturer, enough energy to drive the watch for 2 weeks is stored electrically. If the power needed to drive the watch is 0.1 mW (1×10^{-4} W), estimate the amount of energy stored in the watch.

3.4 *Summing up part 3*

In this part of the unit you have seen how energy can be measured using the concept of work. You have applied the conservation of energy, and formulae for kinetic and gravitational potential energy, to model different sporting situations. Finally you have explored the relationship between power and energy.

ACTIVITY 28 **Summing up part 3**

A good way to reinforce the new ideas you have learned is to produce a 'concept map'. First make a list of all the terms printed in bold in this part of the unit – plus any others that you think important – spread out on a large sheet of paper. Then draw lines between all related terms. Finally label each line with a phrase or equation describing the link.

4 *Stretching and springing*

In this part of the unit, you are going to look at two sports that rely on elastic materials: bungee jumping (Figures 44 and 45) and pole vaulting. In doing so, you will revisit and use ideas from parts 1 to 3 of this unit.

Figure 44 *The popular sport of bungee jumping*

Figure 45 *One of the authors doing research for this unit*

4.1 *Bungee jumping*

Standing on a platform built from the side of a sheer cliff face, I looked down. Forty five metres below me the blue waters lay in wait, glistening in the sun. I had never been so terrified in my life. There was no way my brain was going to let me jump – it was as though an invisible force held me back.

'Stretch your arms out wide' came the voice from behind me, 'and whatever you do, don't grab the rope as you go down.' I tightened my shoelaces once more. 'Are you sure the rope won't slip off my ankles?' I asked.

The two technicians went through the equipment checklist a second time.

'Harnesses.' 'Checked.'

'Static sleeve.' 'Checked.'

'Hey, Bob. This carabiner's a bit loose. Do you think that matters?'

'No. It's been like that for ages.'

Bungee technicians took great pleasure in scaring first-timers.

'Okay, you're on for a jump!'

There was no turning back. Gingerly I stepped forward until my toes were right at the end of the platform. The countdown began. 'Five … four … three ….' The voice of fear in my head was replaced by another:

'How can you face your friends if you wimp out?' I jumped.

For the next three and a half seconds I was weightless – like an astronaut in orbit, but at a fraction of the cost. And what a rush it was! It's hard to describe because it was like being in another world – with no sound and nothing supporting me. My body felt utterly vulnerable, powerless to prevent itself smashing into the water surface at over 100 kilometres an hour.

Panic was beginning to swamp my consciousness, but just then came the reassuring tug on my ankles from the cord above. I knew bungee ropes could stretch to four times their natural length, but it seemed to extend forever. I could feel the tension building up and had to close my eyes. And then I felt the splash of water on my face as my head dipped briefly under, before I was pulled up again. Suddenly I was an enormous yo-yo, reaching fully half way back to the top. Gradually the bounces grew smaller and smaller until I came to rest above the waiting jet boat. The sense of relief was overwhelming.

Bungee jumping is not a new sport. For hundreds of years, men of the island of Pentecost, off Papua New Guinea, have leaped from wooden towers with jungle vines attached to their ankles (Figure 46). For them it's a test of courage – the closer they swoop to the ground, the greater their bravery. Inevitably there have been deaths, one of which happened while Queen Elizabeth II and the Royal Family were watching the ceremony. So how has bungee jumping evolved into a relatively safe activity?

It's got a lot to do with two guys from New Zealand. One is a daredevil businessman called A. J. Hackett, and the other, Henry van Asch, a physicist. Back in the mid-1980s they planned some outrageous stunts to bring bungee jumping to the world's attention, including a leap from the Eiffel Tower. A policeman arrested Hackett after the jump (presumably once he'd stopped bouncing). A. J. Hackett Bungee became the world's first professional bungee operation in Queenstown, New Zealand. Since then, bungee jumping has become established worldwide.

Figure 46 *The origins of bungee jumping*

Analysing a bungee jump

In Activity 29 you are going to put yourself into the position of a bungee designer: given a piece of bungee rope, how do you choose the length to stop someone just short of the ground? Make it too long and they're history; too short and you'll remove a lot of the excitement. Before you do, you will see how can you apply the physics of this unit to working out the correct length of bungee rope.

One approach to solving many problems involving motion is to use forces. The forces on a bungee jumper are shown in Figure 47. Because the tension in the rope varies with extension, the force on the jumper is not constant, which makes it difficult to apply the equations of motion.

Another approach is to use energy conservation. Figure 48 shows the energy transfers at different stages during a jump. As the jumper falls, he loses gravitational potential energy. At first, during free fall, he gains kinetic energy. Then the rope begins to stretch, reducing the jumper's kinetic energy. Energy is transferred to the rope as it stretches, so the rope now has potential energy that we will call **elastic energy** (and symbolise E_{el}). When the jumper comes momentarily to rest at the bottom of the first 'bounce', his kinetic energy is again zero; he has lost gravitational potential energy and the rope has gained elastic potential energy. Energy conservation tells us that the gravitational energy lost ($mg\Delta h$) must be equal to the elastic energy gained by the rope.

Figure 47   *The forces on a bungee jumper*

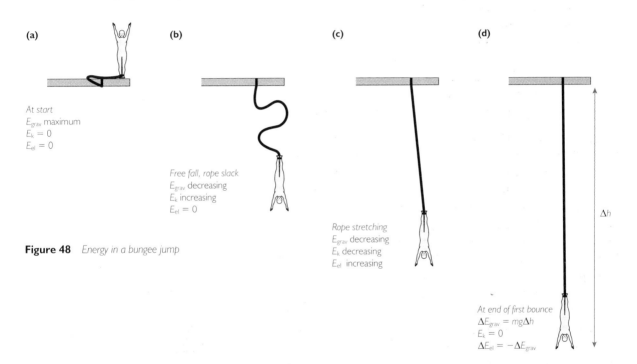

Figure 48   *Energy in a bungee jump*

Measuring elastic energy

You will remember we used the definition of work to derive formulae for gravitational and kinetic energy. Force–extension graphs give us a way to find the work done in stretching a bungee rope. Figure 49 shows a typical force–extension graph. The force varies, so we cannot simply multiply force by distance to find the work done in stretching the sample. But for a small increase in extension, Δx, the stretching force F is *very nearly* constant, so the work done is equal to the area of the strip:

$$\Delta W = F \times \Delta x$$

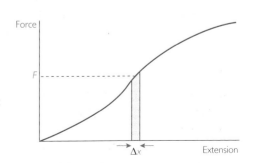

Figure 49   *A force–extension graph*

The total work done in stretching the sample can be found by adding up all the areas of the narrow strips (each with a different height). In other words, the elastic energy stored can be found from the **area under a force–extension graph**.

For a material that obeys Hooke's law, the force–extension graph is a straight line (Figure 50) and there is a simple formula for E_{el}:

$$E_{el} = \tfrac{1}{2}Fx \tag{24}$$

where F is the force needed to produce an extension x. Using equation (14) we can write an expression involving the stiffness k, which is constant for a sample that obeys Hooke's law:

$$E_{el} = \tfrac{1}{2}kx^2 \tag{25}$$

However, with a rubber bungee cord, which does not obey Hooke's law, the graph is curved. We therefore estimate the area by counting the squares of graph paper under the curve. In Figure 51, the values for force and extension are marked on the graph. On the scale shown, the area of each square represents $10\,\text{N} \times 0.1\,\text{m} = 1\,\text{J}$. You can estimate the area by counting only the squares where at least half the area is under the curve, giving 25 squares, i.e. the elastic energy stored is 25 J.

Study note

Notice that this is very similar to finding the distance travelled from a velocity–time graph. See section 1.3.

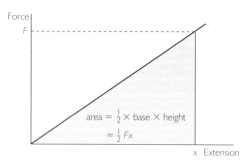

Figure 50   *A force–extension graph for a material that obeys Hooke's law*

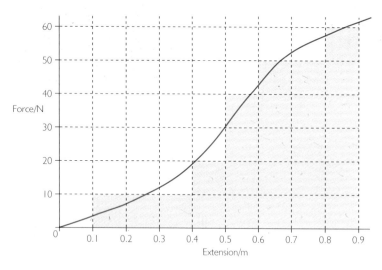

Figure 51   *Estimating E_{el} by counting squares*

ACTIVITY 29   **Bungee challenge**

Set up a model bungee jump, using a piece of elastic. By calculating elastic energy from a force–extension graph, you can work out the height from which a given object can 'jump' with a given piece of elastic, so that it will just miss the floor.

QUESTIONS

34 In a bow and arrow, the wire stretches by 60 cm when the bow is pulled back. If the stiffness of the wire is 0.4 N m^{-1}, how much elastic energy is stored?

35 In most bungee jumps, several cords are used, just in case one of them fails. *The number of cords depends on the jumper's body weight.* Explain the sentence in italics.

36 In February 1992 Greg Rifti set a world bungee record jumping from a helicopter with a rope 250 m long. His cord stretched to 610 m (2000 feet). Calculate (**a**) the gravitational potential energy lost as he fell (take his mass to be 75 kg), (**b**) the stiffness of the cord assuming it obeyed Hooke's law and (**c**) the extension of the cord when he finally came to rest.

4.2 Pole vaulting

Pole vaulters are truly the astronauts of the stadium (Figure 52). The Russian pole vaulter, Sergei Bubka, who has steadily pushed the record up past 6 metres, is effectively jumping over three people, one on top of the other. In the 1960s, there was a sudden rise in the pole vault record heights (Figure 53). It was the result of fibreglass poles being introduced, replacing bamboo and aluminium poles. Fibreglass totally changed the event, allowing the pole to bend nearly into a half circle during the swing.

Can we expect the pole vault record to keep on increasing, or is there a limit? Answer questions 37 and 38 to help you decide.

Figure 52 *Pole vaulting*

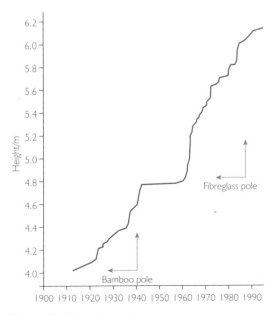

Figure 53 *Pole vault records*

QUESTIONS

37 Write down the labels that you would need to add to Figure 54 so that it shows the energy in a pole vault (like Figure 48 showed for a bungee jump).

38 (**a**) If a pole vaulter can sprint at 10 m s^{-1} (the world sprint record is 10.1 m s^{-1}), through what height can he raise his centre of gravity if all his kinetic energy is used to supply additional gravitational potential energy?

(**b**) Assuming that the vaulter's centre of gravity is 1 m above the ground when running, estimate the height of the vault.

(**c**) Say what, in practice, might (**i**) prevent the vaulter from clearing this height or (**ii**) enable him to exceed this height.

(**d**) Say whether you think the graph in Figure 53 will keep on rising.
(Use g = 9.8 N kg^{-1} = 9.8 m s^{-2}.)

(**a**) The run-up   (**b**) Bending the pole   (**c**) Vaulting over the bar

Figure 54   *Stages in a pole vault*

Further investigations

Investigate the energy transfers in a model pole vault. Devise a way to measure the work done in deforming a springy rod, and the kinetic energy that it imparts to a catapulted mass. Compare the efficiency of the energy transfer obtained with rods of different materials. Scale up the results from your model and compare them with real pole vault records.

4.3 Summing up part 4

In this part of the unit you have seen how to apply the idea of energy conservation and how to measure elastic energy using a force–extension graph. In doing so, you have used and extended ideas from earlier in the unit. Questions 39 to 42 give you further practice in using ideas about energy.

QUESTIONS

Use $g = 9.8 \text{ N kg}^{-1} = 9.8 \text{ m s}^{-2}$ in these questions.

39 An overhead electricity cable between two pylons stretches 50 cm under its own weight. How much elastic energy does it store? (Assume the cable obeys Hooke's law and has $k = 10^7 \text{ N m}^{-1}$.)

40 Itaipu, the world's biggest hydroelectric power station, lies near one of the world's natural wonders – the Iguacu Falls in South America, It supplies 25% of Brazil's energy needs. The power station generates 12 GW of power (one gigawatt, $1 \text{ GW} = 10^9 \text{ W}$), when the flow of water is $10\,000 \text{ m}^3 \text{ s}^{-1}$.

(**a**) Calculate the mass of water flowing per second (take the density of water $= 1000 \text{ kg m}^{-3}$).

(**b**) Estimate the height through which the water drops. What assumption did you make? Will this lead to an underestimate or an overestimate of the height?

41 (**a**) A swimmer moving at constant speed through the water uses a force to do work, but does not increase her kinetic energy. How can this be?

(**b**) Figure 55 is a graph of the energy cost of swimming a kilometre for aquatic animals. For humans, a typical energy cost while swimming is 80 kJ min^{-1} and it takes many minutes to swim a kilometre. Approximately where on the graph would the 'human' data point lie? Comment on this.

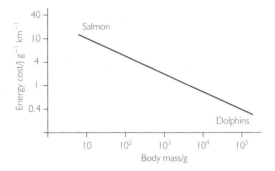

Figure 55   *The energy cost of swimming*

42 Here is an energy puzzle. A rock climber slips vertically, gradually stretching her rope until it supports her, i.e. the tension in the rope is equal to her weight ($F = mg$). She falls through a height Δh and her rope is stretched by the same amount. She has lost gravitational potential energy $\Delta E_{\text{grav}} = mg\Delta h$. But the elastic energy stored in the rope (which obeys Hooke's law) is $\Delta E_{\text{el}} = \frac{1}{2} Fx = \frac{1}{2} mg\Delta h$.

What has happened to the 'missing energy'?

5 *Jumping and throwing*

Many events in the Olympics involve launching objects into the air. The jumping events involve throwing your own body as a **projectile** and the throwing events involve launching another object.

The four Olympic throwing events are discus, shot, javelin and hammer. Despite the varying masses and shapes of all these objects thrown, there are two main aspects that all throwers have to master: a speed-building phase, and a throwing position angle.

The main components of long jump are horizontal speed and vertical lift. International long jumpers should be fast enough to earn a place in their national relay squad. Jesse Owens and Carl Lewis were the world's fastest sprinters in their time and were also the best long jumpers. Heiki Dreschler, one of the world's best ever women long jumpers, was joint world record holder for the 200 m and has a personal best of 10.91 s for the 100 m sprint. Coaching for the long jump involves coaching for sprinting. The long jump also involves achieving sufficient height to stay in the air for a long time. The longer the time in the air and the greater the horizontal speed, the greater the horizontal distance travelled.

5.1 Ski jumping

The Winter Olympic sport of ski jumping is similar to the long jump – the aim is to leave the ramp at high speed in order to travel as far as possible before landing. In this section, you will explore the relationship between the launch speed and the length of the 'jump' and so reach some general conclusions about projectiles that move freely under gravity.

ACTIVITY **30** **Ski jump**

Use the arrangement shown in Figure 56 to see how the launch height h_1 and the height of the vertical drop h_2 affect the horizontal distance travelled.

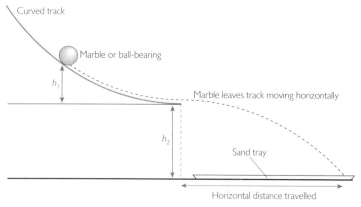

Figure 56 *A model ski jump*

Activity 30 shows that increasing the launch height and the vertical drop both increase the length of the jump. How can these results be explained more precisely? Activity 31 provides a clue.

ACTIVITY **31** **Projectile motion**

Release two squash balls side by side at the same time. Do they hit the floor at the same time? Repeat, but this time launch one squash ball horizontally. Do they hit the floor at the same time?

Figure 57 shows strobe photographs of two balls moving as in Activity 31. Notice that they both hit the floor at the same time. It does not matter that one of them has got a horizontal velocity as well as a vertical acceleration. Notice, too, that the sideways-moving ball covers equal horizontal distances in equal time intervals – its horizontal velocity remains constant and is unaffected by its vertical motion. The two vertical and horizontal components of the motion are *independent of each other*, so we can treat them quite separately.

Projectile motion

The displacement, velocity and acceleration of the projectile (the ball or the skier) are all vectors. We can treat the horizontal components of these vectors completely separately from the vertical components. We will use x and y to indicate horizontal and vertical displacements, and use the labels x and y to indicate components of velocity and acceleration.

If the ball, or skier, leaves the ramp horizontally, the initial velocity vector has no vertical component: $u_y = 0$. In the vertical direction, the force of gravity provides a uniform acceleration, so the vertical component of velocity increases. The vertical motion is described by equations (3b) and (4a) with $a_y = g = 9.8 \text{ m s}^{-2}$, taking downwards as positive:

$$v_y = gt \qquad \text{and} \qquad y = \tfrac{1}{2}gt^2 \qquad (26)$$

In the horizontal direction there is no component of the gravitational force, so there is no acceleration: $a_x = 0$. The horizontal velocity remains equal to its initial value u_x, and the horizontal motion is described by equation (27), which is the same as equation (4a) with $a = 0$:

$$x = u_x t \qquad (27)$$

The horizontal and vertical components combine to give a projectile a **trajectory** (path through the air) that has the shape of a **parabola**. Activity 32 illustrates this.

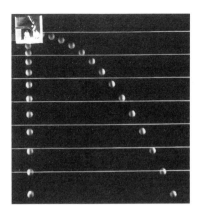

Figure 57   *Strobe photographs of projectiles*

ACTIVITY 32   **Parabolic trajectory**

Use equations (26) and (27) to complete Table 5 and hence to plot the trajectory of a ball thrown sideways at 2 m s^{-1}.

Time t/s	Vertical displacement y/m	Horizontal displacement x/m
1		
2		
3		
4		
5		

Table 5   *Table for Activity 32*

The following example shows how analysis of projectile motion can be useful in police forensic work.

Worked example

Q A car ran off a mountain road and landed 80 m from the foot of a cliff face having fallen 100 m. Was the driver going too fast? The speed limit was 30 mph (about 13 m s^{-1}).

A If air resistance is ignored, the horizontal component of the velocity will not change as the car leaves the road and travels through the air. The horizontal velocity can be estimated if the horizontal distance travelled (80 m) is divided by the time that the car is in the air.

Dealing with vertical motion first to find t:

displacement vertically, $y = 100$ m
initial vertical velocity, $u_y = 0$ m s^{-1}
acceleration downwards due to gravity, $g \approx 10$ m s^{-2}

Using equation (26): $y = \frac{1}{2}gt^2$, so

$$t = \sqrt{\frac{2y}{g}} = \sqrt{\frac{2 \times 100 \text{ m}}{10 \text{ m s}^{-2}}} = 4.47 \text{ s}$$

Now the horizontal velocity can be found using equation (27):

$$u_x = \frac{x}{t} = \frac{80 \text{ m}}{4.47 \text{ s}} = 17.897 \text{ m s}^{-1} \approx 18 \text{ m s}^{-1}$$

So the driver was well over the speed limit and this probably contributed to the accident.

5.2 Throwing

In throwing events such as the discus and shot, and in games such as football and golf, the projectile is *not* launched horizontally. But what launch angle gives the maximum range?

A top British shot putter (ranked third in the UK with a distance of 17.90 m) took part in biomechanical tests to find the limiting factors in his performance. The digitised information from a video of his throwing was analysed by computer. Data on height of release h, projection speed V, and projection angle θ (see Figure 58) were all recorded. By calculating the effect of changing the angle and launch speed, he found that he needed to increase the speed and alter the launch angle. By changing his technique, he increased his personal best by 0.4 m and set a new Scottish National record.

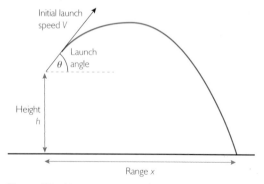

Figure 58 *Measurements on a shot putt trajectory*

The range of a projectile

The motion of a shot can be analysed by resolving the initial velocity into horizontal and vertical components:

$$u_x = V \cos \theta \qquad \text{and} \qquad u_y = V \sin \theta \qquad (28)$$

and then treating the horizontal and vertical motions independently.

For a projectile launched from ground level ($b = 0$), the time of flight can be found by considering the vertical component of its motion and using equation (4a):

$$s = ut + \tfrac{1}{2}at^2$$

With $s = 0$ (the projectile falls back to the ground), $u = u_y = V \sin \theta$ and $a = -g$, we have

$$0 = Vt \sin \theta - \frac{gt^2}{2}$$

so

$$\frac{gt^2}{2} = Vt \sin \theta$$

$$t = \frac{2V \sin \theta}{g} \qquad (29)$$

The horizontal displacement can then be found using equation (27):

$$x = u_x t$$

$$= V \cos \theta \times \frac{2V \sin \theta}{g}$$

$$= \frac{2V^2 \sin \theta \cos \theta}{g} \qquad (30)$$

In this simple situation, the range is greatest for $\theta = 45°$. However, real life is less straightforward – for a start, b is rarely zero. Also, air resistance significantly affects the motion of many projectiles, so the launch angle varies according to the object in question.

The angle of release in a hammer throw is close to 45° because it is launched from near the ground and because air resistance has little effect on its motion. The shot putt requires an angle less than 45° because it is launched from a position higher than where it lands. Because of their shape, a discus and javelin 'float' on the air: the angle of release depends on release speed and headwind, but is always less than 45°. The effects of 'spin' and air resistance make the trajectories of cricket and golf balls even more complicated – again, their best launch angle is less than 45°.

Using a computer model

In Activity 33, you use a computer to calculate the range of a projectile launched from above the ground. The main power of the computer is that it can perform routine calculations very quickly. You, as the scientist, just need to tell it the correct calculations to perform. Once you get an equation of the physics correct and set up a working computer program based on the correct physical equation, you can design problems that may be very difficult or expensive to run for real. If the results do not match up with what happens in a real-world experiment, this tells you that the equation inserted in the program is probably wrong. Refinements can then be made until the computer simulation is closer to reality. Effectively, you can perform a computer experiment and obtain results quickly, cheaply and safely. Engineers design aircraft, cars, buildings and bridges in this way.

ACTIVITY **33** **Range of a projectile**

By carrying out some algebra, derive an equation for the range of a projectile launched from above the ground. Ignore air resistance. Use a spreadsheet to calculate the range for various launch speeds and angles.

5.3 *Summing up part 5*

In this part of the unit you have revisited ideas about vectors and about uniformly accelerated motion and used them to study projectiles. Questions 43 to 45 and Activities 34 and 35 use these ideas in a variety of sporting and non-sporting situations – real and imaginary!

┌─ QUESTIONS ───

43 A skier slides down the slope shown in Figure 59, leaving the ramp at X horizontally at $20\,\mathrm{m\,s^{-1}}$.

(**a**) She drops through 20 m before hitting the mountainside at Y. Calculate the time this takes.

(**b**) Using the time from (**a**), calculate the horizontal displacement R.

(**c**) Explain how each of the following actions affects the distance R:
  (**i**) the skier pushes herself off horizontally when leaving X;
  (**ii**) the skier tries to jump upwards at X before leaving the ramp.

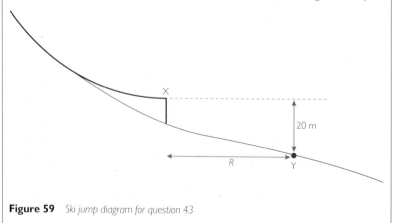

Figure 59 *Ski jump diagram for question 43*

───

44 A cartoon character (like 'Roadrunner' for example) is sometimes shown running off the edge of a cliff (Figure 60). It is only when he looks down and realises that there is no ground at his feet that he stops moving forwards and starts to drop vertically.

(**a**) Explain what *should* happen to his horizontal component of his velocity and the vertical component of his velocity as soon as he runs off the edge of the cliff.

(**b**) Sketch the cartoon trajectory of his motion and also the correct physical parabolic trajectory.

Figure 60   *A cartoon character runs over the edge of a cliff*

45 Figure 61 is from a 16th century book, and shows the supposed trajectory of a cannon ball.

(**a**) What evidence have you seen that shows that such a trajectory is incorrect?

(**b**) Sketch a more realistic path for the cannon ball (ignoring air resistance).

(**c**) If the cannon ball is launched from ground level at a speed of 50 m s^{-1}, calculate its range for launch angles of 30°, 45° and 60°.

Figure 61   *The supposed trajectory of a cannon ball, drawn in 1561*

ACTIVITY **34** **What happens next?**

A James Bond-type super-hero has just spotted a wicked villain climbing over the balcony of a building opposite, intent on some dastardly deed (Figure 62). He takes aim and fires. Just as he does so, the villain notices what's happening and lets go, hoping to drop to the ground and escape. What happens next? Does the villain escape the bullet? Use your knowledge of projectile motion to complete the story.

Figure 62 *What happens next?*

ACTIVITY 35 Force to kick a football

How much force is exerted in kicking a football? Figure 63 shows an experimental set-up that you can use to find out. Discuss how you can deduce the force from the measurements indicated, and then carry them out.

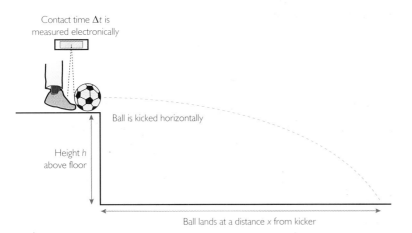

Figure 63   *Apparatus for Activity 35*

Further investigations

Use computer models and experimental measurements to investigate the effect of air resistance on the range of projectiles with various shapes.

6 *Last lap*

6.1 *Summing up the unit*

In this unit you have studied some aspects of motion, balanced and unbalanced forces, and energy. This concluding section is intended to help you to look back over the whole unit and consolidate your knowledge and understanding.

ACTIVITY 36 Sports consultant

Look back through the unit and make sure you know the meanings of the key terms printed in bold.

Use what you have learned in this unit to write a brief guide for a coach, or sports teacher to help them integrate physics into their training. Choose any sport you like which involves one or more of the concepts you have studied in the unit. Here are a few possibilities: high jump, skiing, paragliding, sailing.

Include explanations of the relevant physics principles, and how to apply them to the sport. Write in an appropriate style for your readers.

Throughout this unit, you have seen how graphs can be just as useful as equations in calculating physical quantities. You have used the gradient of a graph and the area under a graph.

ACTIVITY **37** **Using graphs**

Summarise in a table all the different quantities you know how to find using gradients and areas of graphs along with the graph they are measured from.

ACTIVITY **38** **Advertising**

Recently, a tyre manufacturer has introduced a new tyre designed to improve fuel consumption – see Figure 64.

Imagine you are in the marketing department. You have been asked to write the text of a short newspaper advertisement for the 'Energy Tyre', designed to show how much further a tank of petrol will take you, and why – simply. The technical department have supplied the graph shown in Figure 65, and the data given below.

Tyre data:
- Fuel consumption of average family car with normal tyres = 9.5 litres per 100 km
- Reduction in fuel consumption with 'Energy Tyres' = 3%
- The 'Energy Tyre' is the first example of 'low rolling resistance' technology'. Rolling resistance: the absorption of energy and its dissipation in the form of heat, by the tyre, as a result of low-frequency deformation
- High-frequency, microscopic deformation of the tyre also occurs, and results in grip

---

Figure 64 *A new design of tyre*

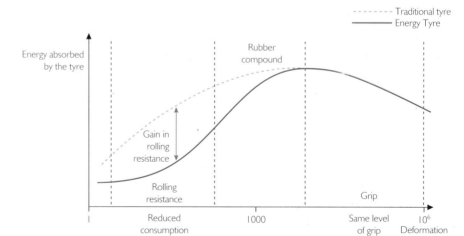

Figure 65 *Tyre data for Activity 38*

1 Hz means 1 deformation per second

6.2 Questions on the whole unit

QUESTIONS

46 A fielder throws a cricket ball of mass 160 g towards the stumps. The wicket keeper catches the ball, which is travelling at 15 m s^{-1}. In bringing the ball to rest, his hands move 0.4 m backwards. What is the average stopping force applied to the ball?

47 In 1976, basketball player Darrell Griffith's standing vertical jump measured 1.20 m. Estimate the speed at which he left the ground.

48 A karate expert sets up a block of wood, mass 500 g, to break with his fist. The energy needed to smash the block is 40 J. Estimate the minimum speed of the karate expert's fist to break it, assuming that all its kinetic energy is transferred to the block.

49 Before a match, a trainer makes his players take in 640 g of carbohydrate food. If 100 g produces 100 kJ of useful energy, estimate the average power expended over a 90 minute game.

50 A ski-lift can carry 100 people at a time up a slope at 20° to the horizontal, at 3 m s^{-1}. Estimate the minimum power of the ski-lift motor.

51 When an aeroplane lands on an aircraft carrier, it can be stopped by a huge steel 'arresting wire', stretched across the deck. A plane of mass 20 t lands at 50 m s^{-1} and the wire has a stiffness $k = 3.3 \times 10^8$ N m^{-1}. (1 t = 1 $\times$ 10^3 kg). Find:

(**a**) the kinetic energy of the plane on landing,

(**b**) the amount the arresting wire stretches (assuming the wire obeys Hooke's law).

52 A car skidded off the road and hit a low stone wall. Glass from the windscreen was found 4.0 m in front of the car windscreen in the field.

(**a**) If the height of the middle of the windscreen was 1.2 m, estimate the speed of the car as it hit the wall.

(**b**) Why is this value likely to be lower than the actual speed of the car when it had been on the road?

53 (**a**) In a sprint race a sprinter of mass 55 kg had an initial horizontal acceleration of 10 m s^{-2}, produced by the force with which her feet pushed against the starting blocks. Calculate the size of this accelerating force.

(**b**) An average net force of 200 N is exerted on a tennis ball, which has a mass of 0.055 kg, while it is in contact with the racket. Calculate the ball's average acceleration during this contact time.

(**c**) A golf club strikes a golf ball with an average force of 6.00 kN, producing an average acceleration of 1.40 $\times$ 10^5 m s^{-2}. What must be the mass of the ball?

6.3 Achievements

Now you have studied this unit you should be able to:

- distinguish between scalar and vector quantities and give examples of each (1.2)*;

- resolve a vector into two components at right angles to each other by drawing and by calculation (2.1, 3.2);

- combine two coplanar vectors at any angle to each other by drawing, and at right angles to each other by calculation (2.1);

- construct displacement–time and velocity–time graphs for uniformly accelerated motion (1.3);

- determine the slope and area of a graph by drawing and (in the case of a straight-line graph) by calculation (1.3, 4.1);

- identify and use the physical quantities derived from the slopes and areas of displacement–time and velocity–time graphs, including cases of non-uniform acceleration (1.3);

- recall and use the expressions $v = \Delta s/\Delta t$ and $a = \Delta v/\Delta t$ (1.2);

- recognise and use the kinematic equations for motion in one dimension with constant velocity or constant acceleration (1.2, 1.3, 5.1, 5.2);

- recognise and make use of the independence of vertical and horizontal motion of a projectile moving freely under gravity (5.1, 5.2);

- recall and use the relationship $F = ma$ in situations where mass is constant (1.4);

- recall and use the independent effect of perpendicular components of a force (2.1, 3.2);

- understand and use the concept of *work* in terms of the product of a force and a displacement in the direction of that force, including situations where the force is *not* along the line of motion (3.1, 3.2);

- calculate power from the rate at which work is done or energy is transferred (3.3);

- recall and use the relationship $E_k = \frac{1}{2}mv^2$ for the kinetic energy of a body (3.1);

- recall and use the fact that the strength of a gravitational field is $g = F/m$ and hence that weight $W = mg$ (1.4, 4.1, 4.2);

- recall and use the relationship $\Delta E_{grav} = mg\Delta h$ for the gravitational potential energy transferred near the Earth's surface (3.1, 4.1, 4.2);

- apply the principle of conservation of energy to examples involving gravitational potential energy and kinetic energy (3.1, 4.1, 4.2).

* Numbers indicate the section(s) that relate to each achievement.

Answers

1 $v = u + a\Delta t$
$\quad = 2.0\,\mathrm{m\,s^{-1}} + 1.5\,\mathrm{m\,s^{-2}} \times 3.0\,\mathrm{s}$
$\quad = 2.0\,\mathrm{m\,s^{-1}} + 4.5\,\mathrm{m\,s^{-1}} = 6.5\,\mathrm{m\,s^{-1}}.$

2 $v = u + a\Delta t$. Assuming he is falling from rest,
$u = 0\,\mathrm{m\,s^{-1}}$.
Taking downwards as positive, $a = g = +9.8\,\mathrm{m\,s^{-2}}$,
$\Delta t = 2.5\,\mathrm{s}$, and so
$v = +9.8\,\mathrm{m\,s^{-2}} \times 2.5\,\mathrm{s} = +24.5\,\mathrm{m\,s^{-1}}.$

3 $a = \dfrac{v - u}{\Delta t}$

$\quad = \dfrac{0\,\mathrm{m\,s^{-1}} - 9.0\,\mathrm{m\,s^{-1}}}{0.003\,\mathrm{s}}$

$\quad = \dfrac{-9.0\,\mathrm{m\,s^{-1}}}{0.003\,\mathrm{s}}$

$\quad = 3000\,\mathrm{m\,s^{-2}}.$

4 $a = \dfrac{v - u}{\Delta t}$

$v = -25\,\mathrm{m\,s^{-1}}, u = 5.0\,\mathrm{m\,s^{-1}}, \Delta t = 0.012\,\mathrm{s}$

$a = \dfrac{(-25\,\mathrm{m\,s^{-1}} - 5.0\,\mathrm{m\,s^{-1}})}{0.012\,\mathrm{s}}$

$\quad = -2500\,\mathrm{m\,s^{-2}}.$

Note that the velocity directions are carefully given positive and negative signs, positive for rightwards velocity and negative for leftwards.

5   (a) $\Delta s = 4.0\,\mathrm{m}$ (s has increased from 2.0 m to 6.0 m) and $\Delta t = 4.0\,\mathrm{s}$, so $v = 4.0\,\mathrm{m}/4.0\,\mathrm{s} = 1.0\,\mathrm{m\,s^{-1}}.$

   (b) If you draw any other triangle on this graph you should get the same velocity.

6   (a) The velocity would be more than $1.0\,\mathrm{m\,s^{-1}}$ – displacement increases by more than 1.0 m in each second.

   (b) The velocity would be negative, i.e. the motion is in the negative direction so the displacement in the positive direction decreases with time – or (if the graph goes below the horizontal axis) the displacement becomes larger in the negative direction.

7   Using the triangle shown, $\Delta v = 7.5\,\mathrm{m\,s^{-1}} - 3.5\,\mathrm{m\,s^{-1}}$
$= 4.0\,\mathrm{m\,s^{-1}}$ and $\Delta t = 2.0\,\mathrm{s}$ so

$\quad a = \dfrac{4.0\,\mathrm{m\,s^{-1}}}{2.0\,\mathrm{s}} = 2.0\,\mathrm{m\,s^{-2}}.$

Using any other triangle would give the same answer.

8   The graph would slope downwards from left to right, showing that the velocity in the positive direction is decreasing, or (if the graph goes below the horizontal axis) that the velocity is increasing in the negative direction.

9   Using equation (3),
final velocity
$v = u + a\Delta t = 8.00\,\mathrm{m\,s^{-1}} + 0.70\,\mathrm{m\,s^{-2}} \times 3.00\,\mathrm{s}$
$\quad = 8.0\,\mathrm{m\,s^{-1}} + 2.1\,\mathrm{m\,s^{-1}} = 10.1\,\mathrm{m\,s^{-1}}.$

displacement
$s = ut + \tfrac{1}{2}at^2$
$\quad = 8.00\,\mathrm{m\,s^{-1}} \times 3.00\,\mathrm{s} + \tfrac{1}{2} \times 0.70\,\mathrm{m\,s^{-2}} \times (3.00\,\mathrm{s})^2$
$\quad = 24.0\,\mathrm{m} + 3.15\,\mathrm{m} = 27.15\,\mathrm{m}$

10 A is ahead (there is a larger area under A's graph).
   A's total displacement can be found by adding together the areas (1–4) of the triangles and rectangles as shown in Figure 66:
displacement $= 37.5\,\mathrm{m} + 75\,\mathrm{m} + 5\,\mathrm{m} + 65\,\mathrm{m}$
$\qquad\qquad\quad = 182.5\,\mathrm{m}.$
   Alternatively, use equation (4) – but remember to treat each 10 s interval separately, since the acceleration is different in each case.

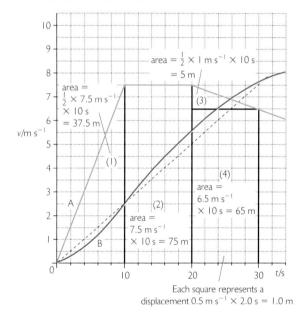

Figure 66   *See the answer to question 10*

B's total displacement can be found by counting the squares under the curved line. Each large square represents a displacement of 1.0 m (see Figure 66). Alternatively (and quicker) notice that B's graph can be approximated to a straight line giving a triangle of 'height' $7.5\,\mathrm{m\,s^{-1}}$ and 'base' 30 s, that represents a displacement of approximately

$\quad \tfrac{1}{2} \times 7.5\,\mathrm{m\,s^{-1}} \times 30\,\mathrm{s} = 112.5\,\mathrm{m}.$

This puts A about 70 m ahead of B after 30 s.
   (You could refine this by estimating the number of graph-paper squares above and below the curved line, and adding and subtracting them from 112.5 m. Using this approach, B's actual displacement is about 5 m greater than 112.5 m – say 118 m altogether.)

11 Using equation (6), net force $F = ma = 65\,\text{kg} \times 2.0\,\text{m s}^{-2}$
$= 130\,\text{kg m s}^{-2} = 130\,\text{N}$.

12 Using equation (6a), $F = m\Delta v /\Delta t$. Taking the initial
direction of motion as positive: $u = +5.0\,\text{m s}^{-1}$,
$v = -25.0\,\text{m s}^{-1}$,
$\Delta v = v - u = -25.0\,\text{m s}^{-1} - 5.0\,\text{m s}^{-1} = -30.0\,\text{m s}^{-1}$
(notice the negative sign) so

$$F = 0.0120\,\text{kg} \times -\frac{30.0\,\text{m s}^{-1}}{0.015\,\text{s}}$$

$$= -240\,\text{N}.$$

The negative signs shows that the force was acting in the
opposite direction to the initial motion – which it would
need to be in order to stop and reverse the motion of
the ball.

13 The answer will depend on your mass – but whatever
the numbers, you should give your answer in newtons
and say that it acts downwards. As you are asked for an
estimate, you can use an approximate value for
$g \approx 10\,\text{N kg}^{-1}$. For example, suppose $m = 64\,\text{kg}$. Taking
downwards as positive, $g \approx +10\,\text{N kg}^{-1}$, $W = mg \approx$
$64\,\text{kg} \times 10\,\text{N kg}^{-1} = 640\,\text{N}$ acting downwards.

14 Taking the initial direction of the ball's motion as positive,
$a = -12\,200\,\text{m s}^{-2}$. $F = ma = 0.024\,\text{kg}$
$\times (-12\,200\,\text{m s}^{-2}) = -292.8\,\text{N}\ (\approx 300\,\text{N})$. The ball
exerts a force of equal size on the racket, in the same
direction as its initial motion.

15 (a) (i) There is a pair of gravitational forces attracting the
diver and Earth towards each other (as in Figure 15).
(ii) In addition to the gravitational forces, as the diver
enters the water there is a pair of forces involving the
diver and the water – the diver exerts a downward force
on the water and the water exerts an upward force that
decelerates the diver.

(b) In an awkward splash landing, the diver comes to rest
rapidly, experiencing a large change of velocity in a short
time, i.e. a large acceleration, so a large, painful, force
must be exerted on the diver by the water. If the diver
enters the water smoothly, the change of velocity is
much more gradual, i.e. the acceleration (and hence the
force exerted by the water) is smaller.

16 (a) Acceleration was uniform from 0 s to 40 s.

Magnitude of uniform acceleration

$$a = \frac{\Delta v}{\Delta t} = \frac{20\,\text{m s}^{-1}}{40\,\text{s}} = 0.5\,\text{m s}^{-2}$$

Magnitude of the instantaneous acceleration at $t = 80\,\text{s}$
is found from slope of graph at $t = 80\,\text{s}$:

$$a = \frac{\Delta v}{\Delta t} = \frac{20\,\text{m s}^{-1}}{130\,\text{s}} = 0.15\,\text{m s}^{-2}$$

(Your answer may differ by $\pm 0.03\,\text{m s}^{-2}$, depending on
exactly how you drew your tangent line.)
At $t = 140\,\text{s}$, acceleration is zero.

(b) Net force $F = ma = 200\,000\,\text{kg} \times 0.5\,\text{m s}^{-2}$
$= 100\,000\,\text{N}$.

(c) Using area under section of graph between 0 s and 40 s:
$\text{displacement} = \tfrac{1}{2} \times 20\,\text{m s}^{-1} \times 40\,\text{s} = 400\,\text{m}$

(Or you could use equation (4) with $u = 0\,\text{m s}^{-1}$, $a =$
$0.5\,\text{m s}^{-2}$, $t = 40\,\text{s}$, which gives the same answer.)

17 The three forces **W** (the weight acting vertically), **H** (the
wind acting horizontally) and **T** (the force exerted by the
support arm at an angle θ to the vertical) are in
equilibrium so must form a triangle (Figure 67).
Measurement on Figure 67 shows that $T \approx 25\,500\,\text{N}$
and $\theta \approx 11°$.

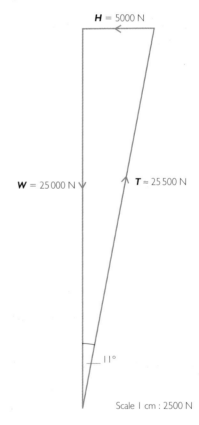

H = 5000 N

W = 25 000 N

T ≈ 25 500 N

11°

Scale 1 cm : 2500 N

Figure 67 *Vector diagram for the answer to question 17*

18 See Figure 68. By Pythagoras,
$R^2 = (500\,\text{N})^2 + (100\,\text{N})^2 = 2.60 \times 10^5\,\text{N}^2$
so $R = 510\,\text{N}$.
$\tan \theta = 100/500 = 0.2$, so $\theta = 11.3°$

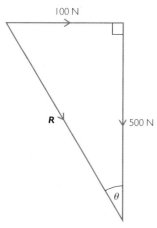

Figure 68 *Diagram for the answer to question 18*

19 See Figure 69. From Figure 25, $\tan \theta = \frac{1}{3}$.
Horizontal force $F = W \tan \theta = 600\,\text{N} \times \frac{1}{3} = 200\,\text{N}$.
By Pythagoras,
$$T^2 = F^2 + W^2 = (200\,\text{N})^2 + (600\,\text{N})^2$$
$$= 4.00 \times 10^5\,\text{N}^2$$
so $T = 632\,\text{N}$.

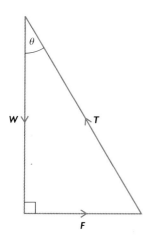

Figure 69 *Vector diagram for the answer to question 19*

20 (a) $T = \dfrac{W}{2 \sin \theta}$, where W is the climber's weight (600 N).
As θ becomes small, then $\sin \theta$ approaches zero and T becomes very large.

(b) Rearranging the expression from (a),
$$\sin \theta = \frac{W}{2T} = \frac{600\,\text{N}}{2 \times 15 \times 10^3\,\text{N}} = 2 \times 10^{-2}.$$
$$\theta = \sin^{-1}(2 \times 10^{-2}) = 1.1°$$

21 (a) Figure 70 shows a space diagram and a force vector diagram for the problem.
The horizontal components of $\boldsymbol{T}_1$ and $\boldsymbol{T}_2$ must be equal and opposite:

$$T_1 \cos 24° = T_2 \cos 23° \qquad\qquad \text{(i)}$$

and the vertical component of $\boldsymbol{T}_1$ acting upwards must equal $\boldsymbol{W}$ plus the vertical component of $\boldsymbol{T}_2$ acting downwards

$$T_1 \sin 24° = W + T_2 \sin 23° \qquad\qquad \text{(ii)}$$

Rearranging (i) gives:

$$T_2 = T_1 \frac{\cos 24°}{\cos 23°} \qquad\qquad \text{(iii)}$$

Substituting (iii) in (ii) gives

$$T_1 \sin 24° = W + T_1 \frac{\cos 24°}{\cos 23°} \sin 23°$$

Rearranging:

$$T_1 \left(\sin 24° - \frac{\cos 24°}{\cos 23°} \sin 23° \right) = W$$

$$T_1 = W \div \left(\sin 24° - \frac{\cos 24°}{\cos 23°} \sin 23° \right) = 5.27 \times 10^6\,\text{N}$$

Substituting this value back into (iii) gives

$$T_2 = T_1 \frac{\cos 24°}{\cos 23°} = 5.23 \times 10^6\,\text{N}$$

(a) Space diagram

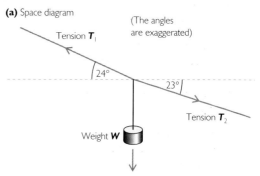

(b) Force vector diagram

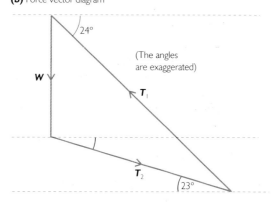

Figure 70 *Diagrams for the answer to question 21*

(b) If $\boldsymbol{T}_1$ and $\boldsymbol{T}_2$ both acted along the same direction, then it would be impossible to draw the closed vector triangle in Figure 70. It is the difference in the vertical components of $\boldsymbol{T}_1$ and $\boldsymbol{T}_2$ that supports the weight of the cable-car.

22 The rope does *not* obey Hooke's law. The load in the second test is three quarters that in the first (600 N/800 N = 0.75), but it does not produce three quarters the extension (0.012 m / 0.020 m = 0.60). In the first case,

$$\text{stiffness} = \frac{800 \text{ N}}{0.020 \text{ m}} = 4.00 \times 10^4 \text{ N m}^{-1} = 40.0 \text{ kN m}^{-1}.$$

In the second case,

$$\text{stiffness} = \frac{600 \text{ N}}{0.012 \text{ m}} = 50.0 \text{ kN m}^{-1}.$$

23 (a) From equation (14), extension

$$x = \frac{F}{k} = \frac{650 \text{ N}}{60 \times 10^3 \text{ N m}^{-1}} = 1.1 \times 10^{-2} \text{ m (11 cm)}$$

(b) Imagine that the 4 m rope is two 2 m ropes joined end to end. Each rope would be subject to the same force (650 N) so each extends by 11 cm, giving a total extension of 22 cm.

24 200 J is 20% of the total energy, so total energy = 5 × 200 J = 1000 J.

25 $E_k = \frac{1}{2}mv^2 = \frac{1}{2} \times 200 \text{ kg} \times (44 \text{ m s}^{-1})^2$
$= 1.94 \times 10^5 \text{ J}$

26 The skier has slightly more kinetic energy than the car (if you guessed 'the same' you were not far out).
Car: $E_k = \frac{1}{2} \times 600 \text{ kg} \times (22 \text{ m s}^{-1})^2 = 1.45 \times 10^5 \text{ J}$
Skier: $E_k = \frac{1}{2} \times 80 \text{ kg} \times (66 \text{ m s}^{-1})^2 = 1.74 \times 10^5 \text{ J}$

27 (a) $\Delta E_{\text{grav}} = mg\Delta h$
$= 65 \text{ kg} \times 9.8 \text{ N kg}^{-1} \times 35 \text{ m} = 2.23 \times 10^4 \text{ J}$
$E_k = 2.23 \times 10^4 \text{ J}$

Rearranging equation (20), $v^2 = \frac{2E_k}{m}$ so

$$v = \sqrt{\frac{2E_k}{m}}$$

$$= \sqrt{\left(\frac{2 \times 2.23 \times 10^4 \text{ J}}{65 \text{ kg}}\right)} = 26 \text{ m s}^{-1}.$$

(b) The mass makes no difference to the speed. This can be shown algebraically:

$$v = \sqrt{\frac{2E_k}{m}} = \sqrt{\frac{2\Delta E_{\text{grav}}}{m}} = \sqrt{\frac{2mg\Delta h}{m}} = \sqrt{(2g\Delta h)}$$

An alternative argument is to say that all free-falling objects have the same acceleration so will fall at the same rate and so reach the same speed.

28 Angle between slope and *vertical* is $\theta = 40°$.
Refer back to question 26: kinetic energy of 80 kg skier moving at 66 m s^{-1} is 1.74 × 10^5 J.

$\Delta W = F\Delta s \cos \theta$ so

$$\Delta s = \frac{\Delta W}{F \cos \theta}$$

$\Delta W = 1.74 \times 10^5 \text{ J}$
$F = $ downward gravitational force on skier
$= 80 \text{ kg} \times 9.8 \text{ N kg}^{-1}$

so

$$\Delta s = 1.74 \times \frac{10^5 \text{ J}}{80 \text{ kg} \times 9.8 \text{ N kg}^{-1} \times \cos 40°} = 290 \text{ m}.$$

Alternatively, start with some algebra to eliminate mass as in question 27:
$\frac{1}{2}mv^2 = mg\Delta h = mg\Delta s \cos \theta$
so

$$\Delta s = \frac{v^2}{2g \cos \theta}$$

$$= \frac{(66 \text{ m s}^{-1})^2}{2 \times 9.8 \text{ m s}^{-2} \cos 40°} = 290 \text{ m}.$$

29 Combining equations (19) and (23), $P = mg\Delta h/\Delta t$
so

$$\Delta t = \frac{mg\Delta h}{P}$$

$$= \frac{60 \text{ kg} \times 9.8 \text{ N kg}^{-1} \times 0.60 \text{ m}}{150 \text{ W}}$$

$$= 2.4 \text{ s}.$$

30 $$\text{Power} = \frac{\text{gain in kinetic energy}}{\text{time taken}}$$

$$= \frac{\frac{1}{2}mv^2}{\Delta t}$$

$$= \frac{1}{2} \times 60 \text{ kg} \times \frac{(10 \text{ m s}^{-1})^2}{3 \text{ s}} = 1000 \text{ W}$$

31 Car must gain kinetic energy $\frac{1}{2}mv^2$.

$$\text{Power } P = \frac{\Delta E}{\Delta t}$$

so

$$\Delta t = \frac{\Delta E}{P} = \frac{\frac{1}{2}mv^2}{P}$$

$$= \frac{\frac{1}{2} \times 800 \text{ kg} \times (30 \text{ m s}^{-1})^2}{60 \times 10^3 \text{ W}}$$

$$= 6.0 \text{ s}$$

32 1 day = 24 × 60 × 60 s = 8.64 × 10^4 s
so energy = 90 W × 8.64 × 10^4 s = 7.8 × 10^6 J.

33 2 weeks = 14 × 8.64 × 10^4 s
so energy = 14 × 8.64 × 10^4 s × 10^{-4} W = 121 J.

34 $E_{\text{el}} = \frac{1}{2}kx^2 = \frac{1}{2} \times 0.4 \text{ N m}^{-1} \times (0.6 \text{ m})^2 = 0.072 \text{ J}.$

35 Each cord contributes just part of the force that acts on the jumper. For example, if a 600 N jumper is supported at rest by six cords, then a 700 N jumper will stretch a seven-cord rope by the same amount – each cord provides a force of 100 N.

36 (a) $\Delta h = 610 \text{ m}$
$\Delta E_{\text{grav}} = mg\Delta h = 75 \text{ kg} \times 9.8 \text{ N kg}^{-1} \times 610 \text{ m}$
$= 4.5 \times 10^5 \text{ J}.$

(b) Extension of cord, $x = 610\,m - 250\,m = 360\,m$.

$$E_{el} = \tfrac{1}{2}kx^2 \quad \text{so} \quad k = \frac{2E_{el}}{x^2} = 6.9\,\text{N m}^{-1}$$

(c) Now the cord must just support his weight, i.e. upward force exerted by cord is $F = kx = mg$, so

$$x = \frac{mg}{k} = \frac{75\,\text{kg} \times 9.8\,\text{N kg}^{-1}}{6.9\,\text{N m}^{-1}} = 107\,\text{m}.$$

37   See Figure 71.

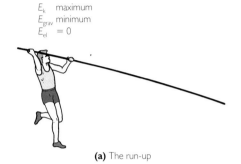

E_k maximum
E_{grav} minimum
E_{el} = 0

(a) The run-up

E_k decreasing
E_{grav} minimum
E_{el} increasing

(b) Bending the pole

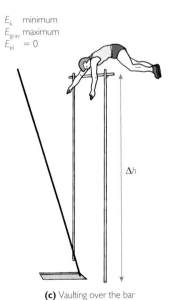

E_k minimum
E_{grav} maximum
E_{el} = 0

Δh

(c) Vaulting over the bar

Figure 71   *The answer to question 37*

38 (a) Initial $E_k = \tfrac{1}{2}mv^2$. Increase in gravitational energy, $\Delta E_{grav} = mg\Delta h$. If all E_k becomes E_{grav}, then $mg\Delta h = \tfrac{1}{2}mv^2$. So

$$\Delta h = \frac{v^2}{2g} = \frac{(10.1\,\text{m s}^{-1})^2}{2 \times 9.81\,\text{m s}^{-2}} = 5.2\,\text{m}.$$

(b) If his centre of gravity just clears the bar, then the height will be 6.2 m.

(c) (i) The energy conversion via bending the pole will not be 100% efficient so not all the initial E_k will become E_{grav}. Also, the vaulter still has some E_k at the top of the vault – he is moving over the bar. (ii) The vaulter is not simply catapulted over, but can push himself further upwards using the pole.

(d) Probably not. Improvements in materials are unlikely to make much difference as the process must already be close to 100% efficient. Athletes may be able to increase the speed of the run-up (though probably not much) and refine their vaulting technique, but these will probably make only a slight difference to the height of the vault.

39    $E_{el} = \tfrac{1}{2}kx^2 = \tfrac{1}{2} \times 10^7\,\text{N m}^{-1} \times (0.5\,\text{m})^2 = 1.25 \times 10^6\,\text{J}$

40 (a) The mass flow rate is $10\,000\,\text{m}^3\,\text{s}^{-1} \times 1000\,\text{kg m}^{-3} = 10^7\,\text{kg s}^{-1}$.

(b) Assume that all gravitational energy lost by the falling water eventually provides electrical energy, i.e. that the overall process is 100% efficient. In 1 second, falling water must transfer $\Delta E = 12 \times 10^9\,\text{J}$. This is achieved by a mass $m = 10^7\,\text{kg}$ falling through a height Δh where $\Delta E = mg\Delta h$, so

$$\Delta h = \frac{\Delta E}{mg} = \frac{12 \times 10^9\,\text{J}}{(10^7\,\text{kg} \times 9.8\,\text{N kg}^{-1})} = 122\,\text{m}.$$

In practice the efficiency will be (much) less than 100%, so the water will have to fall through a (much) greater height in order to generate the same amount of electrical power.

41 (a) She is opposed by an equal force due to the water so she does not accelerate. She transfers energy by heating the water and herself, rather than increasing her kinetic energy.

(b) The data point for humans would lie slightly to the left of the 'dolphin' point at $10^5\,\text{g}$ (100 kg). A human of mass 80 kg would expend about 1 kJ kg^{-1} min^{-1}, which is equivalent to 1 J g^{-1} min^{-1}. Swimming 1 km would take many minutes, and so a human swimmer would expend many J g^{-1} km^{-1}, putting the data point well above the plotted line. Humans transfer considerably more energy while swimming than would an aquatic animal of similar body mass. This is because our bodies are a less suitable shape (less streamlined) so we experience a much greater opposing force than if we were 'designed' for swimming.

42 Some of the energy must have been transferred elsewhere. If she slipped 'gradually' by sliding against a rock face, then friction between her body and the rock would have given rise to heating, which would account for the apparently 'missing' energy. If she fell and 'bounced' before coming to rest (as in a bungee jump) she would initially have some kinetic energy, then heating of air, air resistance and internal heating in the rope would account for the 'missing' energy.

43 (a) Her initial vertical velocity is zero. Using equation (26):

$$y = \tfrac{1}{2}gt^2$$

so

$$t = \sqrt{\frac{2y}{g}} = \sqrt{\frac{2 \times 20\,\text{m}}{9.8\,\text{m s}^{-2}}} = 2.0\,\text{s}$$

(b) Using equation (27): $x = u_x t = 20\,\text{m s}^{-1} \times 2.0\,\text{s} = 40\,\text{m}$.

(c) (i) This would increase u_x, so she would travel further in the time she is in the air. (ii) If she is initially moving upwards, she would take longer to reach the ground, so would travel further.

44 (a) The horizontal velocity remains constant and the vertical velocity increases steadily with a uniform acceleration.

(b) See Figure 72.

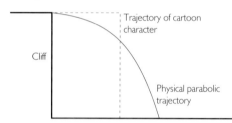

Trajectory of cartoon character

Cliff

Physical parabolic trajectory

Figure 72 *The answer to question 44(b)*

45 (a) You might have seen: long-exposure photographs of projectiles, or stop-frame video or film. Also, if you sketch a parabola on a blackboard, you can throw a small projectile so that it follows the same path – you cannot do this if you sketch the path shown in Figure 61.

(b) See Figure 73.

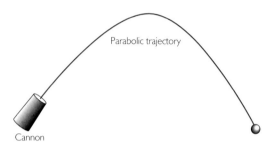

Parabolic trajectory

Cannon

Figure 73 *The answer to question 45(b)*

(c) $\theta = 30°$:

$$\text{range} = \frac{2 \times (50\,\text{m s}^{-1})^2 \sin 30° \cos 30°}{9.8\,\text{m s}^{-2}}$$

$$= 221\,\text{m}$$

$\theta = 45°$:

$$\text{range} = \frac{2 \times (50\,\text{m s}^{-1})^2 \sin 45° \cos 45°}{9.8\,\text{m s}^{-2}}$$

$$= 255\,\text{m}$$

$\theta = 60°$: range $= 221\,\text{m}$ (same as $\theta = 30°$ because $\sin 60° = \cos 30°$ and $\cos 60° = \sin 30°$).

TECHNOLOGY IN SPACE

Figure 1 *A communications satellite*

Why a unit called Technology in Space?

Since the mid 20th century, space technology has played an increasingly important part in our lives, both through satellites orbiting the Earth and through space probes that travel to distant parts of the Solar System.

Communications satellites (Figure 1) transmit radio signals for telephones and television. Meteorological satellites monitor the atmosphere and the Earth's surface, providing data for weather forecasting and adding to our understanding of long-term environmental changes. Astronomical satellites provide clearer views of the cosmos than is possible from the ground. Satellites also play a part in locating oil and other mineral deposits.

The design, building and operation of a satellite or space probe involves the understanding and application of many areas of physics. In this unit you will first see how a self-contained renewable electrical power supply can be designed using solar cells, and then how the interior of a space vehicle can be kept within a suitable temperature range.

In the second year of this course, you will study two more units connected with space and communications: *The Medium is the Message* is about modern telecommunications, and *Reach for the Stars* is about the stars and how we study them.

Overview of physics principles and techniques

In this unit, you will begin by using solar cells and revisiting some ideas about current, voltage and resistance in electric circuits. You will meet the idea of internal resistance, and will learn how resistors and power supplies can be combined in circuits to perform particular functions. You will also learn how, and why, electrical resistance can change with temperature. In the second part of the unit, you will learn about energy transfer to a circulating liquid, and be introduced to ideas about fluid flow.

In the course of the unit, you will also be using and developing some key mathematical and IT skills and techniques – in particular, you will be using algebra and graphs and using a spreadsheet.

Many of the principles and techniques that you meet in this unit will be picked up and developed further in later units. This approach of introducing, revisiting and building on ideas as and when they are relevant to a particular situation is a key feature of this course.

In later units you will do further work on

● dc electric circuits in *Digging Up the Past* and *Transport on Track*;

● fluid flow in *Good Enough to Eat*;

● explanations of why materials behave in certain ways in *Spare Part Surgery*, *Digging Up the Past* and *The Medium is the Message*;

● radiation in *The Medium is the Message* and *Reach for the Stars*.

1 Satellites in space

1.1 A space engineer

Jeremy Curtis is an engineer and Business Development Manager for Space Science at the Rutherford Appleton Laboratory (RAL) in Oxfordshire. His job includes working on the Joint European Telescope for X-ray astronomy (JET-X) (see Figure 2), due to have been launched in 1999 on the Russian Spectrum-X spacecraft. He says 'I trained as a mechanical engineer, but I find space engineering exciting because I have to work with all sorts of experts such as astronomers, physicists, designers, programmers and technicians working around the world.' He was sponsored by RAL during his university degree and then spent several years on designs for a large proton synchrotron (a machine for accelerating protons to very high energies) before moving over to space instrument design. In the following passage, he describes some aspects of space engineering.

Figure 2 *Jeremy Curtis (centre) working on part of the thermal insulation on the JET-X telescope before it is tested at RAL*

Why satellites?

Getting spacecraft into orbit is a very expensive activity with typical launch costs generally measured in tens of thousands of pounds per kilogram. So what makes it worth the bother? There are three key reasons.

First, a satellite is at a good vantage point for studying the Earth's surface and atmosphere – just think how many aircraft would be needed to photograph the whole of the Earth, or how many ships to monitor the temperatures of the oceans.

Second, if we want to study most of the radiation coming from distance parts of the Universe we have to get above the atmosphere. The Earth's atmosphere absorbs nearly everything that tries to get through it – from X-rays to ultraviolet and from infrared to millimetre waves. Only visible light and radio waves can get through. In fact, even visible light suffers – convection in the Earth's atmosphere makes stars seem to jump about or twinkle, blurring telescope images, so a telescope in space produces sharper images than is possible on Earth.

Finally and not least, a communications satellite can beam TV pictures across the globe and link telephone users on different continents.

The problem with space

Once you've gone through the huge trouble and expense of launching your satellite, a new set of problems confronts you in space.

First, a typical spacecraft may need several kilowatts of power – but where do you plug in? The only convenient renewable source of power is the Sun, so most spacecraft are equipped with panels of solar cells. You can see these on the Infrared Space Observatory (ISO) (Figure 3). Unlike on Earth,

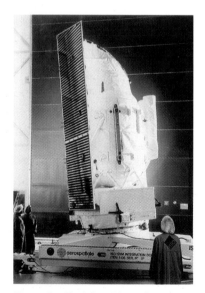

Figure 3 *The Infrared Space Observatory was launched in 1995 by the European Space Agency (ESA) and carries several instruments designed and built in the UK*

there is no worry about what to do on cloudy days, but batteries are still needed for periods when the satellite is in the Earth's shadow (usually up to an hour or two per orbit) and the satellite has to be continually steered to keep the panels pointing at the Sun.

So now we have our spacecraft floating in orbit and pointing the same face to the Sun all the time. Although the solar cells provide partial shade from sunlight this surface starts to heat up, and with no air to convect the heat away the temperature can rise dramatically. To add to the difficulties, the other side of the spacecraft faces cold space (at about 3 K or −270 °C) and so begins to cool down, Unchecked, this would distort the structure, wreck the electronics and decompose the materials that make up the spacecraft. So most surfaces of the spacecraft are covered in 'space blanket' – multilayer insulation made of metallised plastic which reflects the radiation away and insulates the spacecraft. This is the crinkly shiny material you can see in the photo (Figure 4).

Figure 4 *Installing a radiator on the outside of JET-X*

1.2 *Studying with satellites*

The UoSAT satellites are small, relatively low-cost, spacecraft whose purpose is to test and evaluate new systems and space technology and to enable students and amateur scientists to study the near-Earth environment. They are designed and built by the University of Surrey Spacecraft Engineering Research Unit. Figure 5 shows UoSAT 2, also known as Oscar 11. Its sensors record the local magnetic field, providing information about solar and geomagnetic disturbances and their effects on radio communications at various frequencies. Instruments on-board also measure some sixty items relating to the satellite's operation. These include: the temperatures of its faces, its batteries and other electronic devices; the current provided by its solar arrays; and the battery voltages. It can also receive, store and transmit messages to simple radio receivers anywhere in the world. UoSAT's orbit takes it over both poles at a height of about 650 km above the surface, and the spinning of the Earth allows us to receive data six times a day.

Each UoSAT spacecraft is designed to last for several years. Even small spacecraft such as these need electricity to run all the on-board systems, from the computer that controls it all, to the radio transmitters and receivers that send and receive data to and from ground stations on the Earth's surface.

UoSATs are small, each with a mass of typically 50 kg and about 0.5 m across. For comparison, JET-X is about 540 kg in mass and about 4.5 m long. Communications satellites are larger still, with masses of typically 2 to 5 tonnes. At the top end of the scale is the proposed International Space Station (ISS) (Figure 6) – a cooperative venture between 13 nations, including the United Kingdom. Construction and testing started in 1995 and completion is due in 2002. The completed station will have a mass of about

Figure 5 *UoSAT 2 (the frame at the top of the photo is about 0.5 m across)*

470 tonnes, measure 110 m from tip to tip of its solar arrays, and have pressurised living and working space for its crew of six almost equal to the passenger space on two 747 jet airliners. It will have a power demand of over 110 kW.

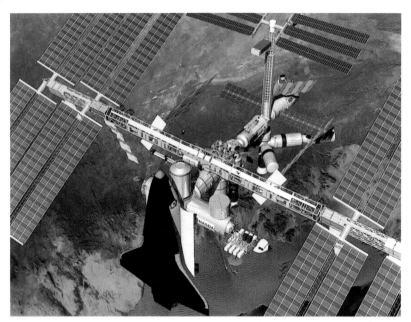

Figure 6   *The proposed International Space Station – a computer-generated artist's impression*

ACTIVITY 1   **Finding out about spacecraft**

Use books, magazines, newspapers, TV programmes and the Internet to find out about space missions as you study this unit. You could collect a folder or scrapbook of notes and cuttings on a particular space mission or on spacecraft in general.

ACTIVITY 2   **Data from space**

Examine some satellite data and see what you can deduce about conditions on-board. Depending on the equipment available to you, you might use data stored on a disk, accessed via the Internet, or direct from a satellite.

Look particularly for information about currents and voltages in power supplies, and about the temperature at various locations in the spacecraft.

Print out a sample of records showing how these measurements vary with time. You will be learning more about these aspects of satellite design and operation as you study this unit.

1.3 Spacecraft power systems

Figure 7 shows the three main elements in a spacecraft power system. The *primary source* involves the use of a fuel to produce electrical power. Primary sources include fuel cells in which a chemical reaction between hydrogen and oxygen produces electricity (with drinking water as a useful by-product), and radioisotope thermoelectric generators (RTGs) in which a radioactive decay process produces heating in a thermoelectric module that generates electricity. In spacecraft, the most common primary source is the photovoltaic cell, powered by solar radiation: here the initial fuel is protons in the Sun, which undergo nuclear fusion.

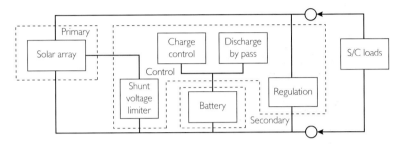

Figure 7 *Schematic diagram of a spacecraft power system*

The *secondary source* is the energy storage system – usually a set of batteries. Sometimes regenerative fuel cells are used in which power from solar arrays electrolyses water to produce hydrogen and oxygen gases during the 'charge' cycle, followed by hydrogen and oxygen recombining to make water during the 'discharge' cycle.

An electronic *power control and distribution system* controls and adjusts the voltage and current inputs and outputs, often using primary and secondary sources together to boost the overall output power.

There are other systems available and these are shown in Figure 8. Information on these can be found via the Internet using the NASA Spacelink page at http://spacelink.msfc.nasa.gov (Figure 9).

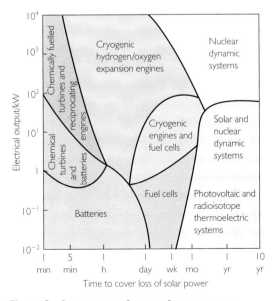

Figure 8 *Power outputs of spacecraft power systems*

Figure 9 *The NASA Spacelink page*

QUESTION

1 Using Figure 8, decide which would be the most suitable power source(s) for a spacecraft needing:

(**a**) 1 kW power output for just one week,

(**b**) 10 kW for five years.

The most common primary source used in satellites is the photovoltaic cell or solar cell. Hundreds to many thousands of such cells are connected together to make up solar arrays. In Figures 5 and 6 you can see the arrays of solar cells on UoSAT 2 and the ISS.

Solar cells have one important characteristic: they only generate electricity when illuminated. Orbiting satellites undergo between 90 and 5500 eclipses, moving into the Earth's shadow, each year (Figure 10). The former is typical of a geostationary telecommunications

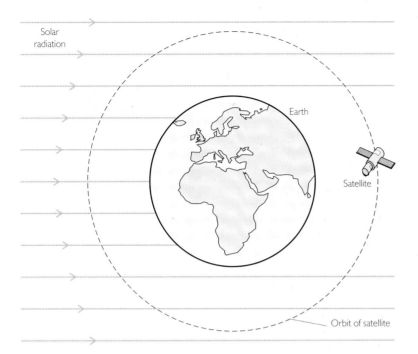

Solar
radiation

Earth

Satellite

Orbit of satellite

Figure 10 *A satellite in eclipse*

Study note

A geostationary satellite is one whose orbit
keeps it always above the same spot on
the Earth's surface. Another term used is
geosynchronous satellite.

satellite, the latter of a satellite in a low orbit like UoSAT 2. The ISS
will have sixteen 30 minute periods of shadow each day. The
secondary power supply is therefore vital, because during eclipse
electrical power has to be supplied by batteries. There are also
occasions when the batteries are needed to provide power in
addition to that of the solar panels.

The spacecraft's solar panels are used to recharge its batteries
when it emerges into sunlight. To do this they must provide a high
enough voltage – higher than the battery's own voltage. (A charger
for a 12 V car battery provides about 13 V.) The power system must
therefore be carefully designed to ensure that the solar panels can
charge the batteries and that the batteries can operate the electrical
equipment on-board.

So what voltage does a solar cell provide? How does this voltage
vary with the brightness of the light? How can we connect up solar
cells in order to charge batteries and operate equipment? These are
questions that you will be exploring in part 2 of this unit.

2 *Solar cells and electric circuits*

In this part of the unit you will learn about solar cells and electric
circuits in order to see what is involved in designing a power supply
for a spacecraft. The things that you learn about circuits can be
applied to electrical systems operated by other types of power
supply – not just to those with solar cells. In later units of this
course, you will be able to learn about some other types of primary
power source.

2.1 *Solar cells*

ACTIVITY **3**   **A first look at solar cells**

In this short activity, your task is to measure the voltage produced by a solar cell under various conditions of illumination.

Connect a voltmeter across just one of the solar cells as shown in Figure 11. Observe how the voltage across the solar cell changes as you vary the separation between the cell and the lamp. Write a sentence summarising what you have observed.

You should have found that even the highest voltage generated was quite small, so, to charge up the on-board batteries, large numbers of solar cells must be connected together.

ACTIVITY **4**   **Solar array voltage**

Have a look at some satellite data and see how the solar array voltage varies with time. Think how these variations might be explained in terms of the illumination of the satellite.

Figure 11   *A solar cell connected to a voltmeter and illuminated*

How does a solar cell work?

A solar cell (technically, a **photovoltaic cell**) is an electrical power supply. Incoming radiation provides energy that is transferred to an electric circuit via the motion of charged particles. Figure 12 shows a schematic diagram of a photovoltaic cell. The two materials are designed so that electrons spontaneously drift from one to the other, giving one a negative charge and the other a positive charge until drifting is halted by the build-up of electric charge. When radiation is absorbed by the cell, some of the electrons gain enough energy to move freely. Some move back across the boundary but most move around the external circuit and are replaced by more electrons drifting across the boundary.

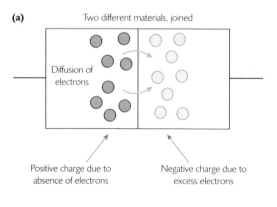

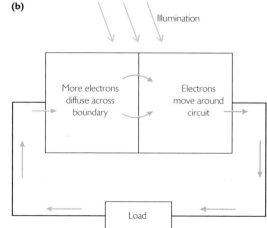

Figure 12   *Schematic diagrams of a photovoltaic cell (a) in the absence of illumination and (b) when illuminated*

Current and charge, voltage and energy

The continuous flow of charged particles constitutes an electric **current**. Current is defined as the rate of flow of charge past a point in the circuit:

$$\text{current } (I) = \text{charge } (\Delta Q) \div \text{time interval } (\Delta t) \tag{1}$$

The SI unit of charge is the coulomb (C) and the unit of current is the ampere or amp (A); $1\ \text{A} = 1\ \text{C s}^{-1}$.

If an amount of charge ΔQ flows past a point in a time interval Δt, then (adapting equation 1) the current I can be written

$$I = \frac{\Delta Q}{\Delta t} \tag{1a}$$

Charge is not created or destroyed (it is **conserved**) and there is no build-up of charge anywhere in a circuit, so the rate at which charge flows towards any point in the circuit must be the same as the rate at which it flows away. So in a circuit where all components are joined in **series** (Figure 13a) the current is the same throughout, and where components are joined in **parallel** (Figure 13b) the sum of currents flowing into a junction is equal to the sum of currents flowing out of it:

$$I = I_1 + I_2 + I_3 \tag{2}$$

Maths reference

Index notation
See Maths note 1.1

Index notation and units
See Maths note 2.2

Maths reference

The delta symbol
See Maths note 0.2

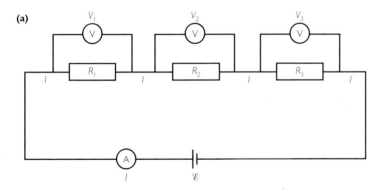

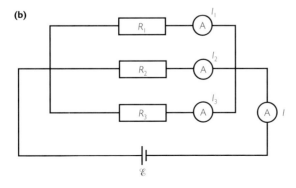

Figure 13 *(a) Resistors joined in series and (b) resistors joined in parallel*

Energy transfers in electric circuits are often expressed in terms of energy per unit charge. The SI unit of energy is the joule (J) and the unit for energy per unit charge is the volt (V); $1\,V = 1\,J\,C^{-1}$. Energy per unit charge is more usually called **potential difference** (pd) or **voltage** and given the symbol V. Using the symbol W for electrical energy:

$$W = QV \qquad (3)$$

The **emf** of a power supply is a measure of the *total* energy that it supplies to each coulomb of charge. Energy cannot be created or destroyed (it is conserved), so the energy transferred *to* the components in a circuit must be equal to the energy transferred *from* the power supply. In the time that it takes for one coulomb to pass any point in the circuit, the energy transferred by the power supply is numerically equal to its emf $\mathscr{E}$, and the energy transferred in each resistor is equal to the pd, V, across it. So the sum of all the pds across all the components in a series circuit (Figure 13a) is equal to the emf of the supply:

$$\mathscr{E} = V_1 + V_2 + V_3 \qquad (4)$$

And when components are connected in parallel (Figure 13b) each has the same potential difference across it:

$$V_1 = V_2 = V_3 = \mathscr{E} \qquad (5)$$

> ## Study note
> Emf stands for electromotive force, but that's a rather misleading term since emf is a measure of energy and not a measure of force.

QUESTION

2 A torch battery (chemical cell) has an emf $\mathscr{E} = 1.5\,V$. When it is connected to a bulb, there is a current of 0.5 A in the circuit.

(**a**) How much charge passes each point in the circuit during a time interval $\Delta t = 2.0\,s$?

(**b**) Use delta notation to write an expression relating the energy ΔW transferred by the cell to a small amount of charge ΔQ.

(**c**) How much energy does the cell transfer to this amount of charge?

In parts (**a**) and (**c**), make sure you show how to manipulate the units as well as the numbers.

Voltages by design

In designing power supplies for spacecraft, it is not sensible for each to be a one-off. Rather, systems are designed using agreed *standards* so that items of equipment can be used 'off the shelf' rather than each having to be purpose-built. In science and engineering the term 'standard' is used to refer to a particular design specification.

In the early days of space exploration the spacecraft of the USA and the former USSR were very different from each other. However, when it was considered a good idea to be able to dock spacecraft with each other (Figure 14), the two countries agreed to have identical docking ports and laid down standards, or specifications, for them.

Figure 14 *Docking an American spacecraft with the Russian space station*

Large organisations such as NASA (National Aeronautics and Space Agency) and ESA (European Space Agency), which are responsible for the design and construction of spacecraft, lay down standards for equipment design. Spacecraft have a lot of electrical equipment on-board and these require specific voltages to operate correctly. To ensure that the required voltages are available, the designers specify a type of circuit, known as a **bus** (Figure 15), into which equipment can be connected. It is much like the ring main that connects the mains sockets in houses, or the wiring harness of a car. In Europe the bus provides voltages of 28 V or 50 V. NASA in the USA has buses supplying voltages in the range 21 V to 35 V.

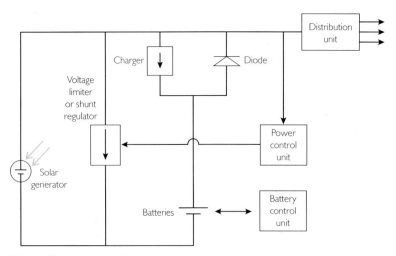

Figure 15   *A power supply bus*

ACTIVITY **5**   **Joining solar cells**

The bus on an ESA spacecraft needs a voltage far greater than that of a single solar cell. Your task for this activity is to see how solar cells can be joined together to provide high enough voltages. Notice that the circuit symbol for a solar cell (Figure 16) is like a dry cell with arrows indicating illumination.

QUESTIONS

3 If a single cell, under specified lighting conditions, generated a voltage of 0.5 V, what voltage would be produced for each of the circuits shown in Figure 16?

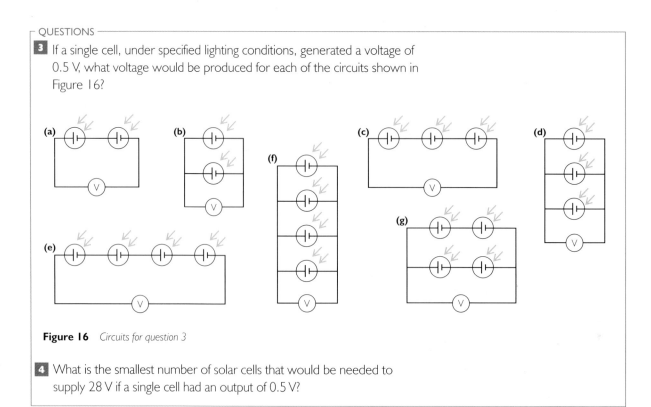

Figure 16   *Circuits for question 3*

4 What is the smallest number of solar cells that would be needed to supply 28 V if a single cell had an output of 0.5 V?

2.2 Cells and circuits

You have seen that instruments on-board satellites are designed to use a standard voltage, and you have seen how to join cells in series and in parallel to produce different voltages. However, there is more to designing a satellite's electrical system than just arranging cells to provide a standard voltage and then connecting up the instruments. The following demonstration illustrates the problem.

| ACTIVITY 6 | **Connecting a load to a power supply** |

The voltmeter in Figure 17 measures the **terminal potential difference** – the pd between the terminals of the power supply. The purpose of this activity is to show what happens to the voltmeter reading and/or to the brightness of the lamps when first one lamp is connected and then more lamps are added in parallel.

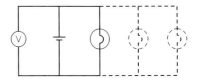

Figure 17   *Connecting a load to a power supply*

Activity 6 raises some important questions that need to be answered in order to design any electrical system:

- Why does the terminal potential difference change when it is connected in a circuit?

- How is this change related to the external load?

- What happens when different loads, or combinations of loads, are connected to the supply?

The answers to all these questions relate to electrical resistance, which is discussed in some detail below.

Study note

The general term 'load' could mean a lamp, motor or heater or something more complex such as a measuring instrument or a radio transmitter.

Electrical resistance

The current in an electrical device connected to a power supply (Figure 18) depends on the potential difference (voltage) applied between its terminals and on its own internal properties. The more easily charge can flow within it, the lower its **resistance** and the greater the current will be for a given voltage. Resistance is defined by the resistance equation:

$$\text{resistance } (R) = \text{potential difference } (V) \div \text{current } (I) \quad (6)$$

The SI unit of resistance is the ohm (Ω); $1 \, \Omega = 1 \, \text{V A}^{-1}$.

A device (or a material) whose resistance remains constant when measured under constant physical conditions (e.g. constant temperature) over a wide range of voltages is said to obey **Ohm's law** and is often called an **ohmic** device, an ohmic conductor or an

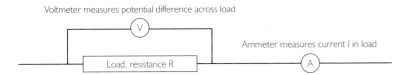

Voltmeter measures potential difference across load

Ammeter measures current *I* in load

Load, resistance *R*

Figure 18   *Defining resistance*

ohmic material. Another way to describe ohmic behaviour is to say that potential difference is directly proportional to current under constant physical conditions, i.e. the graph of pd against current is a straight line through the origin (Figure 19).

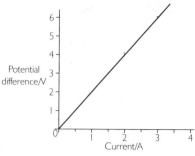

Figure 19 *A current–voltage graph for an ohmic conductor*

QUESTIONS ───────────

5 What is the resistance of the conductor in Figure 19?

6 Which of the graphs in Figure 20 show ohmic behaviour?

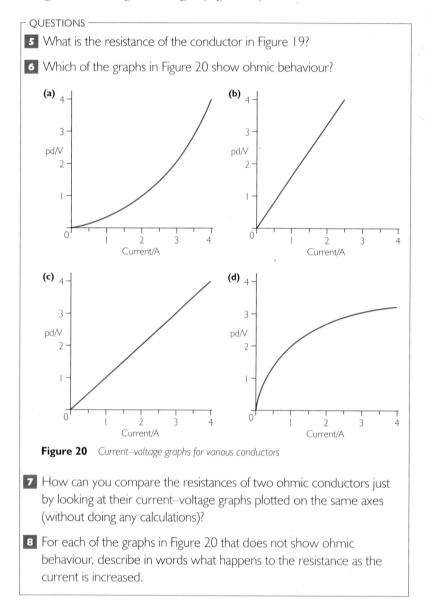

Figure 20 *Current–voltage graphs for various conductors*

7 How can you compare the resistances of two ohmic conductors just by looking at their current–voltage graphs plotted on the same axes (without doing any calculations)?

8 For each of the graphs in Figure 20 that does not show ohmic behaviour, describe in words what happens to the resistance as the current is increased.

Maths reference
....
Graphs and proportionality
See Maths note 5.1
....

Deciding whether a sample obeys Ohm's law

How can you tell, from a set of experimental measurements, whether a conductor obeys Ohm's law? The simple way is to plot a graph of voltage and current and see whether you can join the points with a straight line through the origin. Since experimental measurements on an ohmic conductor will rarely lie *exactly* in a straight line, you need to take account of **experimental uncertainty**: plot **error bars** on the points and use them to draw **error boxes**. If you can draw a straight line through the origin that passes through all the error boxes, then you can say that the conductor obeys Ohm's law *within the limits of experimental uncertainty.*

Figure 21(a) shows some voltage and current measurements plotted without error bars. In this particular example, the uncertainty in the voltage was $\Delta V = \pm 0.5$ V, and that in the current was $\Delta I = \pm 0.25$ A. When these (rather large) uncertainties are plotted in Figure 21(b), you see that the material does seem to obey Ohm's law within the limits of the experimental uncertainty; but if you only had Figure 21(a) it would be impossible to say.

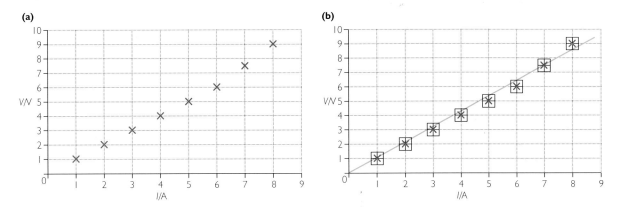

Figure 21   *A plot of some experimental measurements of current and voltage (a) without error boxes and (b) with error boxes*

QUESTION

9 By plotting a graph, decide whether the measurements in Table 1 obey Ohm's law within the limits of the experimental uncertainty.

Current/ A	Uncertainty $\Delta I = \pm 0.1$ A	Potential difference/V	Uncertainty $\Delta V = \pm 0.1$ V
0.5		0.8	
1.0		1.4	
1.5		1.8	
2.0		2.0	
2.5		2.2	

Table 1   *Data for question 9*

Combinations of resistors

To answer the questions raised in the points listed below Activity 6, which relate to designing a circuit for a particular purpose, we need to think what happens when there is more than one resistor in a circuit. Resistors can essentially be combined in two ways. Figure 22 shows some resistors connected in series and in parallel.

Any combination of resistors can be replaced by a single resistor without changing the currents and potential differences in the rest of the circuit. You can show, using equations (4) and (6), that the net resistance of a *series* of resistors is equal to the sum of their separate resistances:

$$R = R_1 + R_2 + R_3 \tag{7}$$

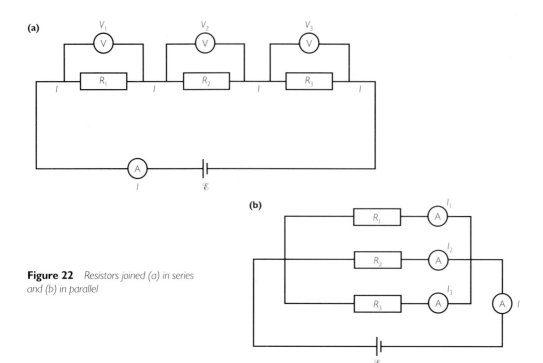

Figure 22 *Resistors joined (a) in series and (b) in parallel*

You can also show, using equations (2), (5) and (6), that, to find the net resistance R of several resistors in *parallel*, you need to add their reciprocals:

$$\frac{1}{R} = \frac{1}{R_1} + \frac{1}{R_2} + \frac{1}{R_3} \qquad (8)$$

Maths reference
....
Reciprocals
See Maths note 3.3
....

The net resistance of several resistors in parallel is always less than the smallest individual resistance – use that to check that your answer is reasonable.

ACTIVITY **7** **Resistors**

Use circuit boards or the *Crocodile Clips* circuit simulator to review your knowledge of resistance.

QUESTION

10 Calculate the net resistance of each of the arrangements shown in Figure 23. Show your working and include units at each step. (When there is a mixture of series and parallel arrangements, you will need to break down the calculations into stages. Begin by looking for groups of resistors that you can easily replace by a single resistor.)

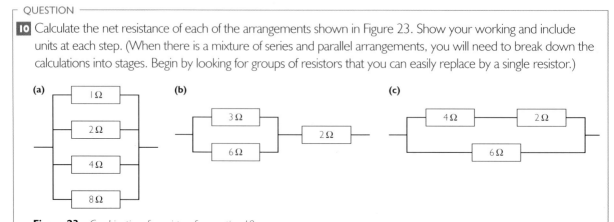

Figure 23 *Combinations for resistors for question 10*

Internal resistance

The drop in terminal potential difference can be explained using the idea of **internal resistance**. Any power supply (a photovoltaic cell, a chemical cell, a dynamo) has some electrical resistance due to the materials from which it is made. This resistance cannot be removed from the power supply, but it is normally shown in circuit diagrams as a resistance r in series with the power supply of emf $\mathcal{E}$ (Figure 24). Often a dotted line is drawn round $\mathcal{E}$ and r to indicate that they are inseparable.

When the power supply is connected to an external load R, there is a current I throughout the circuit – in r as well as in R. Some energy is transferred in the internal resistance of the power supply (it gets warm) as well as in the external load, so the potential difference across the external load (the terminal pd) is less than the full emf of the power supply.

We can apply the resistance equation (equation 6) to the whole circuit

$$\mathcal{E} = IR + Ir \tag{9}$$

and to the external load

$$V = IR$$

so

$$V = \mathcal{E} - Ir \tag{9a}$$

The quantity Ir is sometimes called the **lost volts**.

In your GCSE course, you probably treated the terminal pd of a power supply as being fixed. You have now seen that that is not the case. If you are designing a circuit that uses a real power supply rather than an ideal one, you need to take account of the internal resistance.

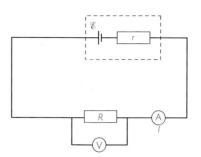

Figure 24 *Internal resistance*

ACTIVITY 8 **How do real power supplies behave?**

Your task is to explore the behaviour of a power supply that has some internal resistance, using a voltmeter, ammeter and various combinations of resistors.

Predict what will happen to the terminal pd and to the current as the external load is varied, and test your prediction.

2.3 *Getting the most from your power supply*

Space engineers have to design spacecraft power systems that operate as effectively as possible. The following passage discusses what this means.

> The output from a power supply depends on what it's connected to, and when we're designing an electrical system for a satellite with a limited energy input (from the Sun), we

want to make sure it operates as effectively as possible. This raises questions about what we mean by 'output' and 'operate effectively'. I think we can say straight away that simply looking at the current [Figure 25] is not a sensible way to measure performance.

The current is greatest when there is a **short circuit** between the terminals – a connection of low (essentially zero) resistance. The current is certainly large, but all that happens is that the power supply heats up because of its own internal resistance. Not only is that not useful, but overheated power supplies have a nasty habit of catching fire or blowing up.

The other extreme – going for the greatest possible terminal pd – is equally useless, though less hazardous. The terminal pd is greatest when the supply is on **open circuit** – meaning that there's an extremely large (essentially infinite) resistance between the terminals – in other words, they are not connected via a circuit at all!

No, to get the best performance out of a power supply, we have to look at maximising the energy transfer to an external circuit, and that involves a trade-off between having a large current on the one hand, and a large voltage on the other. It turns out that there is a fairly straightforward way of designing circuits so that they *do* get the best possible energy transfer from a power supply. You'll come across the terms 'maximum power' and 'impedance matching' in this context – understand those, and you've got it cracked.

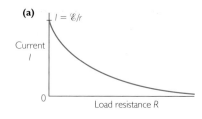

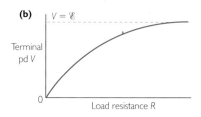

Figure 25 *(a) Terminal pd and (b) current versus load resistance for a power supply with some internal resistance*

Power in electric circuits

Power is the rate at which energy is transferred:

$$\text{power } P = (\text{energy transferred}) \div (\text{time taken}) \qquad (10)$$

Power has SI units of joules per second (J s^{-1}) or watts (W); $1\text{ W} = 1\text{ J s}^{-1}$. Using ΔE to represent energy transfer, equation (10) can be written as

$$P = \frac{\Delta E}{\Delta t} \qquad (10a)$$

The symbols ΔE, ΔW or ΔQ are all used to represent an energy transfer, and you are likely to see all three if you consult other books. ΔW is usually used only for electrical energy and ΔQ for thermal energy – but that is not a hard-and-fast rule.

In an electrical circuit, power is related to current and to potential difference. The current I is the number of coulombs per second flowing past a point in a circuit, and the potential difference V across a load is the number of joules each coulomb transfers to the load. So the rate of energy transfer in the load, the power P, is given by

$$P = IV \qquad (11)$$

If the load has resistance R, we can use the resistance equation (equation 6) to eliminate either V or I:

$$P = I^2 R \qquad \text{or} \qquad P = V^2/R \qquad (12)$$

Maths reference

Index notation and units
See Maths note 2.2

Algebra and elimination
See Maths note 3.4

Worked example

Q For example, if $I = 2$ A ($= 2$ C s^{-1}) and $V = 3$ V ($= 3$ J C^{-1}), in each second 2 coulombs flow into the load, and each coulomb transfers 3 joules to the load, so in each second, 6 joules are transferred:

A $P = 2$ C s$^{-1} \times 3$ J C$^{-1} = 6$ J s$^{-1} = 6$ W.

QUESTIONS

11 A domestic kettle is marked 230 V, 2000 W. When connected to a 230 volt supply, what is the current in the element?

12 What is the resistance of a light-bulb designed to have a power of 60 W when connected to the 230 volt mains supply?

ACTIVITY 9 **Maximising the power**

How can we get maximum power transfer to the external load in a circuit? This activity shows several ways to tackle this question.

Patterns

Calculate the power transferred to various loads by a given power supply, and look for patterns. Try using 'ideal' values that have been made up to give round numbers, and try your own experimental measurements from Activity 8. This may be done on a spreadsheet as shown in Figure 26, or you could use a calculator (which would take much longer).

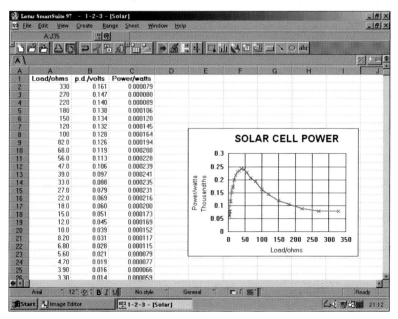

Figure 26 *Using a spreadsheet to calculate power*

Algebra

Starting from $\mathcal{E} = IR + Ir$ and $P = VI$, derive an expression for the power in the load resistance R. Try to eliminate V and I, and end up with an expression that involves *only* P, $\mathcal{E}$, R and r.

The condition for P to have a maximum value depends on the relationship between the external load R and the internal resistance r. To make this relationship clearer, write $R = fr$ and cancel as many common factors as you can. You should get an expression that involves just P, $\mathcal{E}$, r and f:

$$P = \frac{\mathcal{E}^2 f}{(1 + f)^2 r}$$

For a particular power supply $\mathcal{E}$ and r remain fixed. Try calculating $f/(1 + f)^2$ for various values of f (0, 0.5, 1, 1.5, 2, …) and see if you can deduce the value of f that gives the greatest value of P. Compare your result with what you found using the spreadsheet.

Impedance matching

The introduction to this section mentioned the term **impedance matching**. Impedance is a more general term than resistance that relates current to potential difference – there are some types of electrical device where the relationship between current and p.d. is more complicated than that described by the resistance equation, particularly when they are connected to an alternating, rather than a direct, supply. However, when dealing with steady currents and pds, impedance can be treated as meaning the same thing as resistance.

Impedance of solar cells

We have been treating the internal resistance (or impedance) of solar cells as though it had a fixed value for any given cell. In fact, the impedance of a solar cell can vary according to conditions, and this needs to be taken into account when designing a power system for a satellite.

ACTIVITY 10 **Currents and voltages in satellites**

Have a look at some satellite data and see how the battery current and voltage change with time. Think how you might explain any variations in these measurements.

Further **investigations**

When you have been using solar cells, you ensured (we hope!) that the level of illumination remained the same all the time. If you have an opportunity to carry out more detailed investigative work, you might like to explore what happens to the power output and/or internal resistance of a solar cell as the level of illumination changes. You could try using different light sources, or tilting a cell so that it intercepts different amounts of incoming radiation.

Level of illumination is one factor that could affect the internal resistance of a solar cell. You might be able to suggest other factors and explore them experimentally.

Maximum power – maximum efficiency?

In our work we always try to be efficient and, by that, we mean that we make good use of our time and efforts. We also know instinctively what is meant when someone says something is 100% efficient – we know that it cannot be improved. But what does efficiency mean in the context of power supplies?

The **efficiency** of any device or system that transfers energy (such as an electric circuit) has a precisely defined meaning:

$$\text{efficiency} = \frac{\text{energy usefully transferred}}{\text{total energy transferred}} \qquad (13)$$

or

$$\text{efficiency} = \frac{\text{power usefully transferred}}{\text{total power transferred}} \qquad (14)$$

Efficiency is often expressed as a percentage. For example, if a system is 20% efficient, then 20% (one fifth) of the energy supplied by the power source is transferred usefully in the external load, while the remaining 80% is wasted in heating the power supply and the surroundings.

Maths reference

Fractions and percentages
See Maths note 3.1

ACTIVITY **11** **Maximum power – maximum efficiency?**

In an electrical system, is the condition for maximum efficiency the same as that for maximum power? Spend a few minutes discussing the meaning of these two terms, making sure you can distinguish between them. Then try to decide whether the conditions are the same for both. Think what happens to the power output and the efficiency when the load resistance is much greater than the internal resistance, or much smaller, and when the two are equal. You might find it helpful to invent some numerical examples to illustrate what happens.

Designing an electrical system

In Activity 11, you should have convinced yourself that efficiency is greatest when the external load is made as large as possible, which is *not* the same as the condition for maximum power output. When designing an electrical system, should you go for maximum power or for maximum efficiency? If you want to get as much as possible from a small source of power, you aim for maximum power transfer and match the external load to the internal resistance. This is what is generally done in power systems for spacecraft. A circuit where an amplifier delivers power to a loudspeaker is another example where matched impedances are used to achieve maximum output power (speakers are generally labelled with their impedance). However, if the powers involved are large, it is better to aim for a higher efficiency and to reduce the amount of energy wasted due to the internal resistance of the supply. For example, electric vehicles are designed so that the internal resistance of the power supply is as small as possible and the external load resistance is much larger in comparison.

QUESTION

13 Calculate the output power and the efficiency of the circuit in Figure 27. Explain why this arrangement would not be a sensible way to use the power supply.

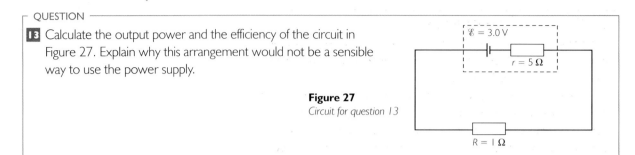

Figure 27
Circuit for question 13

2.4 Summing up part 2

So far in this unit, you have reviewed and extended your knowledge of dc electric circuits, learned how cells and resistors can be combined, and learned about the conditions under which a power supply transfers maximum power to a load.

Activity 12 is designed to help you review your progress, and questions 14 and 15 and Activity 13 are designed for you to reinforce and put into practice what you have been learning.

ACTIVITY **12** **Summing up part 2**

Spend a few minutes checking through your notes – use the following exercises to help you do this.

Skim through part 2 of this unit and make sure that your notes include a clear definition or explanation of each of the terms printed in bold type.

Write a short paragraph, illustrated by a circuit diagram, to explain what is meant by impedance matching and why it is important in designing a power system for a satellite. Include **at least five** of the terms that are printed in bold type in part 2.

QUESTIONS

14 A single 2.0 V cell in a lead–acid battery has an internal resistance, dependent on its state of charge and temperature, of around 0.005 Ω.
  (**a**) If a battery is made up of six cells in series what is (**i**) its total internal resistance and (**ii**) its emf?
  (**b**) This battery is then connected to a load resistance of 2.97 Ω. What is (**i**) the total resistance of the circuit, (**ii**) the current in the circuit and (**iii**) the terminal potential difference?
  (**c**) A car battery is made up of lead–acid cells, and on starting up a car there may be a current of 200 A. If a car's headlamps are on while a car is being started, they are usually seen to dim appreciably. Explain why.

15 Figure 28 shows various arrangements of identical cells.
  (**a**) From (i)–(iv), what can you deduce about the way internal resistances combine? (Do they combine like ordinary resistances?)
  (**b**) What load resistance would you use to obtain maximum power transfer from the arrangement of cells in (v)?

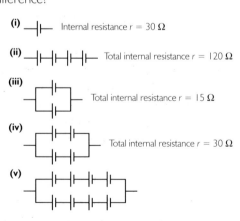

Figure 28 *Combinations of cells for question 15*

Design challenge

This challenge is concerned with designing a solar power supply in order to achieve maximum power transfer to a given load. (It is not intended as a practical activity.)

A single solar cell, under certain conditions, has an emf of 0.45 V and a maximum power output of 0.1 W. An array of identical solar cells, under the same conditions, is required to supply 0.4 W to an external load of 0.506 Ω. If the cells are required each to supply the maximum possible power, how many cells are needed, and how must they be connected? (Hint: start by finding the internal resistance of a single cell, and assume that the internal resistances of these solar cells combine just like ordinary resistances.) Without doing any further calculations, say how many cells would be needed to supply 0.9 W to the same load, and how they must they be connected.

3 *Energy transfer and control*

So far in this unit you have dealt mainly with aspects of electrical power systems and not paid much attention to the solar radiation that provides the energy for their operation. If you look back at what Jeremy Curtis said in part 1 you will see that solar radiation is a bit of a mixed blessing for spacecraft: it supplies much-needed energy, but it also gives the engineer more problems to deal with. In this part of the unit you will see how an understanding of energy transfer processes play a vital part in designing and operating a spacecraft.

3.1 *Facing the right direction*

In the summer of 1997, the Russian space station Mir (Figure 29) faced a series of problems that began when a docking manoeuvre with a supply module went wrong (rather than docking smoothly, the two vehicles crashed together, damaging part of the outer structure of the space station). While working on the repairs, one of the crew accidentally pulled out a cable from the station's main computer. In the words of *New Scientist* magazine (27 July 1997) 'The error left the station almost totally without power and spinning out of control for more than 24 hours.'

But why should disconnecting a *computer cable* leave the station without power? The clue comes in the phrase 'spinning out of control'. The computer controls motors that orient the space station and its solar panels. Unless they are correctly aligned with the Sun, the solar panels do not function effectively.

Power input and radiant energy flux

Figure 30 shows a solar cell and a beam of radiation. The 'strength' of the beam is usually described in terms of the rate at which it transfers energy across unit area square-on to the beam. This

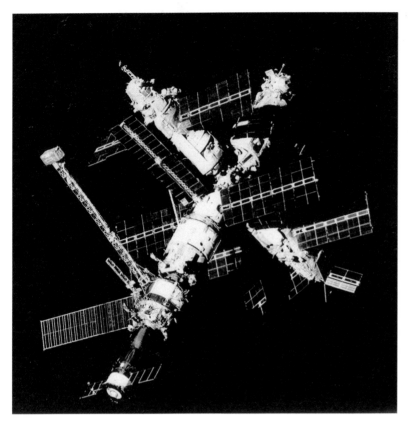

Figure 29   *The Mir space station seen from the Space Shuttle*

quantity is called the radiant **energy flux**, F, or the **intensity**, I, of the beam. (We will use F but you may find I in other books.) The SI units of F (or I) are watts per square metre (W m^{-2}). The rate at which energy is transferred to a surface therefore depends on the flux and the area, A, of the surface:

$$P_{in} = FA \tag{15}$$

Worked example

Q For example, if a beam has $F = 10\ \text{W m}^{-2}$ and shines square-on to a surface of area $A = 2\ \text{m}^2$ (as in Figure 30), then (provided all the incident radiation is absorbed by the surface):

A $P_{in} = 10\ \text{W m}^{-2} \times 2\ \text{m}^2 = 20\ \text{W}.$

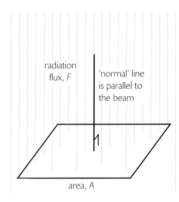

Figure 30   *A solar cell square-on to a beam of radiation*

How large a solar array does a spacecraft need?

The size of solar array depends on the spacecraft's power demands. As you can see from Figure 31 the average power requirements of various spacecraft have risen appreciably since the 1960s. However, even when the power requirements are known, it is still necessary to have information about how efficiently the solar cells transfer energy.

Here, the total energy transferred in the process is the energy of the incident radiation so we could rewrite equations (13) and (14):

$$\text{efficiency} = \frac{\text{useful energy output}}{\text{total energy input}} \qquad (13a)$$

$$\text{efficiency} = \frac{\text{power usefully transferred}}{\text{power input}} = \frac{P_{\text{out}}}{P_{\text{in}}} \qquad (14a)$$

Here, the input refers to the incoming solar radiation flux and the energy is that transferred by the cell.

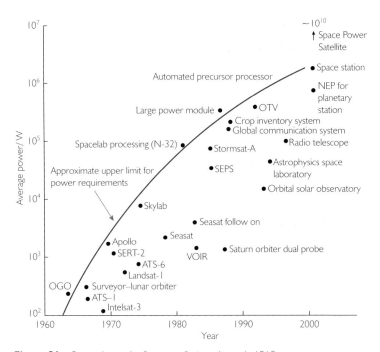

Figure 31 *Power demands of spacecraft since the early 1960s*

Worked example

Q For example, the solar arrays on the Hubble Space Telescope have an area $A \approx 20$ m^2 and are about 10% efficient and the solar flux is $F \approx 1.4$ kW m^{-2}. To find the maximum possible output power:

A $P_{\text{in}} = FA$
    ≈ 20 m$^2 \times 1.4$ kW m$^{-2} = 28$ kW
  P_{out} is 10% of P_{in} so
  $P_{\text{out}} = 0.10 \times 28$ kW $= 2.8$ kW.

ACTIVITY **14** **Sizing up solar arrays**

Use data from Figure 31 to calculate the minimum area of solar array required by Intelsat-3, SERT-2 and Skylab. Assume that *all* their power is supplied from the solar arrays, and that the solar flux is $F \approx 1.4$ kW m^{-2}.

ACTIVITY **15**   **Facing the right direction**

Use a large solar cell and a lamp to explore how the power input to a
solar cell would change if it were not square-on to the incoming
radiation. Look at Figure 30 and think about the radiation that would
by-pass the cell if it were tilted. Think what would happen if the cell
were edge-on to the radiation.

QUESTIONS

16 Write a short paragraph, with at least one diagram, to explain why a breakdown in the computer guidance
system of the Mir space station resulted in a loss of electrical power.

17 The International Space Station (Figure 6), which is planned for construction early in the 21st century, is being
designed with solar arrays that must each produce a peak output power of 16 kW from an incident solar flux
of 1.4 kW m^{-2}. If the efficiency of an array is 11%, what must be its area?

The importance of understanding radiation flux is not limited to
solar panels on spacecraft. Question 18 uses the same ideas in
another situation.

QUESTION

18 In Germany the Daimler-Benz company has incorporated arrays of photovoltaic cells into one of its factories
(Figure 32). The total area of the arrays is 5000 m^2 (about that of a soccer pitch). The company states that the
peak power output from these arrays is 435 kW. If the peak solar flux at this location is 600 W m^{-2}, calculate
the efficiency of these solar arrays.

Figure 32   *Solar arrays on a Daimler-
Benz factory*

3.2 Temperature changes in spacecraft

So far in this unit we have been concerned with designing an electrical power supply system for a spacecraft. Temperature control is another important aspect of designing a spacecraft. All spacecraft, no matter what their task or position, have heating and cooling systems on-board.

ACTIVITY 16 **Getting warmer**

Spend a few minutes 'brainstorming' the following questions. Jot down a list of your ideas.

● Why might the temperature on-board a spacecraft vary markedly if it were uncontrolled?

● What problems might be caused by large changes in temperature on-board a spacecraft?

Think about space probes designed to study the Sun continuously, such as the Solar Heliospheric Observatory (SOHO), or to explore the outermost regions of the Solar System, such as the Voyager and Pioneer probes. Think about manned space stations and moon landers, and about unmanned satellites of all types orbiting the Earth.

Many spacecraft spin about their own axes and so part, at least, keeps going into and out of the sunlight. Others orbit the Earth and so travel in sunlight on the day side and in the dark (cold) on the night side. While space can be as cold as 3 K ($-270\,°C$), a spacecraft can quickly heat up when facing the Sun or through heating due to its own electrical equipment.

Uncontrolled heating and cooling can cause problems. Mechanical parts can suffer from expansion and contraction, as did the Hubble Space Telescope's first solar arrays, which flexed as it moved in and out of the Earth's shadow, and if electrical components get too hot or too cold then they perform less well. For example, chemical batteries and solar cells tend to function better when they are cool. Table 2 shows typical temperature ranges within which various components can operate reasonably well.

Equipment	Temperature range/ °C
electrical equipment	-10 to $+40$
chemical batteries	-5 to $+15$
fuel (hydrazine)	$+9$ to $+40$
microprocessors	-5 to $+40$
mechanical parts	-45 to $+65$
solar cells	-60 to $+55$
solid state diodes	-60 to $+95$

Table 2 *Typical operating temperatures for equipment used in spacecraft*

ACTIVITY **17** **Solar array temperature**

Have a look at some satellite data and see how the temperature of the solar arrays changes with time. Comment on whether the temperatures lie within the ranges given in Table 2.

Sources of heating

As we have just seen, solar radiation is the main source of heating for satellites, but for the Space Shuttle and spaceprobes that enter the atmosphere of the Earth or another planet (or moon), frictional heating is also important. The Space Shuttle, for example, is covered with specially designed heat-resistant tiles.

Figure 33 is an article from a French magazine *Ciel et Espace* ('Sky and Space'). It describes the Cassini-Huygens mission, launched in 1997, that will explore the planet Saturn. Like many space exploration projects, Cassini-Huygens is multinational. The Huygens probe, which is the European part of the project (with major contributions from the UK, France and Germany), will be released from the main Cassini spacecraft into the atmosphere of Titan, one of Saturn's moons. This probe has a heat shield to protect its instruments from the high temperatures that will be reached as it plunges through Titan's atmosphere.

ACTIVITY **18** **The Cassini-Huygens mission**

Have a look at Figure 33 and try to deduce some information about Cassini-Huygens. If you have ever learned any French (even if you did not think you were very good at it!) you will probably be able to guess at most of the meaning of the article. In particular, you should be able to find Cassini's mass, the size of its heat shield, the expected temperature as it is decelerated by Titan's atmosphere, and its initial and final speeds as it approaches Titan.

The article also outlines the scientific aims of the mission – try to work out from the article what aspects of Titan will be studied by the instruments carried by the Huygens probe.

Useful words: fusée = rocket; bouclier = shield; sonde = probe.

Electrical components in space

As you can see from Table 2, batteries and solar cells are particularly sensitive to temperature. The three questions on page 94 illustrate the problem in more detail and indicate the importance of careful choice of materials.

P O I N T · F O C A L

Huygens dans la dernière ligne droite

LES préparatifs de Cassini-Huygens, ultime grande mission interplanétaire de ce siècle, sont entrés dans leur dernière ligne droite. Les nombreuses vicissitudes que les aléas budgétaires ont fait subir, du côté de la Nasa, à cette ambitieuse entreprise américano-européenne semblent désormais appartenir au passé. C'est du moins le vœu qu'exprimait ce printemps Roger-Maurice Bonnet, le directeur des programmes scientifiques à l'ESA. Quant à la petite sonde Huygens, la partie européenne du projet, elle est depuis la fin avril en cours d'assemblage à Ottobrun, chez Dornier, en Bavière. Dans un peu plus de six mois, Huygens devra être livrée à la Nasa, au centre spatial Kennedy, pour une dernière série de tests avant son arrimage sur l'imposante sonde Cassini et un lancement de l'ensemble par Titan 4, la plus puissante des fusées américaines. Date prévue pour le décollage : le 6 octobre 1997.

L'objectif de la mission, qui ne sera atteint qu'en juin 2004, est le monde glacé de Saturne et, plus particulièrement pour ce qui concerne la petite sonde européenne, l'exploration de Titan, le plus gros des satellites de la planète géante. C'est en principe le 27 novembre 2004, vingt et un jours après son largage par Cassini, que cet engin de 343 kg protégé par un bouclier de 2,7 m de diamètre pénétrera dans l'atmosphère de Titan. Un véritable saut dans l'inconnu, puisque les scientifiques ignorent totalement ce qu'ils trouveront à l'arrivée : des lacs ou des océans

de méthane, des terres secouées par des volcans ou grêlées de cratères d'impact. Au point, précise John Zarnecki, de l'université du Kent, en Grande-Bretagne, qu'il a fallu *"tenir compte de six ou sept modèles pour imaginer la surface et concevoir les instruments scientifiques"*. Au total, Huygens emportera six expériences destinées à l'étude de l'atmosphère, de la météo et de la surface de Titan. Parmi ces instruments, une mini-caméra à trois objectifs ultrasensibles qui devrait livrer des images de la surface durant les deux cents derniers mètres de descente. Une gageure.

Gageure également pour les industriels qui ont conçu cet engin de taille certes modeste mais qui devra résister à des conditions extrêmes. Pendant les deux heures et demie que durera le plongeon vers Titan, depuis une altitude de 1270 km et une vitesse de Mach 20 jusqu'à l'arrêt au contact de la surface, Huygens subira un freinage aérodynamique qui, en cinq minutes, fera chuter sa vitesse de 21 600 à 1 080 km/s. Échauffement estimé sur le bouclier de protection : 2 000 °C. Suivra une descente sous une batterie de trois parachutes pour atteindre la surface à 6 m/s. Temps de vie prévu au terme de cette descente : entre 3 et 30 minutes. *"De la protection thermique aux techniques de pilotage hypersonique et de rentrée atmosphérique en passant par les codes de calcul aérodynamique, Huygens est l'un des rares programmes qui ait mobilisé l'ensemble de nos compétences"*, souligne André Motet, directeur adjoint d'Aérospatiale, qui assure la maîtrise d'œuvre de la sonde. Le jeu en vaut la chandelle. Les scientifiques s'attendent à rencontrer dans l'atmosphère de Titan une chimie complexe, voire même de ces grosses molécules qui, sur Terre, ont servi de briques au vivant. Titan détient peut-être des clés qui permettront de percer un peu l'épais mystère qui entoure encore l'apparition de la vie.

Jean-Pierre Defait

Une longue série de tests réalisés sur différents modèles techniques de Huygens — comme ici au centre de la Dasa à Ottobrun, en Allemagne — a précédé le feu vert donné par l'Agence spatiale européenne pour l'assemblage définitif de la sonde.

Figure 33 *The Cassini-Huygens mission*

QUESTIONS

19 Figure 34 shows how one type of battery performed with temperature. 'Available capacity' is a measure of the energy that could be transferred from the battery, expressed as a percentage of the maximum transferable energy.

(**a**) What was the available capacity available at a temperature of (**i**) 50 °C and (**ii**) −20 °C?

(**b**) By how much does the battery's capacity fall in going from 30 °C to 40 °C?

20 Figure 35 shows how the efficiency of solar cells made of different materials depends on temperature.

(**a**) Which material has the highest efficiency at each of the following temperatures?
(**i**) 0 °C, (**ii**) 200 °C, (**iii**) 400 °C.

(**b**) Which material(s) would it not be sensible to use for solar cells if their temperatures were likely to rise above 30 °C?

(**c**) How does the efficiency of a cadmium sulfide (CdS) cell vary when the temperature changes from 0 °C to 400 °C?

21 Some proposed space stations of the near future are likely to need 1 MW of power (1 MW = 1×10^6 W). Suppose such a space station is to have solar arrays made from gallium arsenide (GaAs) and its operating temperature is to be kept below 50 °C. If the incident solar flux is 1.4 kW m^{-2}, what is the smallest area that its solar arrays must have?

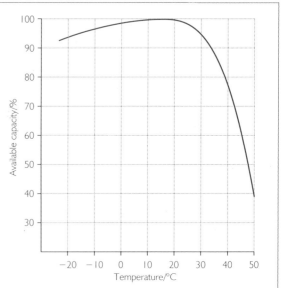

Figure 34   *The performance of a VARTA RS nickel–cadmium battery*

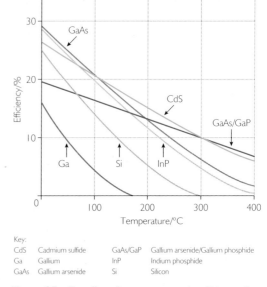

Key:
CdS	Cadmium sulfide	GaAs/GaP	Gallium arsenide/Gallium phosphide
Ga	Gallium	InP	Indium phosphide
GaAs	Gallium arsenide	Si	Silicon

Figure 35   *The effect of temperature on the efficiency of solar cells of various materials*

Resistance and temperature

Not only does temperature affect the performance of solar arrays and batteries, but the resistance of many components also varies noticeably with temperature, as you will see in the following activity.

ACTIVITY 19   **Changing resistance**

Your task is to obtain a set of readings for one component, showing how its resistance changes over the range 0 °C to 100 °C, and to write a short report of your findings to exchange with other students who have used a different component. See Figure 36.

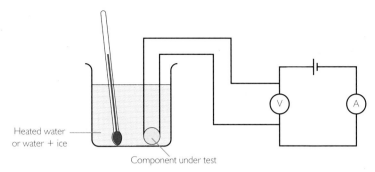

Figure 36 *Apparatus for Activity 19*

You will need to use your tables of results and calculations again later, in Activity 20.

Modelling resistance

The materials used nowadays to make electronic components have been developed to have particular electrical properties. In order to develop 'designer' materials, it is important to describe *how* particular materials behave and also to understand *why*. The change in resistance with temperature is one such aspect of material behaviour that can be explored with the help of scientific modelling.

Scientific modelling

The variation of resistance with temperature raises two questions: *Is there a simple relationship between resistance and temperature?* and *Why does resistance change with temperature?* The second question is of interest when we are trying to understand the behaviour of the natural world and perhaps develop new materials whose resistances change in particular ways. The first question is of particular interest to anyone wanting to know how an electrical system is going to behave. Both these questions involve the important scientific idea of **modelling**.

One of the main goals of science is to describe and understand the natural world – partly for the satisfaction of knowing for its own sake, and partly in order to make use of that knowledge through technology. Exploring the natural world in this way involves the use of **scientific models**. A scientific model is a way of thinking about and visualising objects or processes, often involving a mathematical description. A model in this sense does *not* normally mean a small- or large-scale replica.

Models that represent attempts to understand the world at a fundamental level often need to be adapted and refined depending on what we are using them for, and as our knowledge of the world develops. For example, if you picture atoms and molecules as small spheres as in Figure 37, you are using a model that can explain some large-scale behaviour of materials (differences between solids, liquids and gases, for example). But it does not explain electric currents, nor does it explain how atoms combine chemically – a model of an atom consisting of a small nucleus surrounded by orbiting electrons is more helpful there. In turn, the nucleus-plus-electrons model has to be refined in order to explain radioactive decay. During this course, you will meet several examples of scientific models being developed and refined.

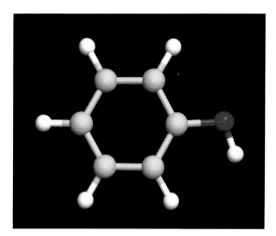

Figure 37　*A simple model explains some of the properties of matter*

Other models are empirical – that is, they are based on observation and experiment, rather than on any fundamental thinking about the underlying processes. Ohm's law ($V \propto I$) is an **empirical model** that describes mathematically the way that some materials behave. Sometimes empirical relationships give clues to something deeper. For example, Isaac Newton observed that all falling objects have the same gravitational acceleration, which led him to an understanding of gravitational force without which we would not be able to launch satellites into orbit.

Even where they do not directly reveal fundamental insights into the laws of Nature, empirical models are extremely useful to scientists and engineers. Ohm's law is just one example of such an empirical relationship. The relationship between resistance and temperature is another.

Model making and model fitting

In principle, making an empirical mathematical model is straightforward. It simply involves collecting some experimental measurements and looking for a mathematical way to describe them – ideally, a fairly simple relationship between two measured quantities. In practice, this can turn out to be less simple than it sounds.

More commonly, you are likely to be concerned with **model fitting**, where you start off with a model and see whether experimental measurements agree with it. You met this in questions 6–8, where you had to decide whether a given material obeyed Ohm's law. Plotting a graph is often a good way to see whether measurements fit a given model – particularly if the expected graph is a straight line, and the experimental values are plotted complete with error bars.

Matching experimental measurements to a mathematical model can help you to find the values of unknown quantities. If a set of current and voltage measurements fit Ohm's law, then you can determine the conductor's resistance. In section 2.3 you used a mathematical model to describe the behaviour of a power supply with internal resistance and hence were able to determine the internal resistance and the emf of the supply.

Is there a simple relationship between resistance and temperature?

Some conductors have a resistance that increases uniformly with temperature. This behaviour can be described by a mathematical model:

$$R_\theta = R_0(1 + \alpha\theta) = R_0 + \alpha R_0\theta \qquad (16)$$

where

R_θ = resistance at temperature θ

R_0 = resistance at 0 °C

α is the **temperature coefficient of resistance**

The coefficient α can be described as 'the fractional increase in resistance compared with the value at 0 °C'. The units of α are $°C^{-1}$, so that the units of $\alpha\theta$ are $°C^{-1} \times °C$, i.e. $\alpha\theta$ has no units – it is just a number.

The value of α can be positive or negative, depending on whether resistance increases or decreases with rising temperature. Resistors that are designed to have a large variation with temperature (i.e. **thermistors**) are often referred to as NTC (negative temperature coefficient) or PTC (positive temperature coefficient) thermistors, depending on the way their resistance changes.

QUESTION

22 The temperature coefficient of resistance of copper is 4.28×10^{-3} °C^{-1}. A piece of copper connecting wire has a resistance of 0.50 Ω at 0 °C. What will be its resistance at 80 °C? In the light of your answer, say whether you think that the connecting wires in a circuit can be ignored when taking account of changes in electrical properties with temperature.

Table 3 lists some very precise values for the resistance of five different material samples, all designed to have a resistance of 1.00000 Ω at 0 °C (i.e. $R_0 = 1.00000$ Ω). By looking at the numbers in each column, you can see that the change in resistance with temperature is linear in each case.

Temperature/°C	Resistance/Ω				
	Carbon	**Copper**	**Constantan**	**Steel**	**Tungsten**
0	1.00000	1.00000	1.00000	1.00000	1.00000
20	0.99000	1.00800	1.00002	1.06600	1.10400
40	0.98000	1.16000	1.00004	1.13200	1.20800
60	0.97000	1.24000	1.00006	1.19800	1.31200
80	0.96000	1.32000	1.00008	1.26400	1.41600
100	0.95000	1.40000	1.00010	1.33000	1.52000

Table 3   *Temperature data for five resistors*

Worked example

Q   Figure 38 shows a graph of resistance R_θ plotted against temperature θ for copper. The graph is a straight line and cuts the vertical axis at $R_\theta = R_0 = 1.00000\ \Omega$. The gradient of the line is equal to αR_0. From Figure 38,

A $\dfrac{\Delta R}{\Delta \theta} = \dfrac{0.40\ \Omega}{100\ ^\circ\text{C}} = 0.0040\ \Omega\ ^\circ\text{C}^{-1} = 4.0 \times 10^{-3}\ \Omega\ ^\circ\text{C}^{-1}.$

$\alpha = \text{gradient}/R_0$

$\quad = \dfrac{4.0 \times 10^{-3}\ \Omega\ ^\circ\text{C}^{-1}}{1.00000\ \Omega} = 4.0 \times 10^{-3}\ ^\circ\text{C}^{-1}.$

Study note

In this example the gradient is numerically the same as α, but that will not in general be the case.

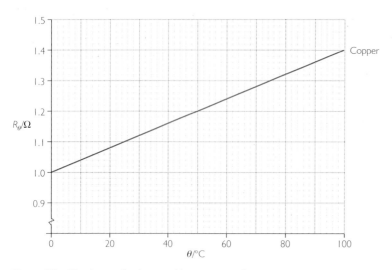

Figure 38   *The change of resistance with temperature for copper*

Maths reference

Linear relationships
See Maths note 5.2

Gradient of a linear graph.
See Maths note 5.3

QUESTION

23 (**a**) Which of the materials listed in Table 3 have a positive temperature coefficient of resistance, and which have a negative coefficient?

(**b**) Suggest a reason why constantan is so called.

(**c**) Choose *one* of carbon, tungsten or steel. Plot a graph, similar to Figure 38, to show its behaviour. Calculate its temperature coefficient of resistance.

ACTIVITY **20** **Model fitting**

Your task is to determine whether your experimental measurements of resistance and temperature from Activity 19 match the mathematical model discussed above, and then to communicate your findings to students who have studied other components.

Your graph of R_θ against θ that you plotted in Activity 19 will enable you to decide whether a particular set of measurements fits the model, and to find the values of R_0 and α.

Why does resistance change with temperature?

You will have seen that different components behave very differently on being heated. Why is this? We can explain the main features using a so-called classical model of materials.

All materials are made up of atoms that are constantly vibrating. As the temperature rises, the atoms vibrate more vigorously. At the same time, a rise in temperature can result in the release of more electrons from atoms. It is the flow of these free electrons that forms an electric current.

As the electrons move through the material, they 'collide' with the vibrating atoms and are scattered, so their flow is disrupted. As the atoms vibrate more vigorously, so the frequency of 'collision' or interaction between the atoms and the electrons also increases. This reduces the rate of flow of the electrons and so the current falls. In other words, the resistance increases (Figure 39a). However, if more electrons are released from the atoms as the temperature rises, then there is a greater rate of flow of charge – the current increases. In other words, the resistance falls (Figure 39b).

The change in resistance with temperature, as illustrated in question 23, depends on which of these two effects 'wins'. In a metal, the temperature has virtually no effect on the number of electrons that can move freely through the material, so the dominant effect is that of atomic vibrations. But in a semiconductor a small rise in temperature leads to the release of a large number of electrons, and this effect now outweighs that of atomic vibrations.

Electronic materials

Space technology relies heavily on 'designer' materials that have been developed to have particular electrical properties. Such materials are essential for the solar cells and the communication and control systems on-board a spacecraft – just as they are for familiar Earth-based electronic devices. The development of electronic devices and materials is usually said to have started with the invention of the transistor in 1947. The following extracts from a newspaper article written fifty years later indicate the importance of this invention. But beware – as is all too often the case with such articles, this one contained a misleading explanation of the science.

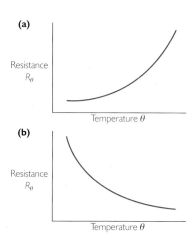

Figure 39 *Schematic diagrams showing the change in resistance with temperature due to (a) thermal vibrations and (b) the release of electrons*

ACTIVITY 21 **Picking holes**

Read the extract from a feature in *The Guardian* newspaper carefully and look out for a misleading explanation of why the electric current in a semiconductor changes with temperature. Discuss what is wrong with the explanation given and suggest how it could be improved.

Huddled secretively in a corner of their laboratory, John Bardeen and Walter Brattain were building a primitive device [Figure 40] whose impact on the world not even these engineering geniuses appreciated. … Cautiously they glued a fragment of gold foil to a wedge of plastic, pressed the wedge on to a sliver of germanium. … When all was ready, Brattain switched on the battery, sending a trickle of power through the circuit … the faint signal leapt to 100 times its strength, a sudden powerful glow on the oscilloscope. …

A week later the experiment was performed in front of their supervisor, William Shockley, and a handful of 'top brass' at their research centre. … Shockley was quick to explain the significance of the work. … No one fully understood then how the crystalline structure of germanium provided different levels of resistance to electrical current that allowed small changes in input to cause large changes in output [but] for the first time you could amplify an electrical signal without the need for a glass vacuum tube. … You were eliminating a fragile, costly and bulky limit to the scope and power of electronics.

The peculiar gadget that clicked into life in Bell Labs back in 1947 was, even then, a culmination of years of research into … a poorly understood group of materials, the semiconductors. The demonstration established solid state physics (the study of the behaviour of electrons in solids) as a promising area of research, now one of the most important areas of science. The first step to producing a reliable transistor was to produce a more robust design. … The second was to produce better quality semiconductor material. It was becoming clearer that the curious behaviour of semiconductors was due in part to naturally occurring impurities that disrupted the crystalline structure of the material, freeing some electrons to move around between atoms. The freed electrons left 'holes' through which current could flow, an effect that could be enhanced by temperature – or by artificially controlling the level of impurity.

Once these techniques were perfected, the transistor shrank in size and grew in significance. [It] became a cultural icon as the heart of the transistor radio, soon followed by TVs, cameras, hi-fi equipment and clocks. Mobile computing, the Internet and wireless communication will one day be joined by electronic business cards, watches that control our central heating, inexhaustible organ replacements and hand-held videoconferencing gear.

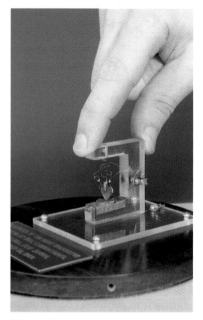

Figure 40 *The first transistor*

3.3 Heating and cooling

You have seen that the performance of electrical devices depends on temperature, so it is clearly important to prevent the temperature on-board a spacecraft from becoming too high or too low. The thermal transfer of energy, giving rise to heating and cooling, takes place in three basic ways: conduction, convection and radiation. Each of these has its place on a spacecraft.

Thermal energy transfer processes

Conduction involves energy 'spreading' through a material by virtue of atomic and molecular vibrations and by the motion of free electrons. Conduction can take place within the spacecraft through metals and through other conducting materials, but since space is virtually a vacuum energy cannot be transferred to or from the spacecraft by conduction.

Convection involves the heating of a fluid (i.e. a liquid or gas) which rises ('floats') due to its reduced density while cooler, more dense, material moves downwards to take its place. In a spacecraft, conditions are often near-weightless, and so there is no 'up' or 'down', but pumped liquids and gases can be used to distribute energy by **forced convection**. As space is an almost perfect vacuum, energy cannot be transferred to or from a spacecraft by convection.

Radiation is the *only* way that energy can be transferred to or from a spacecraft. Spacecraft are heated by solar radiation and, if they are close to the Earth or another planet, radiation (mainly infrared) emitted or reflected by the planet itself. Radiation from the spacecraft itself enables it to lose energy.

> **Study note**
>
> Electromagnetic radiation consists of (in order of decreasing wavelength) radio, microwaves, infrared, visible light, ultraviolet, X-rays and gamma rays.

Temperature control

The temperature within a spacecraft can be controlled by a combination of *passive* control (where processes happen 'naturally' without any intervention) and *active* control (where devices are switched on in order to bring about a desired change). Sometimes the devices are operated remotely, from Earth, but often they are controlled by a thermostat rather in the same way as the immersion heaters or central heating that you might have at home.

Part of the work of the ESA laboratories involves testing spacecraft to see how they absorb solar radiation (Figure 41). Broadly speaking, dull dark surfaces are good at absorbing incident infrared and visible radiation and are also good emitters, while shiny surfaces reflect radiation and are also poor emitters.

Figure 41   *A satellite under solar radiation test*

Some spacecraft have blinds similar to those you might pull down at home to block out intense sunlight. The Giotto spacecraft, which surveyed Comet Halley in 1985, had roller blinds (Figure 42). Some blinds are operated by direct commands from Earth, while others are operated automatically.

Transfer of energy within a spacecraft can be controlled using materials that are good conductors (such as copper) or good insulators. Figure 43 shows one widely used insulating material consisting of layers of plastic (Mylar or Kapton) separated by layers of fine plastic mesh within which there is a vacuum.

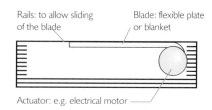

Figure 42 *Roller blinds used on Giotto*

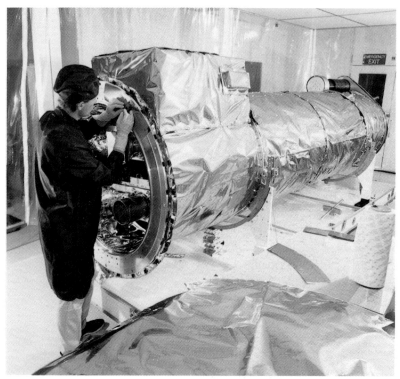

Figure 43 *Mylar/Kapton insulation*

Cooling by liquid circulation

Solid conductors can be used to transfer energy, but heat pipes are more effective and are used extensively (Figure 44). The hollow copper tube contains a volatile liquid: nitrogen or helium for very low-temperature work; acetone, methanol or water at medium temperatures; molten metals such as sodium or lithium at very high temperatures. If one end of the pipe is in a hot area, energy will be transferred to the liquid (cooling the hot area) and evaporating it. The vapour travels along the pipe to be condensed at the other end. On condensing, the liquid transfers energy to its surroundings and then runs (or is pumped) back to the other end of the tube.

Large spacecraft have fluid pumped around them, as in a central heating or air conditioning system, to control their interior temperature. The Space Shuttle is water-cooled. To keep various

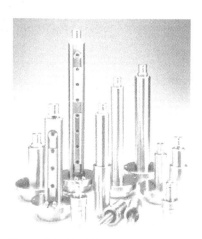

Figure 44 *Heat pipes*

pieces of electronic equipment within their operating temperature ranges, they are sited on 'cold plates' through which the water coolant flows. Air heated by the crew transfers its energy to circulating water in order to keep them relatively cool. The warmed circulating liquids pass through a honeycomb of tubes fitted into radiator panels attached to the Shuttle bay doors. During launch many systems are used at full power so when the shuttle reaches orbit a lot of energy needs to be transferred from the spacecraft to bring the temperature down to a reasonable level. Immediately the Space Shuttle reaches orbit, the payload bay doors are opened (Figure 45) so that energy can be radiated into space.

Figure 45   *Space shuttle in orbit with its doors open*

Astronauts' spacesuits also contain a water cooling system (Figure 46). In what looks like long underwear there are many small plastic tubes through which water circulates. This body-heated water then passes into the back-pack where energy is radiated from the water to the surroundings.

On the Internet the NASA SpaceLink page at http://spacelink.msfc.nasa.gov gives details of a number of cooling systems used on spacecraft. Search under such headings as Water coolant loop system, Shuttle space suit, Active thermal control system, and Heat pipe.

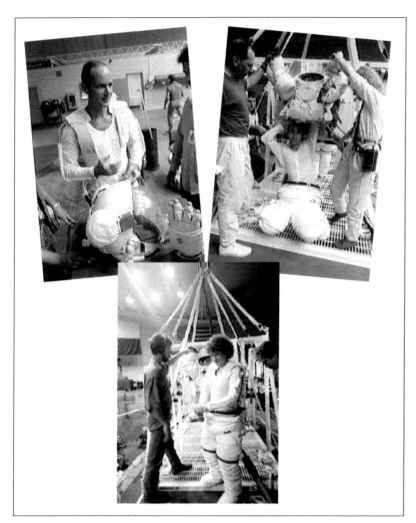

Figure 46 *Astronauts wearing water cooled spacesuits.*

3.4 *Cooling by circulating liquids*

The cooling systems on a spacecraft have to be tested before launch to ensure that they are able to transfer energy at the required rate. One way to do this is to pass a heated fluid (liquid or gas) through the system, measure its fall in temperature and calculate the power or energy transferred from it. In Activity 23 you will model a space cooling system and investigate its energy transfer. But first you need to prepare the ground by thinking how energy transfers can be related to temperature changes of a circulating fluid.

Energy and temperature change

When an object is heated, the resulting rise in temperature ($\Delta\theta$) depends on the amount of energy transferred to it (ΔE), its mass (m) and the material(s) from which it is made:

$$\Delta E = mc\Delta\theta \qquad (17)$$

where c is the **specific heat capacity** of the material. With ΔE in joules (J), m in kg and $\Delta\theta$ in °C, the units of c are $J\,kg^{-1}\,°C^{-1}$. For many materials, specific heat capacity itself depends on temperature so you will often find that you are given an average value over a particular temperature range.

QUESTION

24 A kilogram of water cools from 100 °C to 80 °C in 2 minutes. If the specific heat capacity of water in this temperature range is 4200 J kg^{-1} °C^{-1}, calculate the average power transfer from the water.

ACTIVITY 22 **Heating**

Use an electric immersion heater to heat an aluminium block.
Continue heating until the temperature reaches a steady value. Plot a graph of temperature against time. Calculate the specific heat capacity of the aluminium. Discuss why the temperature does *not* continue to rise indefinitely.

The following example based on a domestic 'radiator' shows how to deal with flowing fluids.

Worked example

Q A domestic 'radiator' has water pumped through it at a rate of 6 kg per minute. Before entering, the water temperature is 60 °C and it leaves at a temperature of 50 °C. Calculate (i) the energy transferred each minute by this heater and (ii) its power output.

A Deal with 6 kg of water. In one minute, this water cools from 60 °C to 50 °C, so you can calculate the energy transferred from it:

$$\Delta Q = 6\,kg \times 4200\,J\,kg^{-1}\,°C^{-1} \times 10\,°C$$
$$= 252\,000\,J\ (= 2.52 \times 10^5\,J)$$

$$\text{power transferred} = \frac{252\,000\,J}{60\,s} = 4200\,W$$

Study note

A domestic radiator in fact transfers most energy by convection, so the name is misleading.

Testing space radiators

ACTIVITY 23 **A model space radiator**

Your task is to use a model radiator system (Figure 47) to find the energy lost from a hot object. Providing a large evacuated space in a school laboratory is not easy, so the 'radiator' used in this activity will be surrounded by air and so transfer energy more by convection than by radiation.

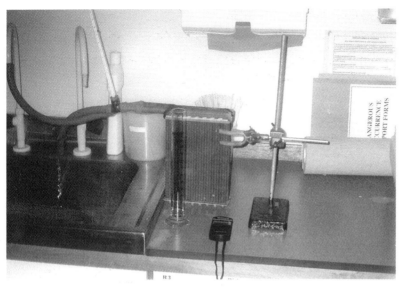

Figure 47 *A model space radiator*

Radiator performance

The performance of a radiator is related to its temperature, its area, the nature of it surface and the temperature of the surroundings. Figure 48 shows data obtained by researchers working at ESTEC in the Netherlands (the European Space Research and Technology Centre, run by the European Space Agency). In these tests, the same type of surface was used throughout, and the input power to the radiator was kept constant. The radiator was allowed to reach a 'steady state', i.e. a steady temperature at which the power radiated balanced the input power. Figure 48 shows how this 'steady state' temperature depends on the surface area and on the temperature of the surroundings. Note that the 'Radiator area' axis has a power or logarithmic scale rising in factors of 10.

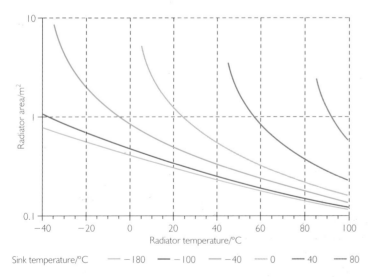

Figure 48 *Radiator performance data*

QUESTIONS

25 Figure 48 gives some radiator performance data. Use this information to answer the following questions.

(**a**) Write a short paragraph (about two sentences) saying how the temperature of the radiator is affected by (**i**) its area and (**ii**) the temperature of the environment or sink.

(**b**) If the environment or sink temperature was 0 °C, what radiator area would be needed to maintain its temperature at 24 °C?

26 In the continuous casting process of steel production, the molten steel has to be cooled before it is straightened, cut and shaped. The steel is poured into a water-cooled mould and further cooling takes place in the curved cooling chamber (Figure 49). This question illustrates the large amounts of energy involved in the process.

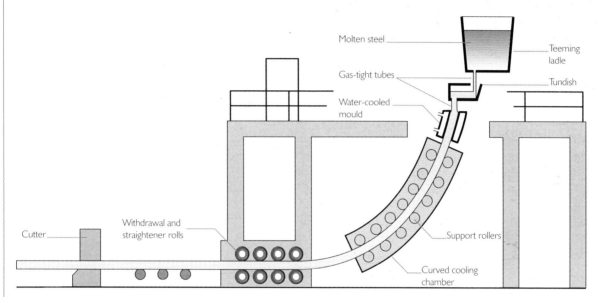

Figure 49   *Cooling molten steel in the continuous casting process*

Water entering the mould passes through each of two wide and two narrow faces. Flow to each of the wide faces is 2400 kg (2400 litres) per minute and to each of the narrow faces 240 kg per minute. The water enters at a temperature of 40 °C and the outlet temperatures are 47 °C on each wide face and 48 °C on each narrow face. The average specific heat capacity of water over this temperature range is $4179 \, \mathrm{J \, kg^{-1} \, °C^{-1}}$.

(**a**) How much energy is transferred to the water in each minute?

(**b**) What is the total power transfer to the water?

Further **investigations**

As you might suspect, the hotter an object is, the more rapidly it loses energy to its surroundings. But how, exactly, does the temperature of an object affect its rate of cooling? And does the temperature of the surroundings make a difference too?

If you have an opportunity to carry out more detailed investigative work you might think about using the apparatus from Activity 23 to explore these and any other related questions that you can think of.

3.5 *Summing up part 3*

In this part of the unit you have learned why it is important to control the temperature on-board a spacecraft, and seen how and why electrical resistance changes with temperature. You have also learned how heating and cooling take place and how such processes can be measured and controlled.

Activity 24 is designed to help you review your progress, and question 27 is designed for you to put into practice what you have been learning.

ACTIVITY **24** **Summing up part 3**

Spend a few minutes checking through your notes – use the following exercises to help you.

Look through part 3 and make sure you know the meaning of each of the terms printed in bold.

Write a short paragraph explaining why the resistance of copper increases with temperature whereas that of carbon decreases.

By means of a labelled sketch and/or a short paragraph, explain how conduction, convection and radiation all contribute to the transfer of energy in the model space radiator used in Activity 23.

┌─ QUESTION ───

27 The passage below refers to Figure 50 and has been adapted from an article in a magazine. When you have read it and studied the diagram, answer the questions that follow.

Sun-catching venetian blinds could help to store the energy transferred from solar radiation and help heat buildings. Each slat has a front reflector made of aluminised plastic. Nested in a bed of insulation below the front reflector is a glass tube containing water. This nests in a second reflector and is protected by a long, narrow window of special glass.

Each front curved reflector bounces the Sun's rays up to the slat above. Here the rays are focused through the narrow glass window and their energy transferred to the water. These water tubes are linked by pipes to the building's hot water system. The slats are re-angled occasionally, but do not need to track the Sun precisely.

During the day the Sun-warmed water passes along the pipes and provides some heating for the room as well as adding hot water to the building's heating system. At night, with the blinds shut, the heated water is circulated back through the water tubes to heat the room. The original prototype transferred 70% of the available solar energy.

(**a**) Why are both the large front reflector and the small rear reflector needed?

(**b**) Why do the blind slats need insulation behind the reflectors? Suggest a suitable insulating material and explain what makes it a good insulator.

(**c**) If the hot water tank is positioned above the level of the blind, explain how the heated water
(**i**) reaches the tank during the day and
(**ii**) circulates through the blind at night.

(**d**) By what thermal energy transfer process(es) is the room heated by the warm water passing through the blind?

(**e**) Taking the various energy transfer processes into account, what properties would be ideal for the material making the water tubes? It is suggested that copper tubes might be better than the glass ones. What advantages and disadvantages might the copper tubes have?

(**f**) In a test of the prototype, the solar flux measured square-on to the blind was 25 MJ per square metre per day, the blind measured 2 m by 2 m, and the water circulated at a rate of 6000 kg per day.

Calculate (**i**) the energy transferred to the water and (**ii**) the resulting temperature rise of the water. Assume that the blind is 70% efficient at transferring energy to the water and that energy transfers from the heated water to the surroundings can be ignored. The average specific heat capacity of water over this temperature range is 4200 J kg^{-1} °C^{-1}.

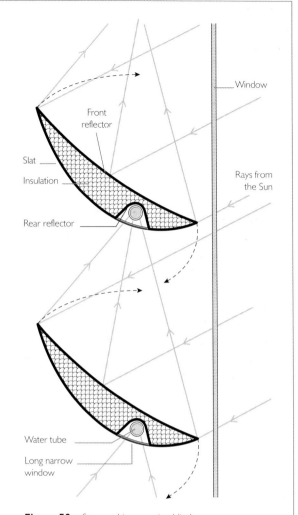

Figure 50 *Sun-catching venetian blinds*

4 *Mission accomplished*

In this unit you have studied some aspects of electric circuits and power supplies and some aspects of energy transfer processes. This concluding section is intended to help you to look back over the whole unit and consolidate your knowledge and understanding.

4.1 *Conservation of …*

In studying this unit you have learned some fundamental pieces of physics that all relate to the important idea of **conservation**. In everyday language, conservation is often used to mean keeping something as it is, not damaging it, not wasting it, or not using it up. For example, you might talk of conserving the countryside, or conserving fuel.

In its scientific sense, conservation means that some measurable quantity remains unchanged. One example is the **conservation of mass**. In Activity 23 you probably took it for granted that the rate of flow of mass into the apparatus was the same as the rate of flow out of it. But other examples of this conservation law are less obvious. For example, if you are dealing with a complex network of pipes (such as in a water or gas supply system) then conservation of mass is important to bear in mind when considering rates of flow through various parts of the system.

The **conservation of charge** is another example: no situation or process has *ever* been found in which the total amount of charge changes. You are probably used to the idea of positive and negative charge and that removing electrons (negatively charged) from an initially uncharged object leaves behind an equal amount of positive charge. The total amount of charge (found by adding up individual positive and negative charges with their correct signs) is always unchanged. We used this fundamental law of Nature earlier in this unit, when we said that the rate of flow of charge (i.e. the current) into a point in an electric circuit must be equal to the rate of flow of charge away from that point. You will probably also have used charge conservation in balancing nuclear and chemical equations.

The **conservation of energy** is another fundamental law of Nature. Even though energy is not 'stuff', nor is it an easily measurable property of matter, it is still possible to define and measure amounts of energy transferred or stored, and no process has *ever* been found in which energy is either created or destroyed. The law of energy conservation underlies much of the work of this unit. For example, in looking at energy in an electric circuit in part 2 we used the fact that the energy supplied by a power source *to* each coulomb of charge must be equal to the energy delivered to the circuit *by* each coulomb.

ACTIVITY 25   **Conservation rules – OK!**

Many of the activities, diagrams and questions in this unit illustrate and use the conservation laws discussed above. By copying and completing Table 4, which lists several of these examples, you will make a chart showing conservation laws in use. Some of the rows of the table have been filled in to give you the idea – but you might decide to design your own chart in a different way, and perhaps to add sketch diagrams and extra notes.

Reference	Illustrates/uses conservation of ...	Notes
Section 2.1, Figure 12 How does a solar cell work?	charge	Electrons drift across boundary leaving positive charge. Overall charge is still zero.
Activity 5	energy	Emf (energy supplied to each coulomb) by cells connected in series is equal to sum of emfs of individual cells.
Resistors in series and parallel	charge	
Resistors in series and parallel	energy	
Activity 9 Maximising the power	energy	Total power supplied by cell = power in external circuit + power in internal resistance.
Questions 16–18		
Section 3.1, Question 20		'Missing' energy can be accounted for by ...
Energy and temperature change	energy	
Activity 23	mass	
Activity 23		
Question 25		

Table 4   *Conservation laws in use*

4.2 *Questions on the whole unit*

QUESTIONS

28 Electric vehicles were first introduced in the late 19th century. At the turn of that century, around 40% of all motor vehicles were powered by electricity, far more than by petrol. Recent years have seen a revival of interest in entirely battery-powered vehicles.

(**a**) The *Elcat Cityvan 2000*, a minivan developed in Finland, has a set of six lead–acid batteries of emf 12.0 V connected to provide 72.0 V. Draw a diagram to show how the batteries must be connected together.

(**b**) The vehicle is powered by a dc motor which, when under the greatest load, draws a current of 300 A from the batteries.
(**i**) Given that each lead–acid battery has an internal resistance of 0.0065 Ω, calculate the voltage (terminal potential difference) across all six batteries under this condition.
(**ii**) Calculate the power transferred by the resistance of each battery while there is a current of 300 A in the circuit.
(**iii**) What effect will this power transfer have on the batteries?

(**c**) The set-up described here does *not* maximise the power transferred by the batteries. Explain why it would in practice be unwise to design the van circuit to maximise the power transfer.

29 The total electrical power generated in the world today is about 10^9 kW. In the rich countries this works out at roughly 1 kW per person. During the next century the world's population is likely to grow to about 10^4 million. To provide everyone with the 'energy standard' of 1 kW, some 10^{10} kW of electricity will need to be produced.

One possible way to achieve this large increase in power might be to build Space Power Satellites (SPS) – a concept first conceived in the 1960s. This would involve building very large solar arrays in geostationary orbit and beaming the power developed by their solar cells to Earth by microwaves (see Figure 51).

(**a**) Calculate the power that could be provided by an SPS array of area 5×10^7 m^2 (50 km^2) if the combined efficiency of the array, transmitter and receiver is 8%, and the solar radiation flux is 1400 W m^{-2}.

(**b**) How many such arrays would be needed to provide 10^{10} kW?

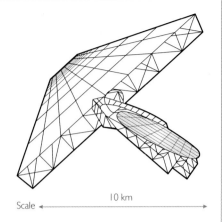

Scale ←————— 10 km —————→

Figure 51 *Artist's impression of a Space Power Satellite*

30 Table 5 shows the energy transferred to a solar water heating panel of area 1 m^2 at latitude 52°N for various times of year and 'angles of tilt' (Figure 52).

(**a**) What angle of tilt would maximise the transfer of energy
(**i**) in January and (**ii**) in July?

(**b**) Explain whether, for this site at latitude 52°N, it would be best to have an angle of tilt of 40°, 50° or 60° to maximise the total energy transferred over a whole year. (It might be helpful to assume that all months are the same length.)

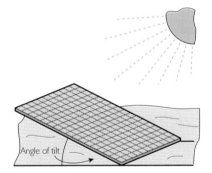

Angle of tilt

Figure 52 *The 'angle of tilt' of a solar panel*

Month	Maximum energy transferred/MJ per day (for angle of tilt shown)									
	0°	10°	20°	30°	40°	50°	60°	70°	80°	90°
Jan	4.0	5.8	7.2	8.6	9.7	10.4	11.2	11.5	11.2	10.8
Feb	6.8	9.0	10.8	12.6	13.7	14.8	15.1	15.1	14.8	14.0
Mar	13.3	15.5	17.6	19.1	20.2	20.5	20.5	19.8	18.4	16.6
Apr	20.5	22.3	23.8	24.8	24.8	24.1	22.7	20.6	18.4	15.1
May	26.3	27.7	28.4	28.8	27.4	25.2	23.0	19.8	16.6	13.0
Jun	28.4	28.8	29.2	29.2	27.4	25.2	22.3	19.1	15.1	11.2
Jul	28.1	28.4	28.8	29.2	27.4	25.6	23.0	20.2	16.2	12.2
Aug	23.0	24.8	25.6	25.9	26.3	24.8	22.7	20.5	17.3	13.7
Sep	16.2	18.7	20.5	21.6	22.3	22.7	21.6	20.5	18.7	16.2
Oct	9.0	11.5	13.7	15.1	16.6	17.3	17.6	17.3	16.6	15.5
Nov	5.0	6.8	8.6	10.1	11.2	12.2	12.6	13.0	12.6	12.2
Dec	3.2	4.7	6.1	7.2	8.3	9.0	9.7	10.1	10.1	9.7

Table 5 *Data for question 30*

31 This question is about a technique used in the oil and gas industry to measure rates of fluid flow. It involves measuring the temperature upstream and downstream of a small heater placed in the path of the fluid as shown in Figure 53. The apparatus is first calibrated by measuring the temperature difference produced by a known heater power for a known gas flow rate. Measuring an unknown flow rate involves readjusting the heater power so that it produces the same temperature change. The following example illustrates how this enables the flow rate to be deduced.

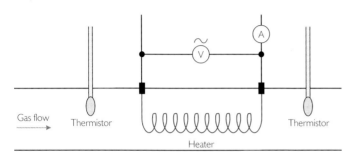

Figure 53 *A technique for measuring fluid flow rate*

(**a**) If the thermistors are the NTC type, how will their resistance depend on the temperature of the gas?

(**b**) (**i**) The voltmeter and ammeter connected to the heater read 240 V and 15 A respectively. Calculate the power transferred by the heater.

(**ii**) At a flow rate of 0.10 kg s^{-1} gas passing the heater rose in temperature by 13 °C. Taking the specific heat capacity of the gas to be 2200 J kg^{-1} °C^{-1} over this temperature range, calculate the power transferred to the gas.

(**iii**) Your answer to (**i**) should not be the same as your answer to (**ii**). Explain why this is the case, and calculate the power that is *not* being transferred to the gas. Which conservation law are you using in this calculation?

(**c**) On another occasion, with the gas at the same initial temperature flowing at a different rate, the power transferred by the heater had to be reduced to 2500 W in order to keep the temperature rise from the same starting temperature to 13 °C and thus to keep the power transfer to the surroundings the same as in (**b**).

(**i**) Using your answer to (**b**)(**iii**), calculate the power transferred to the gas.

(**ii**) Calculate the flow rate of the gas on this occasion.

4.3 *Achievements*

Now you have studied this unit you should be able to:

- describe electric current as the rate of flow of charged particles and recall and use the expression $\Delta Q = I\Delta t$ (2.1, 3.2)*;

- recall and use the expression $V = W/Q$ (2.1);

- define and use the concepts of *emf* and *internal resistance* and distinguish between *emf* and *terminal potential difference* (2.1, 2.2, 2.3);

- recall and use the fact that resistance is defined by $R = V/I$ and that Ohm's law is a special case when $I \propto V$ (2.2);

- recognise and use the relationships between current, voltage and resistance, for series and parallel circuits, and appreciate that these relationships are a consequence of the conservation of charge and energy (2.2);

- recall and use the expressions $P = VI$, $W = VIt$ and derive and use related expressions (e.g. $P = I^2R$) (2.3);

- recall and use the fact that the maximum power transfer from a source of emf is achieved when the load resistance is equal to the internal resistance (2.3);

- recognise and use the expression *percentage efficiency* = {[*useful energy* (or power) *output*]/[*total energy* (or power) *input*]} $\times$ 100% (2.3, 3.1);

- recall that the resistance of metallic conductors increases with increasing temperature and that the resistance of NTC thermistors decreases with increasing temperature (3.2);

- explain, qualitatively, how changes of resistance with temperature may be modelled in terms of lattice vibrations and number of conduction electrons (3.2);

- recognise and use the expression $\Delta E = mc\Delta\theta$ (3.4);

- explain the principles involved in a continuous flow technique to measure thermal energy transfer (3.4).

* Numbers indicate the section(s) that relate to each achievement.

Answers

1 (a) Fuel cells, with or without the addition of cryogenic engines. (The point representing 1 kW, 1 week, lies more or less on the line between these two regions of the graph.)

(b) Solar and nuclear dynamic systems. (Notice that 10^1 kW means 10 kW.)

2 (a) $\Delta Q = I\Delta t = 0.5\ \text{C s}^{-1} \times 2.0\ \text{s} = 1.0\ \text{C}$

(b) $\Delta W = E\Delta Q$

(c) $\Delta W = 1.5\ \text{J C}^{-1} \times 1.0\ \text{C} = 1.5\ \text{J}$

3 In circuits (a), (c) and (e) the cells are in series so their voltages add: (a) 1.0 V, (c) 1.5 V, (e) 2.0 V.
Circuits (b), (d) and (f) all give 0.5 V as the cells are joined in parallel.
In (g) each pair of cells in series gives 1.0 V. The two pairs are joined in parallel so the net output will also be 1.0 V.

4 A single row of 56 cells joined in series gives an output of 28 V. (Several rows of 56 cells could be connected in parallel to give the same output voltage.)

5 2 Ω. Read any pair of values for the graph, e.g. when $I = 3$ A, $V = 6$ V:
$$R = \frac{V}{I} = \frac{6\ \text{V}}{3\ \text{A}} = 2\ \Omega.$$

6 Graphs (b) and (c) show ohmic behaviour – they are straight lines through the origin.

7 The steeper the graph, the higher the resistance. (Graph (b) shows a higher resistance than graph (c).)

8 In (a) the resistance increases at large currents and voltages and in (d) the resistance decreases as the current is increased. You can check this by reading values from the graphs and calculating resistance. For example, in (a), when $I = 2$ A, $V = 1$ V and so $R = 0.5\ \Omega$; when $I = 3$ A, $V = 3$ V so $R = 1\ \Omega$ (an increase). In (d), when $I = 1$ A, $V = 2$ V so $R = 2\ \Omega$, and when $I = 3$ A, $V = 3$ V and $R = 1\ \Omega$ (a decrease).

9 Figure 54 shows a graph of the measurements. It is not possible to draw a straight line through the origin that also passes through all the error boxes, so the material does not obey Ohm's law. (Its resistance decreases as current and voltage increase.)

10 (a) $\dfrac{1}{R} = \left(\dfrac{1}{1} + \dfrac{1}{2} + \dfrac{1}{4} + \dfrac{1}{8}\right)\Omega^{-1} = 1.875\ \Omega^{-1}$

$R = \dfrac{1}{1.875}\ \Omega = 0.53\ \Omega$

(b) First replace the 3 Ω and 6 Ω combination:

$\dfrac{1}{R} = \left(\dfrac{1}{3} + \dfrac{1}{6}\right)\Omega^{-1} = 0.5\ \Omega^{-1}$, so $R = 2\ \Omega$

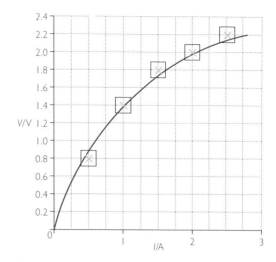

Figure 54 *The answer to question 9*

The complete arrangement is then equivalent to two 2 Ω resistors in series, giving a total resistance of 4 Ω.

(c) First replace the series of 4 Ω + 2 Ω by a single 6 Ω resistor. The complete arrangement is then equivalent to two 6 Ω resistors in parallel:

$\dfrac{1}{R} = \left(\dfrac{1}{6} + \dfrac{1}{6}\right)\Omega^{-1}$, and so $R = 3\ \Omega$

11 $P = IV,\ \dfrac{I}{V} = P = \dfrac{2000\ \text{W}}{230\ \text{V}} = 8.7\ \text{A}$

12 $P = \dfrac{V^2}{R},\ R = \dfrac{V^2}{P} = \dfrac{(230\ \text{V})^2}{60\ \text{W}} = 882\ \Omega.$

13 Current $I = \dfrac{\mathscr{E}}{(R + r)} = \dfrac{3.0\ \text{V}}{(6\ \Omega)} = 0.50\ \text{A}.$

$P_{\text{out}} = (0.50\ \text{A})^2 \times 1\ \Omega = 0.25\ \text{W}$

Total power is

$P_{\text{in}} = (0.50\ \text{A})^2 \times 6\ \Omega = 1.50\ \text{W}$

Efficiency $= \dfrac{0.25\ \text{W}}{1.50\ \text{W}} = 0.17 = 17\%$

Alternatively, efficiency $= \dfrac{R}{(R + r)} = 1\ \Omega/6\ \Omega$
$= 0.17 = 17\%.$

This would not be a sensible arrangement for several reasons. The output power is less than it would be under conditions for maximum power (0.25 W compared with over 0.45 W when $R = r$), but the total power transferred by the battery is *greater* than it would be if $R = r$ (1.5 W compared with 0.9 W), so the battery would run down more quickly. Most of the battery power (80% of it) is wasted due to internal heating in the battery.

14 (a) The cells are in series so the total emf and the total internal resistance are found by adding the separate emfs

and internal resistances.

(i) $6 \times 0.005\ \Omega = 0.03\ \Omega$

(ii) $6 \times 2.000\ V = 12.000\ V.$

(b) (i) The internal resistance and the load form a series circuit, with resistance
$R + r = (2.97 + 0.03)\ \Omega = 3.00\ \Omega.$

(ii) $I = \dfrac{\mathscr{E}}{(R + r)} = \dfrac{12\ V}{(3.00\ \Omega)} = 4.0\ A$ (equation 9).

(iii) Terminal pd $V = IR = 4.0\ A \times 2.97\ \Omega = 11.9\ V.$

(c) If the current in the battery is 200 A, then the 'lost volts' $Ir = 200\ A \times 0.03\ \Omega = 6\ V$. The terminal pd must therefore fall to $12\ V - 6\ V = 6\ V$. If the headlamps are designed to be connected to a pd of 12 V they will dim noticeably.

15 (a) Internal resistances combine just like ordinary resistances in series and parallel, as the following calculations for arrangements (ii)–(iv) show.

(ii) Total resistance $r = 4 \times 30\ \Omega = 120\ \Omega.$

(iii) $\dfrac{1}{r} = \left(\dfrac{1}{30} + \dfrac{1}{30}\right)\Omega^{-1} = \left(\dfrac{1}{15}\right)\Omega^{-1}$ so $r = 15\ \Omega.$

(iv) Each pair of cells in series has resistance $60\ \Omega.$
$\dfrac{1}{r} = \left(\dfrac{1}{60} + \dfrac{1}{60}\right)\Omega^{-1} = \left(\dfrac{1}{30}\right)\Omega^{-1}$ so $r = 30\ \Omega.$

(b) Power transfer will be maximum when the external load resistance is equal to the total internal resistance. Each set of four solar cells has a total internal resistance of $120\ \Omega$. The two sets in parallel have a total resistance of $60\ \Omega$ so the external load must be $60\ \Omega.$

16   Your answer should make the point that input power to solar panels varies with angle. In order to intercept as much radiation as possible, the panels must point directly at the Sun – a change of angle will result in a loss of power. You could go on to say that, provided the panels are within a few degrees of being square-on, the loss of power will not be great. But once the misalignment is more than, say, 20°, then the power drops by a large fraction. A diagram similar to Figure 30 would be suitable.

17   $P_{out} = 0.11 \times P_{in}$

so $P_{in} = \dfrac{P_{out}}{0.11} = \dfrac{16\ kW}{0.11} = 147\ kW = 1.47 \times 10^5\ W$

$P_{in} = FA$

so $A = \dfrac{P_{in}}{F} = \dfrac{147\ kW}{1.4\ kW\,m^{-2}} \approx 10^2\ m^2$

or $A = \dfrac{P_{in}}{F} = \dfrac{1.47 \times 10^5\ W}{1400\ W\,m^{-2}} \approx 10^2\ m^2$

(Notice that you can either use W or kW but you must be consistent and not use a mixture.)

18   Input power is greatest when the arrays are square-on to the incident radiation.

$P_{in} = FA = 600\ W\,m^{-2} \times 5000\ m$
$= 3.00 \times 10^6\ W = 3.00 \times 10^3\ kW.$

Efficiency $= \dfrac{P_{out}}{P_{in}} = \dfrac{435\ kW}{(3.00 \times 10^3\ kW)} = 0.145 = 14.5\%.$

19 (a) (i) about 38%

(ii) about 95%

(b) From about 94% to about 75%, i.e. by about 19% of the maximum available capacity.

20 (a) (i) Gallium arsenide (GaAs)

(ii) Cadmium sulfide (CdS)

(iii) Gallium arsenide/gallium phosphide (GaAs/GaP).

(b) It would not be sensible to use gallium and silicon as their efficiencies have already fallen to zero and so no energy transfer would take place.

(c) At 0 °C a cadmium sulfide cell's efficiency is near 29% but this falls to about 6% at 400 °C.

21   From Figure 35, a GaAs array would have an efficiency of about 25% at 50 °C. If P_{out} is to be $1 \times 10^6\ W$, and P_{out} is 25% of P_{in}, then $P_{in} = 4 \times 10^6\ W.$
If the entire array is square-on to the incident solar flux, then $\theta = 0°$ and $P_{in} = FA$ so

$A = \dfrac{P_{in}}{F} = \dfrac{4 \times 10^6\ W}{(1.4 \times 10^3\ W\,m^{-2})} = 2.8 \times 10^3\ m^2.$

22   $R_\theta = R_0(1 + \alpha\theta) = R_0 + \alpha R_0\theta$
$R_{80} = 50.0\ \Omega\,(1 + 4.28 \times 10^{-3}\ °C^{-1} \times 80\ °C)$
$= 0.50\ \Omega \times 1.324 = 0.67\ \Omega.$

The percentage change in resistance is quite large,

$\dfrac{0.17\ \Omega}{0.50\ \Omega} \approx 34\%.$

However, the resistance of the connecting wires in a circuit is likely to be much less than that of other components, so can usually be ignored. In a circuit that contained a large amount of copper (in coils of electromagnets, for example) the effect of temperature would need to be considered.

23 (a) Copper, constantan, steel and tungsten all have positive temperature coefficients. Carbon is the odd one out with a negative coefficient.

(b) Its resistance is near-constant over a fairly wide temperature range.

(c) Figure 55 shows a plot of all the data from Table 3. The temperature coefficients are carbon $-5.0 \times 10^{-4}\ °C^{-1}$; steel $3.3 \times 10^{-3}\ °C^{-1}$; tungsten $5.2 \times 10^{-3}\ °C^{-1}.$

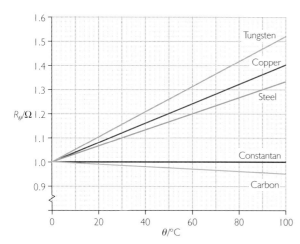

Figure 55 *The answer to question 23*

24 $\Delta E = 1 \text{ kg} \times 4200 \text{ J kg}^{-1}\,^{\circ}\text{C}^{-1} \times 20\,^{\circ}\text{C} = 84\,000 \text{ J}$

$\text{Power} = \dfrac{84\,000 \text{ J}}{120 \text{ s}} = 700 \text{ W}$

25 (a) (i) The larger the radiator's area, the cooler is the radiator.
   (ii) The higher the sink temperature, the higher is the radiator temperature.
   (b) Approximately 1 m².

26 Use equation (17) ($\Delta E = mc\Delta\theta$) and deal with changes that take place in one minute.

For each wide face, $\Delta\theta = 7\,^{\circ}\text{C}$ and $m = 2400 \text{ kg}$
$\Delta E = 2400 \text{ kg} \times 4179 \text{ J kg}^{-1}\,^{\circ}\text{C}^{-1} \times 7\,^{\circ}\text{C}$
   $= 70\,207\,200 \text{ J}$

For each narrow face $\Delta\theta = 8\,^{\circ}\text{C}$ and $m = 240 \text{ kg}$
$\Delta E = 240 \text{ kg} \times 4179 \text{ J kg}^{-1}\,^{\circ}\text{C}^{-1} \times 8\,^{\circ}\text{C}$
   $= 8\,023\,680 \text{ J}$

So the total energy transferred in one minute is
$2 \times (70\,207\,200 + 8\,023\,680) \text{ J} = 1.5646 \times 10^8 \text{ J}.$

(b) Power $P = \dfrac{\Delta E}{\Delta t}$, $\Delta t = 1 \text{ min} = 60 \text{ s}$

$P = 1.5646 \times 10^8 \text{ J}/60 \text{ s}$
   $= 2.6077 \times 10^6 \text{ W}$
   $= 2.6077 \text{ MW} (= 2.6 \text{ MW to two figure precision})$

27 (a) The large reflector focuses the solar radiation onto the water pipes. The smaller reflector 'beams' radiation from the heated water back into the room. Without the smaller reflector most of the radiation not emitted directly into the room would be absorbed by the insulation.

(b) Insulation helps ensure that the absorbed energy is stored in the water and is not transferred directly into the room. Glass fibre or Rockwool (such as used in loft insulation) could be used. These materials trap air within them and prevent it from circulating. The materials themselves are also poor conductors, as is the air. They therefore reduce both convection and conduction.

(c) Warm water is less dense than cold water, so during the day the water circulates within the system by convection: heated water moves upwards to the tank while cooler water descends to the blind. At night, when warm water is required to move downwards from tank to blind, a pump is needed.

(d) Energy transfer will be mainly by convection (warmed air near the blind rises, setting up convention currents in the room) and also by radiation. Transfer by conduction will be minimal, as air is a poor conductor.

(e) Ideally the tubes should be good absorbers of solar radiation (mostly visible and infrared), and good emitters of infrared radiation – preferably their surfaces should be dull black. They should also be good thermal conductors in order to transfer energy to and from the water.
   Copper is a better thermal conductor than glass, so energy would transfer more easily through the tube walls. However, depending on its density and specific heat capacity, more energy might be wasted in heating copper tubes at the expense of the water.

(f) (i) The surface area $A = 4 \text{ m}^2$ so the total amount of solar energy intercepted must be $25 \text{ MJ m}^{-2} \times 4 \text{ m}^2 = 100 \text{ MJ}$. Energy transferred to water is 70% of 100 MJ, i.e. 70 MJ $(= 70 \times 10^6 \text{ J})$.
   (ii) From equation (17), $\Delta E = mc\Delta\theta$, so $\Delta\theta = \Delta E/mc$

$$\Delta\theta = \dfrac{70 \times 10^6 \text{ J}}{(6000 \text{ kg} \times 4200 \text{ J kg}^{-1}\,^{\circ}\text{C}^{-1})} = 28\,^{\circ}\text{C}.$$

THE SOUND OF MUSIC

Figure 1 *Creating electronic music*

Why a unit called The Sound of Music?

The study of sound is surprisingly ancient. Its origin probably lies with Roman architects trying to control echoes in the amphitheatres used for plays and concerts at that time. Since those days, scientists have discovered how a sound is propagated, the speed at which it travels, and precisely what controls its pitch, its loudness and its quality. From its origins in folklore and religion, where it was perceived to be linked with divine and magical properties, music has also become an increasingly important part of many people's lives.

Over the years, the craft of constructing and developing musical instruments has become increasingly scientific. Science has improved the tuning of instruments and the quality and penetration of the sound they produce. New technologies, new materials and modern techniques of mass production have been incorporated into the construction processes. The advent of electronics has heralded a further revolution in music, throwing open the science of sound to the average interested person in the street who can now, with a minimum of effort, generate and combine sounds with infinite variety (Figure 1).

Overview of physics principles and techniques

In this unit you will build on ideas from GCSE about vibrations and waves, looking particularly at how these can be represented graphically. In part 1 you will see how waves combine by a process called superposition and how the waves produced by musical instruments are related to their physical properties. You will use a CD-ROM and computer software first to explore and then to synthesise complex sounds.

Part 2 concentrates on the compact disc. You will discover how a compact disc stores sound and how the CD player retrieves it and how wave properties of the laser light are exploited in order to recover the information. In exploring the components of the CD player, you will learn how light is reflected and refracted by lenses and prisms. You will also see that, while a wave picture allows us to explain many properties of light, we need to introduce a different idea (that of photons) to explain how a laser works.

In the course of this unit you will also be using and developing some key mathematical and IT skills and techniques. Several activities are concerned with the generation and interpretation of graphs – the understanding of exactly what these graphs mean is crucial to the unit. You will also use CD-ROM software, both as a data source and to analyse your own data.

In later units you will do further work on

● travelling waves in *Spare Part Surgery*, *Reach for the Stars* and *Build or Bust?*;

- superposition, interference and standing waves in *Digging Up the Past* and *Build or Bust?*;

- refraction and reflection in *Good Enough to Eat*, *Spare Part Surgery* and *Build or Bust?*;

- photons and energy levels *Digging Up the Past* and *Probing the Heart of Matter*;

- signals in *Transport on Track* and *The Medium is the Message*.

▌ *Making sounds*

1.1 Synthetic sounds

A person steps out on to a stage. Six steel wires are struck sharply. They vibrate only millimetres to either side, too fast to see. Simultaneously, a flood of distorted sound volleys outwards from speakers stacked house-high, and ten thousand people shift their attention forwards. A second person emerges, flicks a few switches and begins to finger a pattern on to rectangular plastic keys. A virtual orchestra of sounds and rhythms emerges from the electronics, skilfully fused together into a recognisable anthem – the band has begun and the audience, down to the very last person at the back of the vast stadium, begins to move to the pulsing of the sound waves washing over them.

This familiar scenario of a modern concert would have been inconceivable a century ago, when an orchestra was an orchestra, consisting of dozens of individuals and their instruments. Nowadays an individual can be an orchestra: musical sounds can be recorded and replayed, time after time. And, most astonishing of all, a simple keyboard or computer can be programmed to reproduce the sounds of any instrument, or in fact any sound, at the press of a button by a process called synthesising. A typical electronic keyboard may contain the 'voices' of several hundred instruments and synthesised effects as well as pre-programmed percussive and instrumental accompaniments.

ACTIVITY ▌   Synthetic sound – how realistic is it?

Listen carefully to two extracts of the same piece of music, one with musicians playing real instruments and one computer-synthesised version of the same piece.

Listen to synthesised versions of common sounds from children's interactive books.

Comment on the quality and realism of the synthesised sounds.

Getting from a real sound to a computer-synthesised version requires an understanding of the physical nature of sound. This is your aim in the first part of this unit.

1.2 Oscillations

All sources of sound involve vibrations.

- A guitar string vibrates to produce a sound.

- The skin of a drum and a table top both vibrate when struck. (Can you suggest why the vibrations of the table top are smaller and die away faster?)

- Your vocal chords vibrate as you make sounds. Feel the vibration with your fingertips placed on the front of your neck as you hum a note.

- The prongs of a tuning fork vibrate. (You can see this if you touch the surface of water with a humming tuning fork.)

A motion that repeats itself over and over again, at regular time intervals, is called a **periodic oscillation**. Behaviour of this type is remarkably common – Figure 2 shows a few examples. Oscillating periodic motion is often referred to as **harmonic motion** because of its relation to sound.

Describing and representing oscillations

The sequence of events that form one 'unit' of a periodic motion is called a **cycle**. In one cycle, the oscillating object moves to and fro, returning to its original position and direction, whereupon the cycle begins again. The time it takes for the system to complete one cycle is called its **time period**. The **frequency** of an oscillation is defined as the number of cycles executed per unit time. One cycle per second is called one **hertz** (Hz) – this is the SI unit of frequency. The frequency f and time period T are related:

$$T = \frac{1}{f} \tag{1}$$

which can also be written

$$f = \frac{1}{T} \tag{1a}$$

As an oscillating object moves, the maximum **displacement** in either direction that it reaches from its **equilibrium position** is called the **amplitude**. The equilibrium position is where the object comes to rest after its oscillations die down.

Displacement–time graphs

We often use displacement–time graphs to represent oscillations. Figure 3 shows such a graph for a metre rule which, when clamped to a bench with about 80 cm of its length projecting, oscillates with an amplitude of 30 mm and a frequency of 2.5 Hz.

A graph such as Figure 3 shows the 'shape' of an oscillation and is often referred to as a **waveform**. Waveforms like that in Figure 3, which have the same simple, smooth shape as graphs of sin θ or cos θ plotted against angle θ, are collectively described as **sinusoidal**.

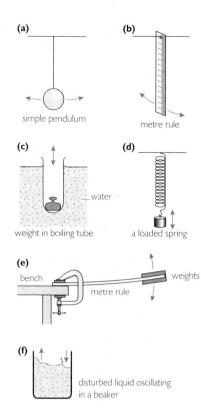

(a) simple pendulum

(b) metre rule

(c) weight in boiling tube — water

(d) a loaded spring

(e) bench — metre rule — weights

(f) disturbed liquid oscillating in a beaker

Figure 2 *Examples of periodic oscillations*

Maths reference

Reciprocals
See Maths note 3.3

Maths reference

Sine, cosine and tangent of an angle
See Maths note 6.2

Graphs of trigonometric functions
See Maths note 6.3

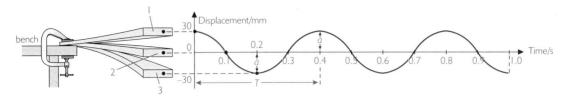

Figure 3 *Displacement–time graph for a clamped metre rule*

Sound waves produced by an oscillating object are detected when they set up oscillations with a similar waveform in a detector such as our ears or a microphone. The oscillations in a microphone can be displayed as a displacement–time graph using a cathode-ray oscilloscope (CRO) or on a computer screen. Their waveform closely matches that of the sound source.

ACTIVITY 2 **Exploring waveforms with an oscilloscope**

Use an oscilloscope to display a waveform produced by a sound source.

Observe how the frequency and amplitude of the waveform are related to the pitch and loudness of the sound.

ACTIVITY 3 **Exploring waveforms with *Multimedia Sound***

Use the sound analysis software *Multimedia Sound* to explore the waveforms of the sound from a variety of sources.

Phase

The term **phase** is used to describe the stage an oscillation has reached in its cycle. The two oscillations shown in Figure 4(a) are exactly in step. They are said to be **in phase**. Oscillations that reach their peaks and troughs at different times are said to have a **phase difference** between them. The phase of an oscillation is often expressed in terms of angles, drawing on the similarity between sinusoidal waveforms and graphs of sines and cosines.

When dealing with phase, angles can be expressed in degrees or, more commonly, in radians. One 'cycle' of a sine or cosine graph corresponds to one complete circle (360° or 2π radians), so oscillations that are exactly half a cycle out of step (Figure 4b) have a phase difference of 180° or π radians. Such oscillations are said to be **in antiphase**.

In Figure 4(c) oscillation A is one quarter of a cycle ahead of B. A leads B by a phase difference of 90° or $\pi/2$ radians – or, put another way, B leads A by $-\pi/2$. Oscillations with a phase difference of $\pi/2$ are said to be **in quadrature**. The general case is shown in Figure 4(d). A leads B by the fraction t/T of a cycle. The phase difference is therefore $(t/T) \times 360°$ or $(t/T) \times 2\pi$ radians.

Maths reference

Degrees and radians
See Maths note 6.1

Study note

When π appears in a description of phase, the units of radians are taken for granted and are sometimes omitted.

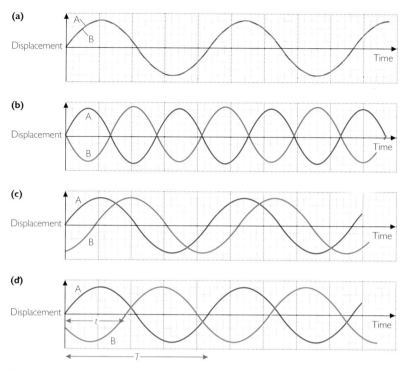

Figure 4 *Graphs showing waveforms for oscillations that are (a) in phase, (b) in antiphase, (c) in quadrature and (d) the general case*

⌐ QUESTIONS ─────────

1 Figure 5 shows three waveforms drawn to the same scale. Write down expressions relating the frequencies of (**a**) A and B, and (**b**) A and C.

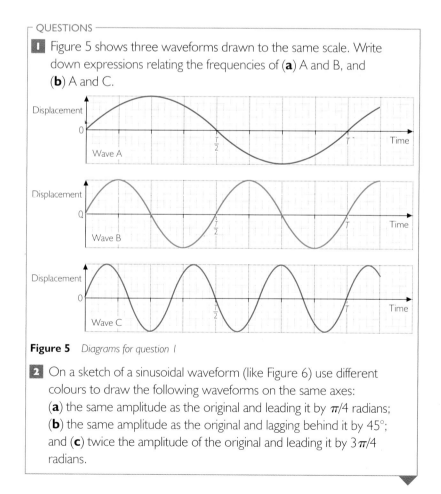

Figure 5 *Diagrams for question 1*

2 On a sketch of a sinusoidal waveform (like Figure 6) use different colours to draw the following waveforms on the same axes:
(**a**) the same amplitude as the original and leading it by $\pi/4$ radians;
(**b**) the same amplitude as the original and lagging behind it by 45°;
and (**c**) twice the amplitude of the original and leading it by $3\pi/4$ radians.

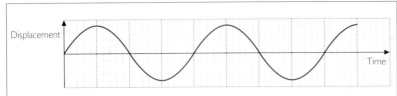

Figure 6 *Waveform for question 2*

3 (**a**) Write down a general expression, in degrees and in radians, for a phase change that would produce a wave identical to the original.

(**b**) What, if any, is the difference between waves that differ from wave A in Figure 5 by each of the following: (**i**) $\pi/8$ radians, (**ii**) 22.5°, (**iii**) $17\pi/8$ radians, and (**iv**) −337.5°?

4 Because the oscillations in Figure 5 have different frequencies, they will only be in phase at certain times. At what times are the following pairs in phase: (**i**) A and B; (**ii**) A and C; and (**iii**) B and C?

5 In the mid-1880s American photographer Eadweard Muybridge took several sequences of photographs showing horses in motion (Figure 7). Treating the leg motion as a simple oscillation, state the phase relationships between the legs of a walking horse.

Figure 7 *A horse in motion*

1.3 Travelling waves

Sound travels by spreading out in all directions from the vibrating source as a **wave** whose properties are closely linked to those of the oscillation. The waves transfer energy from the source to other places without any permanent transfer of matter – this is a property of all **travelling waves**.

There are two main classes of wave, both of which play a part in the production of sound from musical instruments, as you will see in section 1.5. A **transverse** wave involves oscillations at right angles to the direction of wave propagation. In a **longitudinal** wave, the oscillations are along the direction of propagation.

Study note

In the unit *Good Enough to Eat* you will see that light and all other electromagnetic waves are transverse.

ACTIVITY 4 **Waves on a slinky**

Using a slinky, generate and observe some transverse and longitudinal waves (Figure 8).

Mark one loop of the slinky and observe how it moves. Explore how to control the speed of the wave along the slinky. For example, try varying the tension in the slinky. Observe a single pulse as it reaches a fixed or a free end of the slinky.

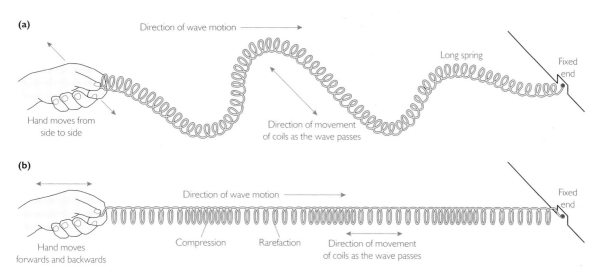

Figure 8   *Using a slinky to generate (a) transverse and (b) longitudinal waves*

In a water wave (Figure 9), the particles circulate rather than just moving up and down. This 'stretches' the surface and will create a normal wave shape at the surface if the amplitude is very small compared with the wavelength. Sharper crests form at larger amplitudes.

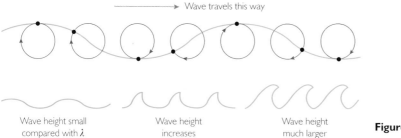

Figure 9   *The movement of particles in a water wave*

QUESTION

6 Use some of the terms introduced so far to describe the following motions:

(**a**) a tablecloth shaken to get rid of crumbs;

(**b**) a train of railway trucks shunted by a locomotive;

(**c**) a 'Mexican wave' in a stadium;

(**d**) the stop–go motion of traffic in a jam.

Sound waves

Sound waves are longitudinal, as can be demonstrated with a loudspeaker cone. As the cone vibrates, it first compresses the air next to it and then immediately allows it to spread out again (rarefy) before repeating the cycle. A series of **compressions** and **rarefactions** travels outwards from the cone. The movements produced by loud sounds can make a candle flame flicker (Figure 10). Sound cannot travel in a vacuum, since the waves need a material that can be compressed or stretched.

Figure 10   *Demonstrating longitudinal oscillations associated with sound waves*

In a human ear (Figure 11) the ear drum (a small membrane) is made to vibrate by the air compressions and rarefactions. These small vibrations are then amplified via a mechanical linkage of tiny bones. These larger pressure variations are detected by nerve endings within the inner ear.

A piezoelectric microphone (Figure 12) works in a very similar way to the ear. Variations of pressure caused by a sound wave exert tiny stresses on a piezoelectric crystal – a material that generates a voltage across it when stressed. This voltage can be detected as a small electrical signal.

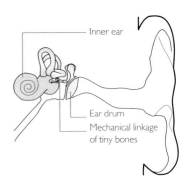

Figure 11   *A human ear*

ACTIVITY 5   **Seeing the pressure change**

Use a CRO to display the voltage from a microphone. The in–out motion of the microphone diaphragm is displayed as an up–down motion of the spot in the screen. Clap your hands by the microphone to produce a voltage spike on the screen.

The passage below was written by someone who was very confused about the science involved in this activity. Discuss what is wrong with it, then write out a corrected version.

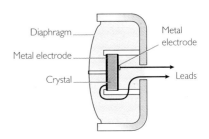

Figure 12   *A piezoelectric microphone*

When hands are clapped, air is squashed between them and exerts an opposing force, pushing the hands apart again. The to-and-fro movement creates a series of compressed and rarefied areas in the surrounding air so that air pressure is changed. The compressions are regions below atmospheric pressure and rarefactions are regions of higher pressure. The compressions and rarefactions travel outwards in the plane of the clapping hands as a sound wave. When the pressure changes reach the loudspeaker, they are immediately converted into electrical signals, generating a voltage which flows onto the oscilloscope and onto the screen. This makes the oscilloscope trace appear to jump.

Graphs of transverse travelling waves

There are several ways in which we can use graphs to represent travelling waves. Since transverse waves are perhaps easier to visualise, we will deal with them first and then apply the same ideas to longitudinal waves.

ACTIVITY 6   **Freezing a travelling wave**

Generate a travelling transverse wave on a rubber cord, rope, or chain. If you do this in a darkened room, a strobe light can be used to 'freeze' the motion if the frequency of the strobe and the wave are suitably adjusted.

> ⚠️ **Safety**
> **Strobe lighting can cause fits in epilepsy sufferers, especially at frequencies below about 20 Hz. Do not take part in this activity if you think you might be affected.**

Displacement–distance graphs

The 'snapshot' that you should have seen in Activity 5 looks something like Figure 13, a displacement–distance graph. We can use such a diagram to define the **wavelength** λ as the distance between adjacent crests or, more generally, the distance between two points that are in phase.

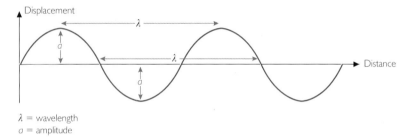

λ = wavelength
a = amplitude

Figure 13   *A displacement–distance graph of a travelling transverse wave*

The motion of each particle in Figure 13 is slightly out of phase with that of each of its neighbour particles, and so the wave pattern travels, as shown in Figure 14.

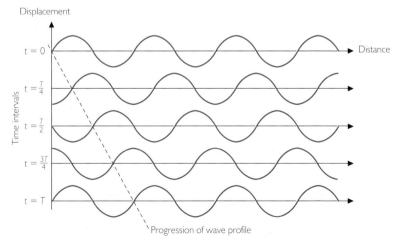

Figure 14   *Successive 'snapshots' of a travelling wave*

The wave equation

The wavelength λ and the frequency f of the wave are connected via the **wave equation**

$$v = f\lambda \qquad\qquad (2)$$

where v is the speed of propagation of the wave. Note that equation (2) applies to *all* types of wave.

QUESTION

7 The human ear is sensitive to sounds between about 20 Hz and 20 kHz. (The ability to hear high frequencies diminishes with age. It can also be greatly reduced by prolonged exposure to loud sounds.) Taking the speed of sound in air as $340\ \mathrm{m\ s^{-1}}$, calculate the corresponding range of wavelengths.

Displacement–time graphs

We can represent the wave by drawing a displacement–time graph for just one particle in the material through which the wave is travelling, as we have already done for oscillating objects. You will have noticed that displacement–time and displacement–distance graphs have very similar shapes. To be sure of distinguishing between these two sorts of graphs, make sure you *always* label the axes.

QUESTIONS

8 Figure 15 shows a wave travelling in the positive x direction, away from the origin.

   (**a**) What are the wave's (**i**) wavelength and (**ii**) time period?

   (**b**) Sketch a displacement–time graph for the particle marked A.

9 A travelling wave whose speed is $300\ \mathrm{m\ s^{-1}}$ has the displacement–time graph shown in Figure 16. Sketch a displacement–distance graph for this same wave.

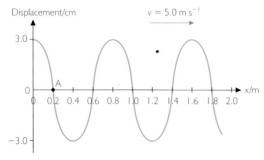

Figure 15   *Diagram for question 8*

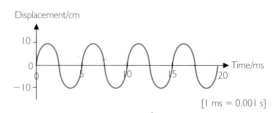

Figure 16   *Diagram for question 9*

Graphs of longitudinal travelling waves

Figure 17(a) shows a schematic diagram of the compressions and rarefactions in a sound wave. As you will see, there are various ways in which we can represent such a wave on a graph.

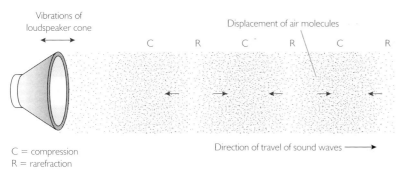

C = compression
R = rarefraction

Figure 17 *A 'snapshot' of a sound wave*

Pressure–distance and displacement–distance graphs

Perhaps the most obvious way to turn Figure 17 into a graph is to plot pressure against distance, and to define the amplitude as the maximum pressure increase (or decrease) caused by the wave. It can also be useful to use a displacement–distance graph. However, the maximum displacement of the particles does not correspond to the maximum pressure.

ACTIVITY **7** **Graphs for a longitudinal wave**

Figure 18 shows a row of 20 undisplaced particles, and below it the same particles displaced by the passage of a longitudinal wave. By tracing the motion of each particle, generate graphs of displacement versus distance and pressure versus distance.

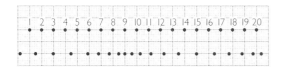

Figure 18 *Diagram for Activity 7*

Figure 19 shows the pressure–distance graph for the wave of Figure 17 and the displacement–distance graph at the same instant. As you should have found in Activity 7, the two graphs are *not in phase*: pressure variations are zero where there is maximum displacement, and vice versa. Notice, too, that these graphs look 'transverse' even though they represent a longitudinal wave – in particular, the displacement is measured *along* the direction of wave motion in the same direction as the distance even though it is plotted on the *y*-axis of the graph.

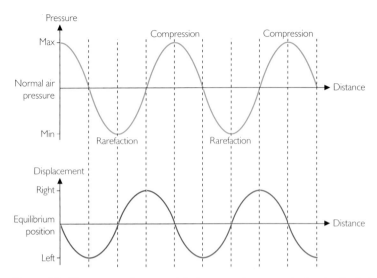

Figure 19 *The pressure–distance and displacement–distance graphs for a longitudinal wave*

Displacement–time and pressure–time graphs

We can also use displacement–time or pressure-time graphs to represent longitudinal wave motion in exactly the same way as transverse waves. If you look back at questions 8 and 9, you will see that there is nothing in either question to indicate the type of wave they were dealing with – they apply equally to either type.

1.4 Superposition and standing waves

You have seen how an oscillating object can produce a sound wave. But what controls the frequency (the pitch) of the sound? How can a musical instrument be tuned to give a desired note? And why do notes of the same pitch sound different when played on different instruments? What determines the 'quality' of a sound?

Superposition

The answers to all the questions above involve **superposition** – the combination of two or more waves. When two or more waves arrive at the same place at the same time, the resultant displacement is equal to the sum of those due to the individual waves. The effect is most noticeable if the waves combined are **coherent**, meaning that they are of the same frequency (or wavelength) and with a constant phase relationship. Figure 20 shows the result of combining two waves of the same frequency and phase but different amplitude.

The displacement–time graphs in Figure 20 show the effect of the resultant wave on just one particle: the first two graphs are simply added together to produce the resultant displacement–time graph. If the two superposing waves are both travelling along 'on top of one another' we can simply add their displacement–distance graphs to produce a 'snapshot' picture of the resultant wave. For sound waves, we could plot graphs using pressure rather than displacement: these, too, can simply be added together.

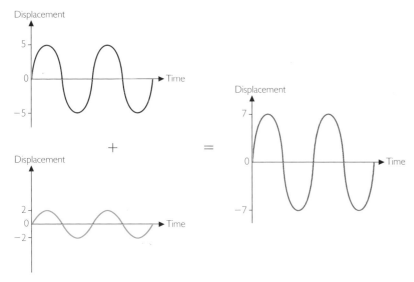

Figure 20　*Superposition of two waves*

ACTIVITY **8**　**Superposition**

Using *Multimedia Sound*, investigate what happens when two or three simple sinusoidal sound waves superpose.

In Activity 8 you should have seen examples of two special cases of superposition. If two waves combine so that they are *always* reinforcing one another, this is called **constructive superposition**; and if they are always cancelling one another, this is called **destructive superposition**.

QUESTIONS

10 Sketch graphs similar to Figure 20 to show the resultant wave in each of the following cases:

(**a**) coherent waves of identical amplitude superposed in phase;

(**b**) coherent waves of identical amplitude superposed with a phase difference of 90° or $\pi/2$ radians;

(**c**) coherent waves of identical amplitude superposed with a phase difference of 180° or π radians.

11 The driver of the jet-propelled car 'Thrust' that broke the world land speed record in 1997 sat directly between two high-powered jet engines. He would have been deafened but for a technique called 'active sound suppression', which involves generating sounds in the driver's headphones to cancel out the engine noise. What can you say about the sounds that would need to be generated?

12 What conditions must two waves satisfy if they are to undergo (**a**) maximum constructive superposition and (**b**) maximum destructive superposition?

Standing waves

Interesting things can happen when waves of a single frequency (or wavelength) travel back and forth 'on top of one another', as might happen if waves are reflected back and forth. Figure 21 shows the superposition of a 'red' wave travelling from left to right with a 'green' wave of the same frequency travelling in the opposite direction.

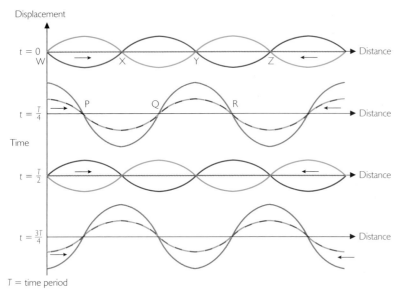

Figure 21 *Superposition of travelling waves*

The waves could be …

● transverse, with the *y*-axis representing transverse particle displacement,

● longitudinal, with the *y*-axis representing particle displacement along the direction of travel,

● longitudinal, with the *y*-axis representing changes in pressure.

Superposition of the 'red' and 'green' waves gives the 'blue' resultant wave, which doesn't travel in either direction, but merely remains where it is and changes profile as shown in Figure 22. The wave goes through the sequence 1,2,3,4,5,4,3,2,1 in one cycle. This type of wave is called a **standing wave** (or, in some books, a **stationary wave**). A point on the standing wave such as P, Q, or R where the value plotted on the *y*-axis is always zero is called a **node** (there is ***no*** change). A point such as W, X, Y or Z where the amplitude reaches a maximum is called an **antinode**.

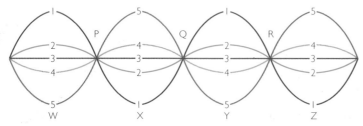

Figure 22 *A standing wave*

ACTIVITY 9   Standing waves

Generate and study some standing waves of various types. Examples might include: water waves in a bowl; waves on a cord or a slinky; sound waves in a tube.

QUESTIONS

13 What is the distance on the standing wave between two adjacent nodes? (Express your answer in terms of the wavelength of the travelling waves.)

14 What is the phase relationship of all the oscillating particles between a pair of adjacent nodes? How does that compare with the phase of wave particles between the pair of nodes either side?

1.5   Musical notes

In this section, you will apply ideas about waves to two sorts of musical instrument and see how they produce notes.

Wind instruments

Getting a note from a wind instrument (such as a saxophone or a flute) can be surprisingly difficult for a person trying it for the first time. The process is, however, straightforward to describe at a basic level.

ACTIVITY 10   Playing a wind instrument

Read the passage below and answer questions 15 to 20 that follow. Answers to many of the questions can be found in the passage and in earlier sections of this unit. Skim read the passage first to get an idea of what is in it and then read the questions, so that on your second, more careful, reading of the article you will be able to pick out the important points.

Wind instruments (Figure 23) rely on the column of air molecules inside the tube of the instrument being made to oscillate as a standing wave. This can be done in several ways. Trumpets and other brass instruments are played with lip vibrations causing the air to oscillate; oboes and clarinets rely on a flexible reed vibrating as it is blown; whilst recorders have a notched air vent at the top which protrudes into the air column slightly, setting up eddies in the air which generate molecular oscillations.

The standing wave of air vibrations makes the instrument and the air around it vibrate at the same frequency, generating a sound wave that travels outwards in all directions.

There are two basic categories of wind instrument:

● Open tubes – a flute or a recorder behaves like this type of tube, with both ends open.

Figure 23   *Wind instruments*

● Closed tubes – a clarinet behaves like this type of tube, with one end open and one closed; the closed end is the reed end.

The standing waves are set up because sound waves are reflected from either a closed or an open end. The wavelengths of the standing waves are governed by the following end conditions:

● At a closed end, air molecules are not free to move so their amplitude of vibration is zero (a displacement node) but the changes in pressure are maximum.

● At an open end, the amplitude of air molecule vibrations is a maximum (a displacement antinode) but the pressure does not change (a pressure node).

These conditions mean that a given tube can only sound certain precisely fixed frequencies that are known as its **resonant frequencies**. [Figure 24] shows the longest standing wave that can be set up in an open tube, and [Figure 25] shows the longest standing wave that can be set up in a closed tube of the same length. The lowest frequency that can be produced from a given tube is called its **fundamental frequency**.

When an instrument is played, the pitch is controlled by opening or closing the holes along the tube. At an open hole, the air molecules can move freely but the pressure does not change. So opening or closing the holes effectively alters the length of the tube in which a standing wave can be set up.

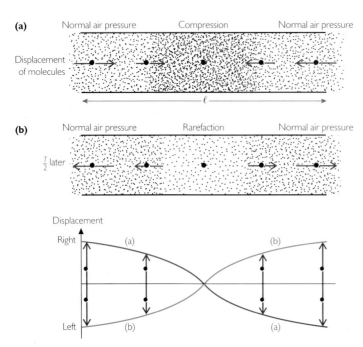

Figure 24 *Fundamental standing wave in an open tube*

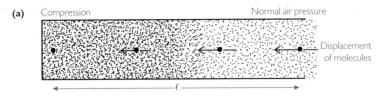

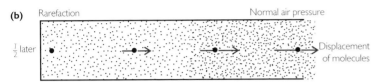

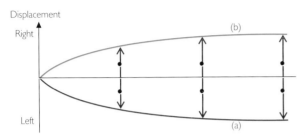

Figure 25 *Fundamental standing wave in a closed tube*

QUESTIONS

15 Explain why the air molecule displacement graphs in the diagrams in Figures 24 and 25 have both positive and negative values.

16 Sketch graphs showing how air pressure will vary with distance along each tube in Figures 24 and 25.

17 What fraction of a wavelength λ corresponds to the tube length ℓ for (**a**) an open tube fundamental and (**b**) a closed tube fundamental?

18 (**a**) From your answer to question 17, work out an expression for the fundamental frequency of an open tube in terms of its length, ℓ, and the speed of sound in air, v.

(**b**) Repeat (**a**) for a closed tube.

19 What properties of a recorder do you think determine the fundamental frequency of the instrument?

20 When playing a recorder you cover up different numbers of holes to get different frequencies. In Figure 26 a black circle indicates a covered hole. On a sketch of Figure 26 mark the effective length of the tube in each case. Which of the two cases shown would give the lowest pitch (frequency) of note?

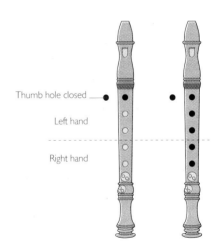

Figure 26 *Fingering for two different notes on a recorder*

ACTIVITY 11 **Can your recorder tell you the speed of sound?**

Your answers to question 18 involved a relationship between the frequency of a note, the length of the tube and the speed of sound in air. Using this relationship, and with the help of *Multimedia Sound*, measure the speed of sound with a recorder.

Stringed instruments

Stringed instruments such as guitars or violins (Figure 27) produce a transverse standing wave on a string held between two fixed supports. The particles in the string are normally set into oscillation by plucking or bowing, but piano strings are struck by felted hammers.

The standing wave is generated by the superposition of the waves travelling along the string and being reflected at the support. A phase change of 180° (π radians) takes place at the reflection (Figure 28a) so the incident and reflected waves always superpose destructively at that point and there will be a displacement node at both supports (Figure 28b).

Figure 27   *Stringed instruments*

(a)

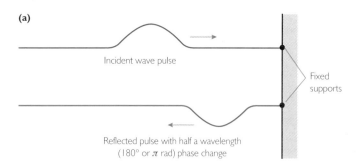

Study note

You can see the phase change if you send a single pulse along a slinky that is fixed at one end. You might have seen this in Activity 4.

(b)   These diagrams show a single full wave being reflected.
Ⓘ = incident part of wave. Ⓡ = reflected part.
Snapshots (i) (ii) & (iii) are half a time period apart.

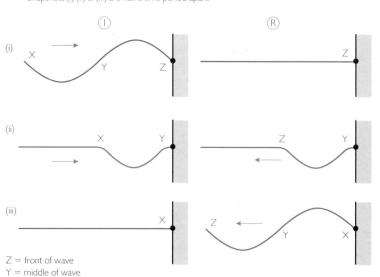

Z = front of wave
Y = middle of wave
X = back of wave

Figure 28   *Reflection at a fixed boundary (a) produces a phase change which (b) ensures that there is a node at the boundary*

QUESTION

21 **(a)** Sketch a diagram showing the lowest-frequency standing wave that can be produced on a string with two fixed ends.

(b) Write down **(i)** a relationship between the wavelength λ of this wave and the length ℓ of the string, and **(ii)** a relationship between the length ℓ of the string and the frequency f and speed v of this wave.

(c) When we refer to 'the wavelength' and 'the speed' in part **(b)**, do we mean the wavelength and speed of transverse waves travelling along the string, or the wavelength and speed of the resulting sound waves in air?

The sound box of a stringed instrument

As the string oscillates as a standing wave, it generates a succession of compressions and rarefactions in the air, which travel outwards as a sound wave (Figure 29).

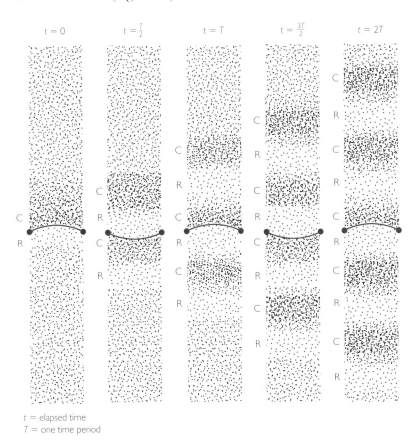

$t =$ elapsed time
$T =$ one time period

Figure 29 *An oscillating string generates a sound wave*

If the string were the only thing vibrating, then the sound would be barely audible because the string itself affects very little air. To make the sound louder, the string is attached to a sound box, which resonates with the string and sets a greater mass of air in motion, so the sound is louder.

QUESTIONS

22 Classical guitars have a very obvious sound box to 'resonate' the sound. How do electric guitars achieve the same effect?

23 Figure 30 shows part of a violin under construction, being tested by driving it at two of its resonant frequencies, with tea leaves on the surface of the wood. Explain what is happening to the tea leaves.

Figure 30   *Testing the sound box of a violin*

Notes from a stringed instrument

Even if you are only vaguely familiar with a guitar (or any other stringed instrument), you will know that there are several ways in which the player can control the pitch (frequency) of the note.

ACTIVITY 12   **What factors affect the note produced by a string?**

Use a guitar or a sonometer (Figure 31) to explore one factor that affects the pitch of its note. Try to deduce a mathematical relationship between frequency and the factor you are investigating.

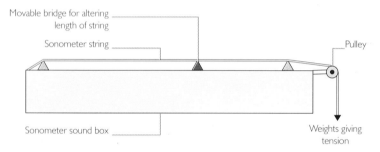

Movable bridge for altering length of string

Sonometer string

Pulley

Sonometer sound box

Weights giving tension

Figure 31   *A sonometer*

In question 21, you saw that the lowest-frequency standing wave that could fit on to a stretched string of length ℓ has a wavelength λ where

$$\lambda = 2\ell$$

This wavelength is related to the frequency f of oscillation by the wave equation (2)

$$v = f\lambda$$

where v is the *speed of the transverse waves travelling along the string*. We can therefore write

$$f = \frac{v}{\lambda} = \frac{v}{2\ell} \tag{3}$$

In Activity 12, you should have found that f is inversely proportional to the length ℓ of the string. The shorter the string, the higher the note – as described by equation (3).

You should also have found that the frequency does indeed depend on the tension and the mass per unit length of the string. Both of these factors affect the speed of transverse waves travelling along the string. In Activity 4 you will have seen that you can control the speed of waves along a slinky: the greater the tension, the greater the speed. The speed also depends on the mass per unit length of the string (or spring): the heavier the string, the lower the speed. The speed v is in fact related to the tension T and mass per unit length μ by the following equation:

$$v = \sqrt{\frac{T}{\mu}} \qquad (4)$$

Combining equations (3) and (4) gives an expression for the frequency of the fundamental standing wave on a string:

$$f = \frac{1}{2\ell} \sqrt{\frac{T}{\mu}} \qquad (5)$$

QUESTIONS

24 Explain which one of the following pairs of similar instruments (Figure 32) should produce notes with a higher range of frequencies:

(**a**) a bass guitar and a banjo

(**b**) a piccolo and a flute

(**c**) a side drum and a timp.

Figure 32 *Pairs of similar instruments*

25 Explain in words how equation (5) accounts for the following:

   (**a**) Before being played, stringed instruments are tuned by twisting a series of screws or pegs.

   (**b**) Violinists and guitar players press their fingers against the strings while playing.

   (**c**) In a piano, the strings that sound the high notes are much thinner than the strings that sound the low notes.

26 A guitar string is 0.5 m long, has a mass per unit length of $3.75 \times 10^{-4}\,\text{kg m}^{-1}$ and is held under a tension of 15 N.

   (**a**) What is the frequency of its fundamental vibration?

   (**b**) If the guitar player wishes to produce a note of frequency 400 Hz from this string (without re-tuning), how far along the string should the finger be placed?

27 You may have witnessed a person breathing in helium gas and then speaking – the voice sounds much higher in pitch. Suggest a physical explanation for this effect.

Further investigations

If you have an opportunity in future, there are several aspects of this section that you could investigate further. Here are some suggestions:

- The frequencies of note produced by tapping a bottle partly filled with water or by blowing over its top
- Two-dimensional standing wave patterns on a metal sheet attached to a vibration generator
- The tensions, thicknesses and lengths needed to produce a given note from guitar or violin strings made from different materials
- The notes produced by wind instruments of various sizes
- The design and performance of sound boxes for stringed instruments
- The measurement of speed of sound in air and other materials.

1.6 Complex sounds

Most people can recognise when a note produced in two different ways has the same frequency. Vocalists, for example, often need to hear a note from a piano to adjust their voice to the right key. They can hear the note and produce a note at the same frequency. But why do these two notes sound different? And why does a trumpet or a guitar, or a didgeridoo for that matter, sound different again?

Speech tells us the answer

A waveform of human speech (Figure 33) gives a clue. At first sight, the wave looks complex and 'untidy', but you can see that it actually has a clear repetitive pattern or **periodicity**. You can pick out a basic period of about 10 ms, corresponding to a frequency

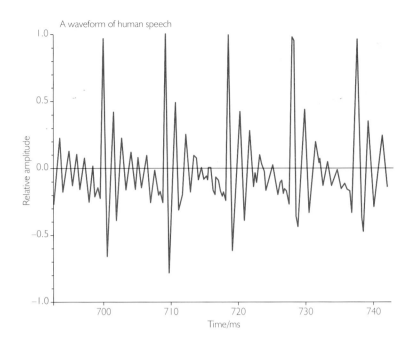

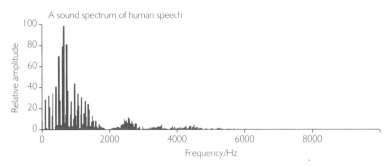

Figure 33 *A waveform of human speech and its sound spectrum*

ACTIVITY **13** **A note about notes**

Use *Multimedia Sound* to explore the waveforms and frequency spectra of notes that sound similar in frequency and yet are different in quality. Look for waveforms that have similar periods (similar 'repeat distances' on the screen).

---

of about 100 Hz. But the waveform clearly does not correspond to a simple sinusoidal wave. In Activity 8 and question 10, you saw that the superposition of sinusoidal waves with different frequencies can produce waveforms with different shapes. The waveform in Figure 33 takes this to extremes – it can be reproduced by the superposition of a very large number of sinusoidal waves.

The frequencies and amplitudes of sinusoidal waves needed to make up a given sound can be found with an instrument called a **spectrum analyser**, which analyses (splits up) the sound into its component frequencies – rather as a prism splits light into its different frequencies or colours. The spectrum analyser produces a **sound spectrum**, which is a plot showing the frequencies and amplitudes of these component sinusoidal waves. The spectrum of the human speech (Figure 33) has a very large number of components, dominated by frequencies of a few hundred hertz.

Sounds from different instruments or other sources may have similar pitch due to similar periodicities in their waveforms, but they may have very different tones or qualities due to the presence of other components. Each individual sound will have its own characteristic frequency spectrum. Because the patterns in speech sounds are recognisable, spoken words can be converted into digital code by a computer and a program can recognise the digital code as a particular word. This technology is used in software that allows you to 'speak' the instruction into an instrument (Figure 34).

Figure 34

QUESTION

28 For the waveform shown in Figure 35, determine its period and (fundamental) frequency.

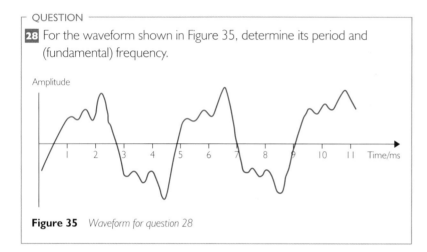

Figure 35   *Waveform for question 28*

Harmonics and overtones

A dictionary may define musical 'harmony' as 'a pleasing combination of concordant sounds'. Exactly what property makes one combination of sounds 'pleasing' to the ear, and another not, fascinated ancient scholars such as Pythagoras. Early experiments found patterns and mathematical links between lengths of strings, for example, which produced concordant sounds when plucked.

You have already seen that, if a string or air column is made to vibrate in its fundamental mode, it will emit a sound corresponding to the longest standing wave that will fit within the boundaries.

Putting more energy into the system, by blowing harder into a recorder for example, may produce higher-frequency standing waves. Sounds from these higher-frequency standing waves are called **overtones** or **harmonics.** Strictly speaking, harmonic frequencies are always whole-number multiples of the fundamental frequency: if the fundamental frequency is f_0, then the harmonic frequencies f_n are expressed as

$$f_n = n \times f_0 \qquad\qquad (6)$$

where n is a whole number. Overtones do not have to be whole-number multiples.

ACTIVITY **14**   ## Standing-wave harmonics on a string

Use a signal generator to produce standing waves of various frequencies on a string as shown in Figure 36. Predict other frequencies at which you would expect to produce standing waves on the same string, and test your predictions.

It is less easy to see the standing waves in an air column. In Figures 24 and 25 you saw one common way of representing such a wave, which is repeated in Figure 37. Remember that the lines which look like a transverse standing wave represent the *longitudinal* displacement of air molecules.

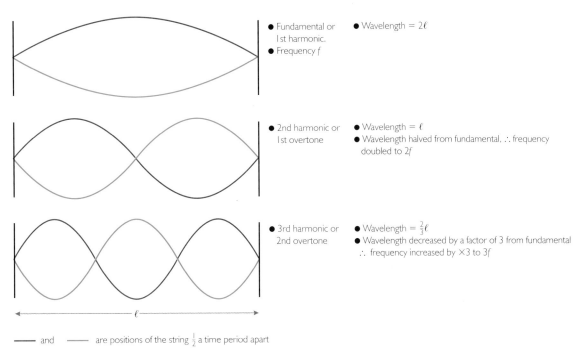

- Fundamental or 1st harmonic.
- Frequency f

- Wavelength $= 2\ell$

- 2nd harmonic or 1st overtone

- Wavelength $= \ell$
- Wavelength halved from fundamental, $\therefore$ frequency doubled to $2f$

- 3rd harmonic or 2nd overtone

- Wavelength $= \frac{2}{3}\ell$
- Wavelength decreased by a factor of 3 from fundamental $\therefore$ frequency increased by $\times 3$ to $3f$

——— and ——— are positions of the string $\frac{1}{2}$ a time period apart

Figure 36   *Standing–wave harmonics on a string*

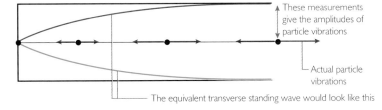

These measurements give the amplitudes of particle vibrations

Actual particle vibrations

The equivalent transverse standing wave would look like this

Figure 37   *Representing the fundamental standing wave in a closed tube*

ACTIVITY **15**   ## Harmonics in air columns

By making use of the 'end conditions' for open and closed tubes, sketch a series of diagrams showing the standing waves that can be set up in an open and a closed tube of length ℓ. Derive expressions for the wavelengths and hence the frequencies of these standing waves.

Musical notes and other sounds

When you produce a note on a musical instrument, you set up several standing waves simultaneously – the string or air column does vibrate at its fundamental frequency, but at the same time there will be several harmonics, or overtones, present. The resulting sound wave is a superposition of waves with all these frequencies, and it is the mix of overtones that give the note its particular 'quality'. You should have found in Activity 15 that the harmonics in an open tube follow the same pattern as those for a string (Figure 36), but in a closed tube only odd-number multiples of the fundamental frequency are present.

ACTIVITY **16**   **Overtones in a recorder**

Use *Multimedia Sound* to analyse the overtones present in notes from a recorder. Relate your findings to the pattern of frequencies that you found in Activity 15.

ACTIVITY **17**   **Analysis of many sounds**

Use *Multimedia Sound* to explore the sound spectra of many sounds – preferably non-musical. Then try to identify some unknown sounds from their waveforms and frequency spectra.

QUESTIONS

29 Figure 38 shows a standing wave on a stretched wire at 234 Hz. Assuming the tension in the wire does not change, what will be the frequency of the wire's (**a**) fundamental, (**b**) the $n = 3$ harmonic and (**c**) the $n = 7$ harmonic?

Figure 38   *Diagram for question 29*

30 It is possible to get higher notes from a guitar string by plucking it hard and then touching the string lightly at particular positions. Describe where the guitarist should touch the string to achieve notes with (**a**) twice and (**b**) three times the fundamental frequency.

31 By holding a plastic metre ruler at its centre and vibrating it with your hand at about 6 Hz, you can make it vibrate at its fundamental frequency (Figure 39).

(**a**) Sketch the ruler vibrating at its first harmonic frequency, and state what that frequency will be.

(**b**) If the ruler were held at one end, what would be (**i**) the fundamental frequency and (**ii**) the frequency of the first overtone?

Figure 39   *Diagram for question 31*

32 A vibrating wire produces a note at 648 Hz. The distance between nodes of the standing waves is 28 cm. What are (**a**) the wavelength and (**b**) the speed of the travelling waves on the wire?

33 A standing wave in an air column in a pipe has four displacement nodes and five displacement antinodes. It is emitting sound at a frequency of 1244 Hz.

(**a**) Is the pipe open or closed?

(**b**) Which harmonic is being generated?

(**c**) Write down an expression for the length ℓ of the pipe in terms of the wavelength λ of the sound being emitted.

(**d**) Calculate the wavelength λ, assuming the speed of sound in air is 340 m s^{-1}.

(**e**) Calculate the length, ℓ, of the pipe.

34 Figure 40 is a representation of the frequency spectrum for a wind instrument playing a certain note. The amplitude of each component is indicated by the intensity of its line.

(**a**) Is it a closed or an open pipe instrument?

(**b**) Do you think it is being blown softly, normally or hard?

(**c**) Estimate the effective length of the instrument when creating the note that gave rise to the spectrum.

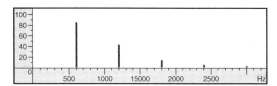

Figure 40   *The frequency spectrum of a wind instrument (see question 34)*

1.7 Synthesis – Summing up part 1

You should now be well versed in the science of sounds. You should be aware of what makes sounds different and how complex waveforms can be treated as combinations of simple sinusoidal waves. Activity 17 uses these ideas in the **synthesis** of familiar sounds. Synthesis means 'bringing together'. Activity 17 is about synthesis of complex sounds from simple components, and it also involves bringing together what you have learned in part 1 of this unit.

The idea is simple: if, by analysing a sound spectrum, you can pick out the main frequencies present in their correct proportions, then by reproducing those frequencies simultaneously you should get a reasonable copy of the sound. The more of the constituent frequencies you can reproduce, the better the copy will be. This method of reproducing sounds is often used by electronic devices and less sophisticated keyboards.

ACTIVITY **18**   **Synthesising sounds**

Use *Multimedia Sound* to reproduce some musical and other sounds. Comment on the quality of the reproduction.

As a final word, it is worth mentioning sampling – the method by which better keyboards achieve much more realistic musical instrument copies.

The main disadvantage of reproducing a sound as in Activity 17 is that the constituent frequencies and their relative proportions may change considerably during the duration of the sound. Sampling gets round this by recording digitally the make-up of a sound at specific stages during the sound.

We can also think of this as making a detailed digital copy of the shape of the sound's waveform. You can improve a sample in several ways: Firstly by increasing the sampling rate, i.e. how many times you record information about the sound per second. Secondly, you can increase the number of digital bits – pieces of digital code – that represent each tiny section of the sound. You will meet the idea of digital signals again in part 2 of this unit.

Further investigations

If you have the opportunity, here are some things that you might like to investigate:

● the frequency spectrum of a clarinet (or other instrument) as it plays through its complete range;

● the frequency spectrum of notes from a plucked elastic band;

● sounds produced from simple percussion instruments, e.g. a block of wood suspended and struck with a hammer;

● the quality of sounds synthesised by a cheap keyboard (the cheaper the better!).

---

2 *The compact disc player*

Sometimes we want a permanent record of a famous voice, some favourite music or the strange sounds of whales. If so, it is more than likely that the permanent storage of that recording will be on a compact disc (CD), as that is the most popular format for sounds as well as computer programs. In part 2 of this unit you will explore many of the aspects of physics required to manufacture a CD player (Figure 41).

2.1 *What's on the discs?*

Compact discs store information in a way quite unlike the previous generations of discs, as we now discover.

Figure 41 *A CD player*

Before the CD

Thomas Edison was the first to record sound on wax cylinders. It was another American, the German-born Emile Berliner, who invented the flat disc-type record in Philadelphia in May 1888. In the early part of the 20th century the records were played back rotating at 78 revolutions per minute, so were called 78s. Later a way was devised to store more music on vinyl discs that rotated more slowly – hence the name long-playing record or LP.

ACTIVITY 19 **Comparing discs**

Examine the surfaces of a CD and an LP (Figure 42), and their playback systems (just the visible exterior parts). Use any magnification available. Briefly describe the appearance of each surface and comment on how many grooves (if any!) you can see. Which surface is 'read' during play?

Listen to two extracts of music, one from an LP and one from a CD played through the same amplifier. Comment on any difference in the quality of sound from the two systems you heard.

(a)
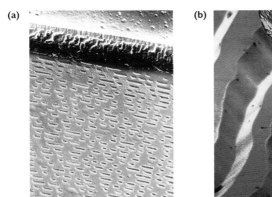

(b)

Figure 42 *Magnified views of (a) a CD and (b) an LP surface*

ACTIVITY 20 **CDs – the sound of science**

Read the article below and answer questions 35 to 42 that follow. Answers to many of the questions can be found in the article. If you skim read the article first, you will get an idea of what is in it. Then read the questions so that on your second, more careful, reading of the article you will be able to pick out the important points. Have a dictionary at hand to assist with any unfamiliar words.

The sound of science

Only 12 cm in diameter, the laser-scanned digital compact disc makes conventional long-playing records look almost as archaic as 78s. Compact discs offer better sound quality with up to an hour's uninterrupted playing time and, most important perhaps, they are infinitely more durable than vinyl discs. A compact disc will still play back perfectly even with a 2 mm hole drilled through the playing area, and handling a compact disc presents no problems as they are immune to scratches, dirt and grease. There are no grooves in the surface of the compact disc, and the CD player has no stylus. The audio information or signal recorded on to the disc is processed and stored there in a fundamentally new way, which is where computer electronics come in.

Storage and retrieval

All conventional music reproduction systems, and this includes tape as well as discs, are analogue storage-and-retrieval systems; digital disc recording requires a radically different approach. For the compact disc, Philips developed an elegant optical scanning system, using a low-powered laser to 'read' tiny bumps in a reflective metal surface [Figures 43 and 44].

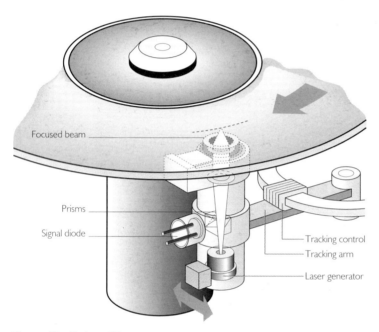

Figure 43 *Playing a CD*

Study note

'Analogue' means that the way the information is stored is a copy (an analogue) of the original sound wave. The grooves on an LP mimic the sound waves – they are an analogue of the sound. 'Digital' means that information is stored as a sequence of numbers.

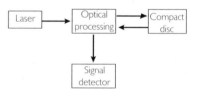

Figure 44 *Block diagram of a CD player system*

Metallic layer

Sandwiched by a protective plastic coating, the silver metallic layer in the compact disc is etched with a spiral track of bumps of literally microscopic proportions. The pitch of the spiral is in fact 1.6 μm, which makes the 'micro grooves' of a conventional LP look quite big. When light, in fact a beam of highly concentrated laser light, is focused on this pattern, a reflected light signal is received from the flat surface, which is compared with the light reflected from the bumps. In the player's optics, both reflected rays are passed to a photodiode, where superposition produces a series of electrical 'ones' and 'zeros'. Here the fundamental benefit of working with digits can be realised – it does not matter exactly how much light is received, because anything above a predetermined level is read as a 'one' and everything below that level as a 'zero'. Because the playback system only has to identify these two conditions, fidelity to the original information is theoretically perfect. The laser is accurately focused on the reflective metal layer so dust particles or marks on the plastic coating are ignored.

QUESTIONS

35 What is meant by the statement that CDs are 'durable'?

36 (**a**) Does the CD system of sound recording use a digital or an analogue method?

(**b**) In a couple of sentences, explain the difference between the two methods.

37 What do you think the author means by 'optical scanning'? What is the equivalent for an LP?

38 The distance between one turn of the spiral track and the next is called its 'pitch'.

(**a**) Write down the size of the pitch of a CD expressed in standard form.

(**b**) How broad can the light beam be if it is to distinguish between one set of bumps and another?

39 The article mentions two materials. The compact disc has a 'reflective metallic layer' and a 'protective plastic coating'.

(**a**) What property, other than protective, must the plastic coating have?

(**b**) What is important about the metallic layer?

(**c**) Which reflection is more important, that from the metal or that from the plastic?

40 Sketch diagrams to show (**a**) what is meant by a focused beam and a parallel beam and (**b**) how it is possible for an accurately focused beam to ignore dust particles and marks on the plastic surface.

41 Reflection is mentioned many times. Jot down what you understand by the term.

42 The article includes a labelled diagram. What are: a signal diode; a tracking arm; and a prism?

Maths reference

Standard form
See Maths note 1.2

2.2 Optical scanning

The digital information is coded on a CD as a series of small raised areas created as the playing disc is pressed from a master disc in which pits have been etched (Figure 45).

The pits are made, using a **binary code**, from audio measurements made 44 100 times a second. Each binary number represents the sound signal at one instant in time converted to a sequence of bumps or no bumps (rather like Braille) on a spiral track. Using this system we only have to read binary 1 or 0. For an optical reader this means detecting whether a light signal is 'on' or 'off'.

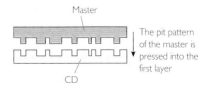

Master

The pit pattern of the master is pressed into the first layer

CD

Figure 45 *Pressing a CD from a master disc*

Superposition

Somehow a series of bumps on a disc have to turn the light on and off as it scans over them. It is all done by waves – in particular the property of waves known as **superposition**.

The following discussion, with questions 43 to 45 and Activity 21, shows how superposition of coherent waves plays a key part in reading a CD.

Study note

Superposition is discussed in section 1.4 of this unit.

QUESTIONS

43 This question is about light waves A, B and C:
- wave A has frequency f and amplitude a;
- wave B has frequency f and amplitude $1.5a$, and is in phase with A;
- wave C has frequency f and amplitude a, and is $180°$ out of phase with A.

State what an observer would see in each of the following situations. Give the frequency and amplitude of the resulting wave in each case and sketch graphs to illustrate your answers.

(**a**) (**i**) A is combined with B to give wave P.
   (**ii**) A is combined with C to give wave Q.

(**b**) Wave B becomes $180°$ out of phase with A before combining with it to give wave R.

(**c**) Wave C becomes in phase with A before superposing with it to give wave S.

44 For digital use the signal detector requires two states – the light is on or off.

(**a**) Look at your answers to question 43 and decide which results are equivalent to 'on' and which to 'off'.

(**b**) What are the requirements for two waves to produce total cancellation?

In practice an electronic circuit can be calibrated to recognise 'on' signals for anything above a predetermined level of brightness, and if the light level falls below that the circuit records 'off'. In our example the conditions for cancellation could then be set so that the two waves had to have the same period, be out of phase and their amplitudes only need be similar, not identical.

QUESTION

45 If 'on' is taken to mean 'has an amplitude greater than a' and all other brightness levels are deemed 'off', reconsider your answer to question 44.

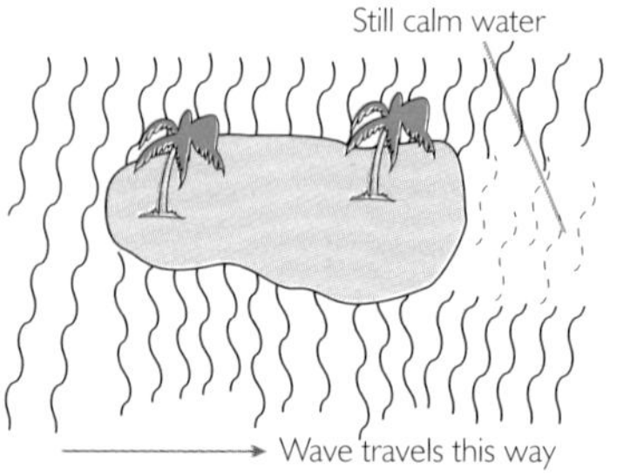

Coherent waves

To get a steady signal from the superposition of two waves, they need to be coherent, otherwise the signal keeps changing (see question 43). Light waves from two separate sources will be incoherent because the light is emitted in short random bursts each lasting about a nanosecond. One way to be sure of getting coherent waves is to use a single beam of light. But how could a phase difference be caused across a single beam? It can be caused in several ways. Two parts of the wave could start together in phase, travel different distances and meet up again (Figure 46). Or part of the wave could be **reflected** and meet up with the unreflected part (Figure 47).

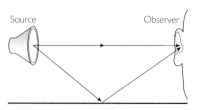

Figure 46 *Superposition of waves that have travelled different paths*

Figure 47 *Superposition of reflected waves*

Superposition in a CD player

In a CD player the laser light source produces a single beam with a diameter equal to twice that of a raised bump. In the absence of a bump, all the light is reflected from the background surface with no phase difference across it – so it produces constructive superposition, i.e. the signal diode detects that the light is 'on' (Figure 48).

In the presence of a bump, half the light will go to the background surface and back and get out of phase with the part

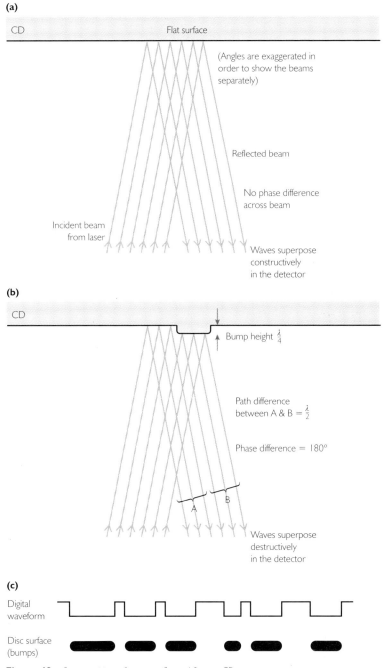

(a)

CD Flat surface

(Angles are exaggerated in order to show the beams separately)

Reflected beam

No phase difference across beam

Incident beam from laser

Waves superpose constructively in the detector

(b)

CD

Bump height $\frac{\lambda}{4}$

Path difference between A & B = $\frac{\lambda}{2}$

Phase difference = 180°

A B

Waves superpose destructively in the detector

(c)

Digital waveform

Disc surface (bumps)

Figure 48 *Superposition of waves reflected from a CD*

reflected from the shorter route via the top of the bump. If the path difference is carefully arranged, this light will destructively interfere. The light is recorded as 'off' by the signal diode even if the cancellation is not absolutely complete. The light beam moving over the spiral track gives a sequence of on–off signals, which is then processed to reconstruct the original sound.

In the case of the CD, one part of the light beam can destructively interfere with the other part because of a difference in the distance they both travel. This will only work if the laser light is **monochromatic** (i.e. of a single frequency) and **coherent** (we will return to this in section 2.6).

ACTIVITY 21   Microwave scanner

Use the apparatus shown in Figure 49 to illustrate reading a CD. The 500 nm wavelength laser light used in a CD player is far too fine for laboratory use, so this apparatus uses electromagnetic waves with a wavelength of 3 cm to model the action. The size of the bumps is scaled up by the same factor as the wavelength.

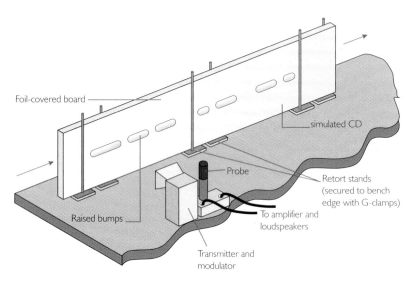

Figure 49   *A large-scale model of a CD scanner*

QUESTION

46 (**a**) If two beams of light are to interfere destructively, what is the smallest possible difference in the paths travelled?

   (**b**) If two beams of light interfere constructively, what are the possible differences in the paths travelled?

   (**c**) If the wavelength of the light is 500 nm, how high must the bumps on a CD be to produce destructive interference?

2.3 *The coating on the disc*

One of the great selling points for CDs is that the surface is protected by a transparent coating – no spills, scratches, etc., can alter the sound quality. But strange things can happen to light as it enters and leaves a transparent material (i.e. crosses a boundary between different materials). What are the consequences for the optical scanning system? This section explores a behaviour, known as **refraction**, and show its consequences for the CD player. But first some terminology.

Figure 50 shows a ray of light crossing a boundary, labelled with the conventional terms. Note the convention of measuring all the angles with the **normal** and not with the surface.

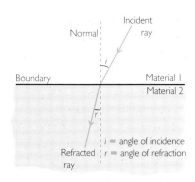

Figure 50 *A light ray crossing a boundary*

QUESTION

47 (**a**) There are two materials in Figure 50. If they are air and glass, which is which? What helped you to decide?

(**b**) If you interchanged the materials, what would be different?

(**c**) If a ray is incident along the normal, what happens to it in the second material?

(**d**) Now imagine the materials are altered so that the ray of light is refracted less. How would the angle, *r*, alter?

Light changes its direction in this way because it travels at different speeds in different materials. The speed is greatest in a vacuum (almost the same as in air) and smaller in all other materials. It is only when light meets a surface at an angle that the effect of this becomes apparent. We get a similar experience when a car swerves into the kerb because the inside wheels meet a large puddle of water. The slowing effect turns the vehicle.

Snell's law of refraction

It is not enough to be able to say which way the ray will 'turn' as it crosses a boundary. We need to be able to predict the exact path from a given angle of incidence. Figure 51 shows waves crossing a boundary.

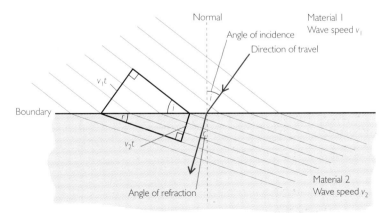

Figure 51 *Waves crossing a boundary*

In a time t, the waves in material 1 travel a distance $v_1 t$ while the waves in material 2 travel a distance $v_2 t$. By drawing right angled triangles as shown in Figure 51, we can write down some useful relationships. The triangles share a hypotenuse, so

$$\frac{v_2 t}{\sin r} = \frac{v_1 t}{\sin i} \qquad (7)$$

Cancelling t, multiplying by $\sin i$ and dividing by v_2, we can write the relationship known as **Snell's law**:

$$\frac{\sin i}{\sin r} = \frac{v_1}{v_2} \qquad (8)$$

For any two given materials, the ratio v_1/v_2 is constant, and is known as the **refractive index**, and given the symbol $_1\mu_2$:

$$_1\mu_2 = \frac{\sin i}{\sin r} = \frac{v_1}{v_2} \qquad (8a)$$

Strictly, we should always talk of the refractive index *between* two materials and use the labels 1 and 2 before and after the μ. But when dealing with light we often talk of the refractive index *of* a material, taking it for granted that the other material is air (or a vacuum) and dropping the labels.

Maths reference

Sine of an angle
See Maths note 6.2

Study note

In some books you will find the symbol n rather than μ.

ACTIVITY 22   Measuring refractive index

By tracing rays of light through a rectangular-block of transparent material and measuring the angles at the interfaces (Figure 52), use Snell's law to calculate the refractive index of that material.

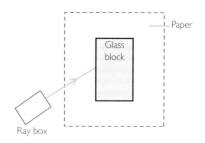

Figure 52   *Diagram for Activity 22*

QUESTIONS

48 A ray of light travels from air into another transparent material. Use Snell's law to determine the missing values in Table 1.

Angle of incidence, i	Angle of refraction, r	Refractive index, μ
40°	A	1.33
B	30°	1.47
64°	36°	C

Table 1   *Data for question 48*

49 (**a**) Extend Table 2 by adding your own experimental values of refractive index from Activity 22.

   (**b**) Given that light travels at 3.00×10^8 m s^{-1} in air, what is the speed of light in each material in Table 2?

Material	Refractive index between air and material
glass	1.47
water	1.33
polystyrene	1.60

Table 2   *Data for question 49*

Study note

There are many different types of glass, and the refractive index of each type depends on its composition. Table 2 refers to just one type.

Changing the wavelength

Refraction means that we have to look again at the value of the wavelength of the light used in a CD player. Earlier the height of a bump was set at 125 nm based on a wavelength of 500 nm. But this is inside the plastic coating. Will the light have the same wavelength in the air?

Have another look at Figure 51. Notice that when the waves slow down they get closer together. Frequency remains constant. Starting from the link $v = f\lambda$ between speed v, frequency f, and wavelength λ of a wave (equation 2 in part 1) we can answer the question as follows.

Worked example

Q If $\lambda = 500$ nm in plastic with refractive index 1.55, what is the wavelength in air?

A Using the labels a = air and p = plastic:

$$_a\mu_p = 1.55 = \frac{v_a}{v_p} \qquad \text{and} \qquad \lambda_p = 500 \text{ nm}$$

We can write

$$f_a = \frac{v_a}{\lambda_a} \qquad \text{and} \qquad f_p = \frac{v_p}{\lambda_p}$$

Frequency f does not change and so $f_a = f_p = f$ and therefore

$$\frac{v_a}{\lambda_a} = \frac{v_p}{\lambda_p}$$

which we can rearrange to give

$$\frac{\lambda_a}{\lambda_p} = \frac{v_a}{v_p} = {_a\mu_p}$$
$$\lambda_a = 1.55\,\lambda_p$$
$$\lambda_a = 1.55 \times 500 \text{ nm} = 775 \text{ nm}$$

This wavelength is much longer in air than it was inside the plastic coating of the CD. This alters the specification for the laser in a CD player.

From the worked example above, we get an important general result that extends equation (8):

$$_1\mu_2 = \frac{v_1}{v_2} = \frac{\lambda_1}{\lambda_2} \tag{8b}$$

Study note

You will do further work on refraction in the unit *Good Enough to Eat*.

2.4 A focused beam

The bumps on a CD are so small and so close together that they can only be detected by a very narrow beam of light. As you have seen in section 2.1, the diameter of this beam must be about 1.6 μm across. In this section you will see how a lens is used to narrow the laser beam down to a small spot just at the surface of the CD.

Converging lenses

Any lens that is fatter at its centre than at its edge will converge (bring together) a beam of light (Figure 53). Such lenses are known as **converging** or **convex lenses**. In Figure 53(d) the lens is reducing the divergence of the beam, i.e. converging it. Figures 53(a) and (c) show beams converging through a point.

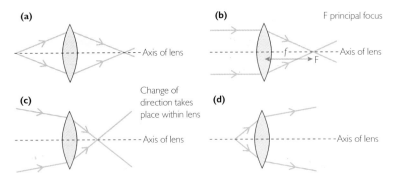

Figure 53 *Converging a beam of light*

Figure 53(b) shows a parallel beam converging through a point F known as the **principal focus** of the lens. (There is one on either side of the lens.) The distance from the lens to this point is called the **focal length**, f, of the lens. Opticians prefer to use a measure, called the **power of a lens**, P, which is the reciprocal of the focal length in metres:

$$P = \frac{1}{f} \tag{9}$$

The unit for the power of a lens is the **dioptre**, D. Note that the stronger the lens, the shorter its focal length. It is often useful to rearrange equation (9) by taking the reciprocal of each side:

$$\frac{1}{P} = f \tag{9a}$$

Maths reference

Reciprocals
See Maths note 3.3

QUESTIONS

50 (**a**) If a lens has a focal length of 20 cm, what is its power?

(**b**) What is the focal length of a 4 D lens?

51 A parallel beam of light enters a 2 D lens. If the lens has a diameter of 4 cm, what would you see on the other side of the lens (**a**) less than 50 cm from the lens, (**b**) at 50 cm from lens and (**c**) more than 50 cm from the lens?

52 Figure 54 shows two rays about to enter a magnified section of a lens. Copy the diagram and continue the paths to show how Snell's law of refraction predicts convergence.

53 In the scanning system of a CD player, a diverging beam passes through two strong converging lenses: the first makes the beam parallel and the second brings it to a point on the playing surface (see Figure 43). If the second lens is 2 mm from the surface, what must be (**a**) its focal length and (**b**) its power?

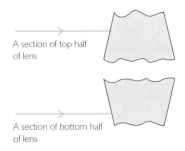

A section of top half of lens

A section of bottom half of lens

Figure 54 *Light rays approaching a lens*

Lens formula

In a CD player, the lens and its distance from the CD have to be such that the beam is focused at exactly the right position. How is this done? To explore the behaviour of a convex lens, it is useful to introduce the idea of an image.

When a lens converges light, it carries with it an image of the source object correct in every detail – the sort you can see in a cinema. This type of image that can be projected on to a screen is called a **real image**. To project a clear image on to a fixed screen it is necessary to place the object an exact distance from the lens (see Figure 55). The equation connecting the distance of an object from the lens and the distance for its image is

$$\frac{1}{u} + \frac{1}{v} = \frac{1}{f} \tag{10}$$

where u is the object-to-lens distance, v is the image-to-lens distance and f is the focal length.

Maths reference

Reciprocals
See Maths note 3.3

Adding and subtracting fractions
See Maths note 3.5

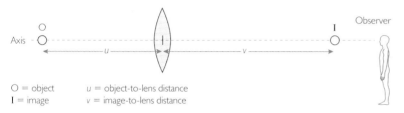

O = object u = object-to-lens distance
I = image v = image-to-lens distance

Figure 55 *Producing a focused image with a converging lens*

Real is positive

The lens equation applies to both converging and **diverging lenses**, and can predict the sort of image (called a **virtual image**) that does not project on to a screen but can only be seen by looking through the lens – as with a magnifying glass. To fit all possible situations the lens equation comes with a sign convention (referred to as the 'real is positive' convention):

● the focal lengths of converging lenses are positive

● the focal lengths of diverging lenses are negative

● real objects and images have positive distances

● virtual distances are negative.

If your experiments or calculations give you a negative image distance, that means you will not be able to project the image on to a screen.

Study note

You will do further work on lenses, including diverging lenses, in the unit *Spare Part Surgery*.

ACTIVITY **23** **Converging lens**

Use a convex lens and two small coloured light sources (Figure 56) to find the focal length of a convex lens and explore some other properties of the image that it produces.

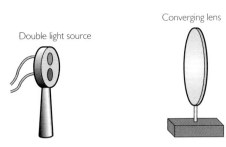
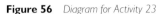
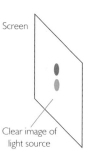

Figure 56 *Diagram for Activity 23*

There are two common ways of locating the position of an image. Putting the data into the lens formula is very precise, but there is an alternative. It is possible to locate an image position by construction: plotting the paths of individual rays of light. An advantage of this method is that it gives a clearer picture of what is happening.

Drawing a ray diagram

Rays leave a light source, like the one in Activity 23, in all directions. At the image all the rays from the original source converge together. To locate the exact site of this image we only need to follow the paths of two rays (or three to be extra certain). Which rays are the easiest to plot?

1 Any ray that goes through the centre of a lens will continue travelling in the same direction.

2 Any ray that travels parallel to the axis will be deflected to pass through the principal focus.

3 Any ray passing through a principal focus before it gets to the lens will emerge parallel to the axis.

Figure 57 shows how to draw a ray diagram to locate the image of a lamp, 2 cm high, placed 30 cm from a 5 D lens.

Look carefully at Figure 57. The object must be drawn a little off the axis. All you can say about points along the axis is that they have their images on the axis too. Notice that the vertical and horizontal scale factors do *not* have to be the same! Note, too, that so far we have drawn a fat lens out of all proportion to reality, but when we draw a ray diagram we assume that all the refraction takes place in the middle, and so we show the lens simply as a straight line.

The light, X, is to the left of the diagram with its top, point O on the diagram, 2 cm above the axis. The rays are numbered 1, 2, 3 as in the list above. Look carefully to see how the construction is completed according to the guidelines. Follow each ray from its start on the top of X (point O) to the right of the diagram. The rays do not stop at I. Note that the position of the top of the image, point I on the diagram, is used to predict where the bottom of it will be seen, Y.

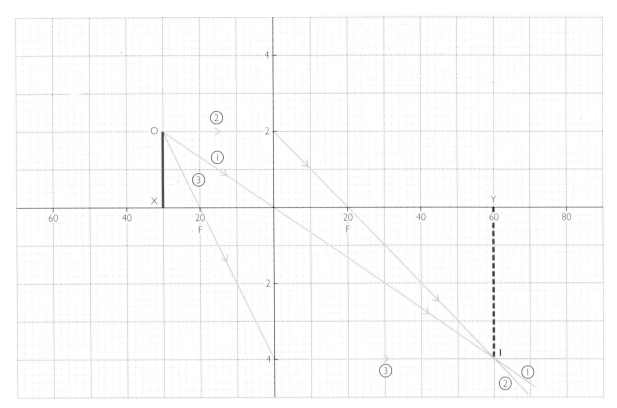

Figure 57 *Drawing a ray diagram*

Several facts can be established from Figure 57:

● The value of v, i.e. the position of the image:

● The fact that the image is inverted. Look again to see how this is obvious.

● The size of the image and its **magnification**, which is defined as height (size) of image ÷ height of object.

Study note

Note that a magnification of less than 1 would correspond to a diminished image; while a value greater than 1 shows that the image is larger than the object.

QUESTIONS

54 Study Figure 57.

    (**a**) Give the scale used (**i**) for u, v and f and (**ii**) for the object height.

    (**b**) Determine the magnification of the image of X from the diagram.

55 Use the values of u and f from Figure 57. Substitute into the lens formula and find the image distance, v. Does it give the same value as the construction method?

56 Construct accurate ray diagrams to determine the position of the images for the situations listed in Table 3. Describe the image fully, i.e. give its size, magnification and say whether it is inverted. For each example, check your answer by calculation. NB: Drawing accurately to scale takes patience at first. Choose your scales for each example carefully and be prepared to start again if your first choice doesn't work very well.

Situation	Focal length f/cm	Object distance u/m	Object height/ cm
a	15	30	6
b	30	45	2
c	40	40	5
d	50	60	10
e	50	300	10

Table 3   *Data for question 56*

57 From your answers to question 56, identify the situation where the magnification is 1. What do you notice about the values of u, v and f in this case?

58 Suppose a manufacturer wished to use a single converging lens to focus the laser beam on to the CD surface (see question 53 and Figure 43). If the lens is to be 2 mm from the CD surface and 1.5 cm from the point of origin of the beam, what must be its focal length?

Absence of image

For some object positions it is not possible to focus an image on the screen. This occurs when the object distance is smaller than or equal to the focal length: $u \leqslant f$.

2.5 Splitting the beam

So far we have seen how a focused beam shines on the prepared surface of a compact disc and is reflected from it, full of coded information. It's not much help if it then gets mixed up with the incident light. Somehow it must retrace a different route to reach a detector and be decoded. Activity 24 shows how a beam can be split.

ACTIVITY 24   **Ray tracing on the way out**

Using blocks of various shapes (as in Figure 58), look at light as it comes out of a block and see how a single beam can be split into two parts.

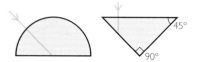

Figure 58   *Block shapes for Activity 24*

Reflection and refraction at a boundary

In Figure 59 light emerges from a dense material into a less dense one, for example from a Perspex block into air. It is incident on a boundary where both reflection and refraction are possible. Your sketches from Activity 24 will show that reflection is always possible but refraction not always. The largest possible internal angle of incidence that will allow light to emerge is called the **critical angle**, C. If the light cannot refract out of the block we say that there is **total internal reflection** (sometimes abbreviated to TIR).

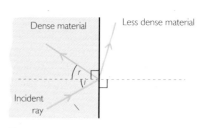

Figure 59   *Light emerging from a block*

ACTIVITY **25** **Connections**

Decide how you could apply the laws of refraction to light emerging from the block to derive a relationship between critical angle and refractive index.

Look back at your results for Activity 24 and find the size of the critical angle for one of the blocks. Use this value to determine the refractive index for the material of the block.

Splitting the beam in a CD player

The actual use of total internal reflection inside a CD player is a neat trick. The player has a pair of prisms (Figure 60) each made of a choice of material designed to have a particular critical angle. The laser light going towards the disc is not totally internally reflected but passes straight through. The returning light meets the internal boundary at an angle greater than its critical angle and is totally internally reflected.

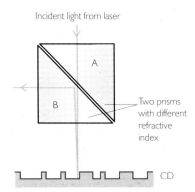

Figure 60 *The prisms in a CD player*

QUESTIONS

59 Light is incident at 42° at the inner surface of a transparent material. For each of the materials listed in Table 4, decide whether it will be split.

Material	Refractive index
glass fibre	1.55
Perspex	1.48
water	1.33
optical (flint) glass	

Table 4 *Data for question 59*

60 The silvering on the back of a mirror can deteriorate with time, so instruments often use a prism as reflector in preference to a conventional mirror. Draw diagrams to show how a prism with angles 45°, 45°, 90° can be used (**a**) to reflect a beam totally through 90° and (**b**) to reflect a beam through 180°.

2.6 *Why does it have to be a laser?*

In section 2.2 we said that the light beam in a CD player had to be monochromatic (single coloured) – i.e. have a single frequency. The way to achieve this is to use a laser. In order to explain what is special about laser light, we will first look at light from sources that are *not* monochromatic.

Coloured light

You will probably have seen all the colours that make up white light separated out by a prism and displayed as a spectrum. This shows us what is there but doesn't explain how it got there. To understand about the lasers used in CD players, we need to develop a theory about light production.

In Activity 26 you will observe the spectra from various light sources. To display the spectra you need a **spectrum analyser** (a device that separates out the different frequencies present). This could be a prism, but a filter called a diffraction grating allows you to spread the colours over a wider range of angles so that they are more easily distinguished.

ACTIVITY **26**   **Observing spectra**

Use a prism or a diffraction grating to observe the colours that make up the light from various sources. See Figure 61.

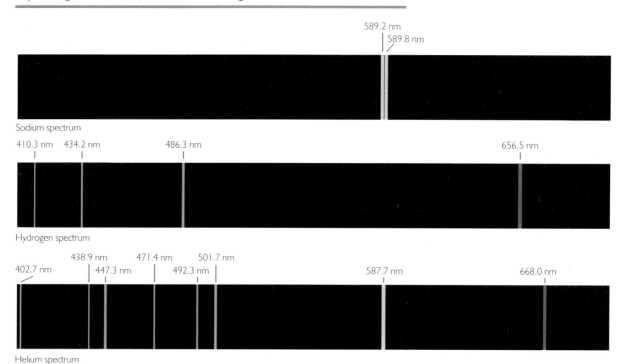

Sodium spectrum

Hydrogen spectrum

Helium spectrum

Figure 61   *Light from various sources observed through a diffraction grating*

Modelling light

In our first encounters with light it was enough simply to say that we need it in order to see. Then, perhaps through physics lessons, you learn that it involves energy transfer, and then you observe the phenomenon of superposition, which convinces you that light has wave properties. This helps to explain colour and refraction – different colours are attributed to different wavelengths, and refraction is linked to the wave speed. So, is it enough to say that light is a wave? Well, no. Once we get to the point of having to explain what is happening as light is created or absorbed, we need another way of looking at this thing called light; we need another **model**.

The energy emitted by a light source is the result of millions of individual events. Each event radiates a packet of energy, which means light also has to be modelled as a particle. A light particle is called a **photon**. These two models, wave and particle, describe different aspects of the phenomenon of light. Which one we use depends on the particular situation.

Both models can be used to describe colour. According to the wave model, colour depends on frequency: violet light has a higher frequency than red light (about twice as high). But according to the particle model, colour depends on energy: a violet photon transfers more energy than a red photon (about twice as much). The two models are related via the Planck equation

$$E = hf \qquad (11)$$

where E is the energy of the photon and f is the frequency of the wave. The constant h is known as Planck's constant: $h = 6.63 \times 10^{-34}\,\text{J s}$.

Maths reference
....
Units
See Maths note 2.2
....

QUESTIONS

61 (**a**) Copy and complete Table 5 so that it contains data relating to the wave and photon models of light.

Colour	Wavelength λ/nm	Frequency f/Hz	Photon energy E/J
infrared	775		
red	656		
green	486		
blue	434		
purple	410		
ultraviolet	389		

Table 5 *Data for question 61*

Study note
....
For questions 61 and 62 use speed of light $c = 3.00 \times 10^8\,\text{m s}^{-1}$, Planck's constant $h = 6.63 \times 10^{-34}\,\text{J s}$.
....

(**b**) How do the values of photon energy help explain warnings about sunburn?

62 Power is the rate at which energy is transferred. A power of 1 W corresponds to 1 J s^{-1}. A laser for a CD player has a power of 0.2 mW and a wavelength of 775 nm.

(**a**) What is the frequency of the light?

(**b**) At what rate does the laser emit photons?

(**c**) What difference would it make to your answers if the laser had a smaller wavelength but the same power?

Maths reference
....
Manipulating powers on a calculator
See Maths note 1.4
....

Atomic line spectra

In Activity 26 you will have seen some **line spectra** – light that contains only a few distinct colours separated by gaps, rather than a continuous range. This light was emitted by atoms in an electrical discharge tube. Each element has its own distinctive set of colours.

The photon model can help explain the origin of atomic line spectra. In a discharge tube, energy is transferred from the electrical supply to the atoms in the gas, giving their electrons additional energy. The electrons lose this extra energy by emitting light – each photon given out corresponds to a single electron losing energy. When electrons are bound in an atom, they can only have certain energies, which are known as electronic **energy**

levels, and the photons they emit correspond to electrons making transitions between these levels. By analysing the energies of photons given out by excited atoms, it is possible to work out their energy levels.

As hydrogen is the simplest element (just one electron), its line spectrum is the one most readily worked out. Some of the calculated energy levels for hydrogen are shown in Figure 62, with arrows indicating some of the possible energy transitions.

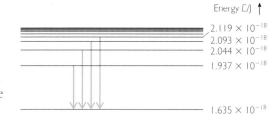

Energy E/J ↑
2.119 × 10⁻¹⁸
2.093 × 10⁻¹⁸
2.044 × 10⁻¹⁸
1.937 × 10⁻¹⁸

1.635 × 10⁻¹⁸

QUESTIONS

63 Calculate the energy transitions corresponding to the four arrows in Figure 62, and match them up with four of the lines listed in your answer to question 61.

64 Without doing any calculations, what can you say about the photon emitted when an electron makes a transition to the lowest energy level in Figure 62 (called the ground state)?

Wave–particle duality

If light can be represented as a wave *and* as a stream of particles, what exactly *is* light and what do you have to do about it? Both models are 'right' in that they each explain some aspects of the behaviour of light, and we have to treat light as behaving *like* waves part of the time and *like* particles at others – notice that we have not said that light *is* either of these!

0

Figure 62 *An energy level diagram for a hydrogen atom*

QUESTIONS

65 Given a choice between the wave and photon models, say which you think best explains each of the following: (**a**) a lens refracts a beam of light, (**b**) a light source produces a line spectrum and (**c**) a ray of light is reflected.

66 'A photon is the means by which the energy carried by the waves is ultimately delivered and takes effect.'

(**a**) What does the speaker of this quotation mean about energy being delivered?

(**b**) How does this short statement indicate when to use the wave and particle models?

Laser light

A **laser** emits light of just one frequency. In other words, it has a special sort of line spectrum, corresponding to just one energy transition. Laser light has two other unusual properties, both of which are useful in the CD player.

● The light is emitted in a narrow beam rather than coming out in all directions.

● The light is coherent – different atoms emit light in phase with one another, rather than randomly.

The name laser stands for **l**ight **a**mplification by **s**timulated **e**mission of **r**adiation. This phrase relates to the way that a laser produces light, which is in turn related to the light's special properties.

A directed beam of coherent monochromatic light is produced if excited atoms are stimulated to emit a photon in a chosen direction. An identical photon will do this. One photon enters the excited atom and two leave (the light is 'amplified'). The photons travel in the same direction, have the same wavelength and are in phase with one another (see Figure 63).

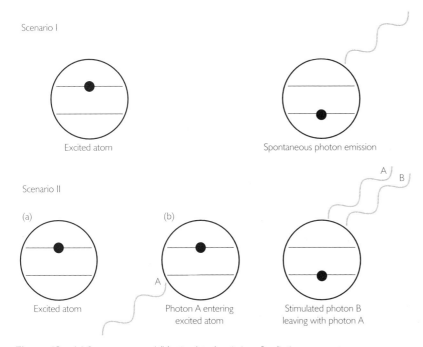

Figure 63   *(a) Spontaneous and (b) stimulated emission of radiation*

The first consideration is how to get the atoms excited. The energy from an electric current or discharge through the material works well. Almost immediately photons will be spontaneously emitted. Mirrors are used to make sure some of these photons are kept travelling up and down the space, stimulating others to 'get in step'. A small hole in one mirror allows a small proportion to escape as a laser beam.

ACTIVITY **27** **Jelly laser**

A simple demonstration (Figure 64) shows the principal elements in a laser.

   Safety
Do not allow light from the flash gun or the laser to shine directly into your eye.

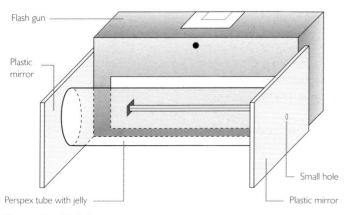

Flash gun

Plastic mirror

Perspex tube with jelly

Small hole

Plastic mirror

Figure 64   *A jelly laser*

Various types of laser

Many types of material can be made to 'lase'. Sometimes a gas is used; but to get a compact, robust portable laser, solid materials are used. The laser for a CD player must be extremely small. To get an intense monochromatic light from a small component, the answer is to use a semiconductor material – most commonly gallium arsenide. The disadvantage of a semiconductor laser is that the beam spread is about 10°, hence our attention to focusing in section 2.4.

Detecting the signal

Our journey around the working of a CD player is almost complete. There is just space for a word or two about the light detector. The digital signal is going to need electronic decoding and processing before the final sound is heard. All this requires a transfer of energy from a light to an electrical signal. A suitable component is a photodiode (Figure 65). When a photon hits its surface, the energy is absorbed by an electron, which moves, i.e. it contributes to an electric current.

2.7   Summing up part 2

This second part of the unit has covered many of the bits and pieces contained within a compact disc player. To summarise what you have learnt, it is a good idea to bring all the parts together. Activities 28 to 30 and the questions that follow are designed to help you do this.

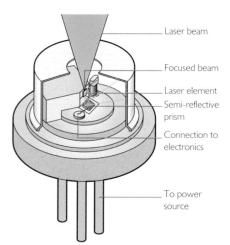

Laser beam

Focused beam

Laser element
Semi-reflective prism

Connection to electronics

To power source

Figure 65   *Detecting the signal*

ACTIVITY 28   **Summing up part 2**

Skim through part 2 of this unit and make sure that your notes include a clear definition or explanation of each of the terms printed in bold type. Look back at the article *The sound of science* in section 2.1 and see how it relates to what you have been learning.

How it works

Imagine you are helping to put together a page of the 'How it Works' type for a daily newspaper or magazine. The page is on the CD player. Decide who your imaginary readership might be. The page is to consist of a large diagram (similar to Figure 66) showing the path of light through it, with plenty of explanatory labels that give a brief outline of the physics behind each of the components on your diagram.

A moment or two spent planning the final appearance of your layout can save you time in the end.

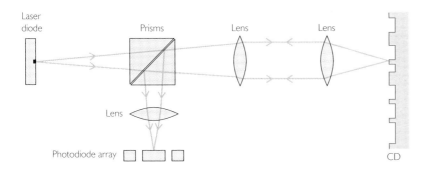

Figure 66 *Diagram for Activity 29*

ACTIVITY **30** **A model CD player**

Set up a large-scale model, using lenses and blocks like those in Activities 22, 23 and 24, of the optical system of a CD player that could be displayed at an open day or parents' evening. Prepare a brief explanation of your model (either written or spoken) suitable for GCSE students or other visitors.

Further **investigations**

In this part of the unit, you have measured the refractive index of some materials using a beam of white light. You have also seen that white light consists of a mixture of colours and that colour is related to the frequency (and wavelength) of light. For most materials, refractive index depends on wavelength – which is why a prism can act as a spectrum analyser.

If you have an opportunity, you could measure the refractive index for different colours of light and compare various transparent materials to see how good they are at dispersing light (i.e. separating it into components of different wavelength). You could relate your findings to information about materials that are chosen for particular purposes because of their dispersive properties.

┌─ QUESTIONS ──

67 Bicycle reflectors are made from sheets of small plastic prisms that reflect light (e.g. from car headlamps) back towards the source (Figure 67a).

  (**a**) Using the terms *critical angle, total internal reflection* and *refractive index*, explain what happens to the light in Figure 67(a) after it enters the prism.

  (**b**) Figure 67(b) shows a light ray entering the same prism at a different angle.
    (**i**) Using values from Figure 67, find the refractive index of the plastic.
    (**ii**) By calculating the critical angle, decide whether this prism would act as a good reflector when light enters as shown in Figure 67(b).

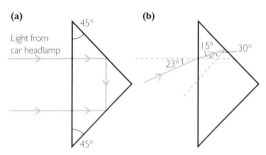

Figure 67   *Using a prism as a reflector (a) 'square-on' and (b) when light enters at an angle*

68 Alice is talking to Oliver about the lack of an image on the screen in her experiment (Activity 23). She has a converging lens of focal length 30 cm and has placed her lamp object 20 cm from it. She suggests that the light cannot get through the lens. Oliver says that is a daft idea, and light gets through but the rays are all jumbled up. Comment on both points of view.

└──

3 *Encore*

In this unit you have studied several aspects of the behaviour of sound and light. This concluding section is intended to help you to look back over the whole unit and consolidate your knowledge and understanding.

3.1 *Waves*

In studying this unit you have learned some fundamental pieces of physics which all relate to **waves**. You have been studying sound waves in air, waves on stretched strings, and light waves. Much of what you have learned about waves in this unit can be applied to other natural and man-made phenomena that can be described and explained in terms of waves – earthquakes, microwave ovens and starlight are just three examples in addition to those you have met in this unit. But there are also some important differences between the various types of waves.

ACTIVITY **31** **Waves**

Table 6 lists properties of waves that you have studied in this unit. Copy the table. Use ticks and crosses to show which properties apply to which type of wave, and which are common to waves of all types. If you made a large copy of this table you could add brief notes in each box – as has been done in the second row.

Property	Type of wave			
	Sound waves	**Waves on string**	**Light waves**	**All**
obeys wave equation $v = f\lambda$				
speed depends on material	✓ [to be done in *Spare Part Surgery* unit]	✓ $v = \sqrt{\dfrac{T}{\mu}}$ ref. index	✓ ref. index $\mu = \dfrac{v_1}{v_2} = \dfrac{\sin i}{\sin r}$	
can travel in a vacuum				
transverse				
longitudinal				
undergoes reflection				
phase change of π when reflected at 'hard' boundary				
undergoes superposition				

Table 6 *Summary of wave properties for Activity 31*

3.2 *Questions on the whole unit*

69 In the manufacture of microchips, sizes and positions have to be measured very precisely. This may be done using a laser, as shown schematically in Figure 68.

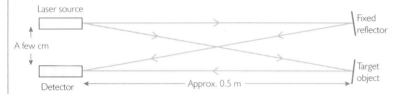

Figure 68 *Measuring small changes in position*

The detector measures the intensity of light produced by the superposition of the two light beams. Small changes in the intensity indicate small changes in position of the 'target' object. Using light of wavelength 600 nm, changes in position as small as 0.15 nm can be measured.

(**a**) Figure 69 shows two waves arriving at the detector in phase. Suppose the 'target' is moved away from the source through 150 nm. How much further, approximately, does the light beam now have to travel via the target to reach the detector?

Figure 69 *Waves arriving at a detector*

(**b**) Draw a diagram to show the two waves that now arrive at the detector, and the resultant signal.

70 Ruari and Rachel are talking about different kinds of waves. Ruari is certain that both sound and light from a spaceship travel through outer space so that you can hear and see the engine. Rachel says that you only get sound effects in *Star Wars* films. What do you think?

71 This question is about the vivid colours seen in the wings of many moths, butterflies and birds. These so-called *iridescent* colours are produced by superposition when light is partially reflected and partially refracted by one or more thin layers of cuticle (scaly material) and then recombines as shown in Figure 70.

Figure 71 shows the light paths through a single cuticle layer. If light of a particular wavelength *undergoes constructive superposition*, when beams

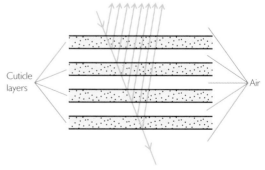

Figure 70 *Reflection and refraction by thin layers*

2 and 3 recombine, then the cuticle layer appears to 'shine' with light of that colour.

Suppose that light is incident on the cuticle at an angle of $\theta = 0°$. In order for constructive superposition to occur, the wavelength of the light in air, λ_a, and the cuticle thickness, d, must be related by the expression

$$2d = (n + \tfrac{1}{2})\frac{\lambda_a}{\mu}$$

where n is any whole number (0, 1, 2, ...) and μ is the refractive index of the cuticle. The following questions show how this expression comes about.

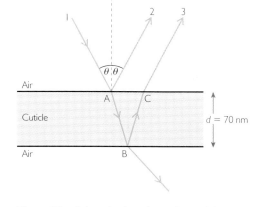

Figure 71 *Light paths through a single cuticle layer*

(**a**) (**i**) Explain what is meant by *constructive superposition*.
(**ii**) How must the *phases* of beams 2 and 3 be related if constructive superposition is to take place when they recombine?

(**b**) Light reflected at A, the upper surface of the cuticle, *undergoes a phase change of 180° or π radians*. Explain what is meant by this phrase in *italics*.

(**c**) In order for beams 2 and 3 to superpose constructively when $\theta = 0°$, what must be the relationship between the wavelength, λ, and the thickness, d?

(**d**) The expression in (**c**) must involve the wavelength of light in the cuticle. If the cuticle has a refractive index of μ, show how the wavelength in the cuticle, λ_c, is related to the wavelength λ_a of the same light in air.

(**e**) When $n = 0$, the expression given earlier in the question is satisfied by one particular colour of visible light. The cuticles in a *Urania* moth wing have a refractive index $\mu = 2.45$. Given that visible light has a wavelength range from about 400 nm (violet) to 700 nm (red), what will be the colour of a *Urania* moth wing when viewed at $\theta = 0°$?

3.3 Achievements

Now you have studied this unit you should be able to:

- understand and use the terms *amplitude*, *frequency*, *period*, *speed* and *wavelength* (1.2, 2.3)*;

- recall and use the wave equation $v = f\lambda$ (1.3, 2.3);

- recall that a sound wave is a longitudinal wave which can be described in terms of the displacement of molecules or changes in pressure (1.3, 1.5);

- recognise and use the expression $v = \sqrt{(T/\mu)}$ for the speed of a wave on a string or wire (1.5);

- use graphs to represent transverse and longitudinal waves, including standing waves (1.3, 1.4, 1.5);

- explain and use the concepts of *coherence*, *path difference*, *superposition* and *phase* (1.2, 1.4, 1.5, 1.6, 2.2);

- explain what is meant by a *standing wave*, how such a wave is formed, and identify nodes and antinodes (1.4, 1.5);

- identify the physical factors (e.g. length, tension, mass per unit length) which affect the pitch of musical note produced by a string and by a pipe, and hence explain how the pitch may be controlled (1.5);

- distinguish between analogue and digital signals (2.1, 2.2);

- use ray diagrams to trace the path of light through an optical system (2.4, 2.5);

- understand and use the terms *focal length*, *power* (of a lens) and *critical angle* (2.4, 2.5);

- explain how the behaviour of light can be described in terms of waves and photons (2.2, 2.3, 2.6);

- recognise and use the expression $E = hf$ to relate the frequency of radiation to a transition between known energy levels (2.6).

* Numbers indicate the section(s) that relate to each achievement.

Answers

1 (a) $f_A = \dfrac{f_B}{2}$ because the period of A is twice that of B.

   (b) $f_A = \dfrac{f_C}{3}$ because A has three times the period of C.

2 See Figure 72

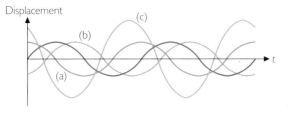

Figure 72 *The answers to question 2*

3 (a) The phase difference must correspond to a whole number of cycles, i.e. by $360n°$ or by $2\pi m$ radians, where n is a whole number.

   (b) They are all the same.

   $\dfrac{\pi}{8}$ radians $= 22.5°$ so (i) and (ii) are the same.

   $\dfrac{17\pi}{8} = 2\pi + \dfrac{\pi}{8}$ so (iii) is the same as (i) and (ii).

   $-337.5° = 22.5° - 360°$ so (iv) is also the same as (i), (ii) and (iii).

4 (i) A and C are in phase at times 0 and T. (ii) A and C are in phase at times 0, $T/2$ and T. (iii) B and C are in phase at times 0 and T.

5 The order in which the feet are placed on the ground is front right, rear left, front left, rear right, front right, ... So the two front legs move in antiphase with one another, as do the two rear legs. Each front leg is a quarter of a cycle (90°) behind the rear leg on the same side.

6 (a) The motion of the cloth approximates to a travelling transverse wave pulse, with an amplitude and frequency that depends on how it is shaken.

   (b) The motion of the trucks approximates to a travelling longitudinal wave pulse.

   (c) The Mexican wave is a travelling transverse wave of roughly constant amplitude and speed.

   (d) If the traffic is confined to one lane its motion approximates to a series of longitudinal pulses. If lane changing is possible, then there is also some transverse motion.

7 Using equation (2), wavelength

   $$\lambda = \dfrac{v}{f} = \dfrac{340 \text{ m s}^{-1}}{20 \text{ Hz}} = \dfrac{340 \text{ m s}^{-1}}{20 \text{ s}^{-1}} = 17 \text{ m}.$$

   Similarly, when $f = 20$ kHz,
   $\lambda = 17 \times 10^{-3}$ m $= 17$ mm.

8 (a) (i) $\lambda = 0.8$ m

   (ii) $f = \dfrac{v}{\lambda} = \dfrac{5.0 \text{ m s}^{-1}}{0.8 \text{ m}} = 6.25 \text{ s}^{-1}$ (= 6.25 Hz).

   $T = \dfrac{1}{f} = \dfrac{1}{6.25 \text{ s}^{-1}} = 0.16$ s.

   (b) See Figure 73

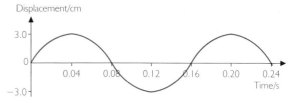

Figure 73 *The answer to question 8(b)*

9 See Figure 74. The period T is 5 ms (5×10^{-3} s), so the wavelength can be found using equations (1) and (2):

   $$\lambda = \dfrac{v}{f} = v \times T = 300 \text{ m s}^{-1} \times 0.005 \text{ s} = 1.5 \text{ m}.$$

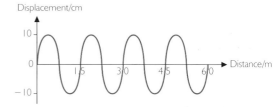

Figure 74 *The answer to question 9*

10 See Figure 75

(a)

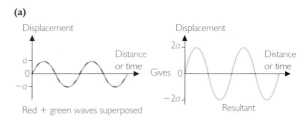

Red + green waves superposed

(b)

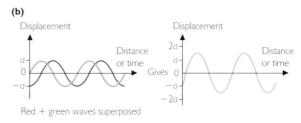

Red + green waves superposed

(c)

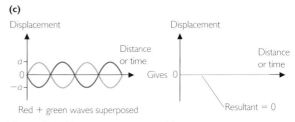

Red + green waves superposed

Figure 75 *The answers to question 10*

11   The sound must have the same amplitude as the engine noise, but be in antiphase with it.

12   In both cases the waves must have the same amplitude and frequency. For (a) they must be in phase and for (b) they must be in antiphase.

13   Distance between nodes $= \dfrac{\lambda}{2}$

14   All particles between a given pair of nodes oscillate in phase. They are in antiphase with particles immediately beyond each of those nodes.

15   Sign indicates the direction of displacement, and the molecules oscillate first to one side of their equilibrium position and then to the other.

16   See Figure 76

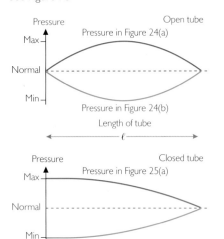

Figure 76   *The answers to question 16*

17   (a) Open tube: there is a displacement antinode at each end, so $\ell = \dfrac{\lambda}{2}$.

   (b) Closed tube: the length of the tube is the distance from node to antinode, i.e. $\ell = \dfrac{\lambda}{4}$.

18   (a) From equation (2), $f = \dfrac{v}{\lambda}$. For an open tube, $\lambda = 2\ell$ (see question 17) so $f = \dfrac{v}{2\ell}$.

   (b) For a closed tube, $\lambda = 4\ell$ so $f = \dfrac{v}{4\ell}$

19   The fundamental frequency depends primarily on the length of the air column from the tip of the mouthpiece to the nearest open hole. (The width of the tube might also affect the frequency, as would the overall pattern of uncovered holes.)

20   Case (b) gives the lower note because it has a longer air column than (a) – it has a longer uninterrupted row of covered holes.

21   (a) There is a node at each end and an antinode in the middle. See Figure 77.

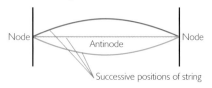

Figure 77   *The answer to question 21(a)*

   (b) $\ell = \dfrac{\lambda}{2}$ so $f = \dfrac{v}{2\ell}$. (Compare with the answers to question 17 about waves in an open tube.)

   (c) We are referring to the transverse waves on the string, because it is these waves that superpose to form the standing wave that defines the fundamental frequency of the string's vibration. (The sound waves that are generated in the air have the same frequency as these vibrations, but travel at a different speed and so have a different wavelength.)

22   In an electric guitar, the vibrations are amplified electronically.

23   As the wood vibrates, the tea leaves are set in motion and settle at places where the wood is not moving, i.e. at the nodes. The pattern of tea leaves therefore reveals a two-dimensional standing wave (such standing waves are sometimes called Chladni vibrations after the 19th century scientist who first investigated them).

24   (a) banjo, (b) piccolo, (c) side drum.
   In each case, the smaller instrument produces the higher-pitched notes, because the standing waves that correspond to its fundamental vibration will be shorter and hence of higher frequency. (We can only compare *similar* instruments in this way, because there are other factors that affect the speed of the waves set up within the instrument and hence the frequency of the fundamental vibration.)

25   (a) Twisting the screws adjusts the tension in the strings so that they produce the desired notes. The greater the tension, the higher the frequency of vibration of a given string, and so the higher the pitch of its note.

   (b) Placing a finger on the string shortens the length that is free to vibrate. The shorter the string, the higher the frequency of its vibration, and so the higher the note it produces.

   (c) Reducing the mass per unit length of a string increases the frequency of its vibration and hence raises the pitch of its note. (If all the strings of a piano were the same thickness, they would have to have a very large range of lengths, and the high-note strings would have to be held under much greater tension than the low-note strings. Using strings of different thickness reduces the extremes of length and tension that are needed, making the instrument easier to construct and use.)

26 (a) Substituting values into equation (5)

$$f = \left(\frac{1}{1\,\text{m}}\right) \times \sqrt{\frac{15\,\text{N}}{3.75 \times 10^{-4}\,\text{kg m}^{-1}}}$$

$$= \sqrt{(4 \times 10^4)}\,\text{s}^{-1} = 200\,\text{Hz}$$

(b) The frequency is to be doubled, therefore the length of vibrating string must be halved, so the finger must be placed 0.25 m from the end.

27 You can treat the 'voice box' as a hollow cavity, in which standing waves are set up whose wavelengths depend on the size of the cavity. In helium, the frequency of a standing wave of given wavelength is higher than when the person breathes air, indicating that sound travels faster in helium. (This is indeed the case. Sound speed in a gas is governed by the speeds of the molecules. Helium molecules are lighter than the nitrogen and oxygen molecules that make up air, and at a given temperature they move faster.)

28 (a) Time period $T \approx 4.3$ ms, so $f \approx \dfrac{1}{0.0043\,\text{s}} = 233\,\text{Hz}$.

29 The wave shown is the $n = 2$ harmonic, $f_2 = 234$ Hz.
   (a) $f_2 = 2f_0$ so the fundamental is $f_0 = 117$ Hz.
   (b) $f_3 = 3f_0 = 351$ Hz. (c) $f_7 = 7f_0 = 819$ Hz.

30 (a) This note must have a wavelength half that of the fundamental, so the string should be touched half way along.

   (b) Similarly, a note of one-third the wavelength is made by touching the string one-third of the way along.

31 (a) There must still be a node in the middle (Figure 78), so the wavelength is one-third the fundamental wavelength and the frequency is 18 Hz.

Figure 78   *The answer to question 31(a)*

   (b) Now there is a node at one end and an antinode at the other, i.e. the wavelength of the fundamental has been doubled so the fundamental frequency is halved to 3 Hz and the next frequency to 9 Hz.

32 (a) $\lambda = 2 \times 28$ cm $= 56$ cm $= 0.56$ m
   (b) $v = f\lambda = 648$ Hz $\times 0.56$ m $= 363$ m s^{-1}.

33 (a) Open (a closed pipe would have equal numbers of nodes and antinodes). See Figure 79.

Figure 79   *Diagram for the answer to question 33*

   (b) This is the $n = 4$ harmonic. (The fundamental has one node, the $n = 2$ has two, the $n = 3$ harmonic has three.)
   (c) From Figure 79, $\ell = 2\lambda$ (the distance between nodes is $\lambda/2$).
   (d) $\lambda = \dfrac{v}{f} = \dfrac{340\,\text{m s}^{-1}}{1244\,\text{Hz}} = 0.273$ m
   (e) $\ell = 2\lambda = 0.546$ m.

34 (a) Open pipe, since all multiples of the fundamental frequency are present.
   (b) Many overtones are present, so the instrument is not being blown softly. But overtones do not dominate, so it is not being blown hard. It is most likely being blown 'normally'.
   (c) Fundamental frequency $f \approx 600$ Hz.

$$\lambda = \frac{v}{f} \approx \frac{340\,\text{m s}^{-1}}{600\,\text{Hz}} = 0.57\,\text{m}.$$

   For the fundamental of an open pipe,

$$\ell = \frac{\lambda}{2} \text{ so } \ell \approx \frac{0.57\,\text{m}}{2} = 0.28\,\text{m}.$$

35 A CD does not easily wear out. Scratches (or small holes), dirt and grease do not affect play-back, and the stylus does not wear down the disc surface.

36 (a) Digital.
   (b) An analogue method replicates the waveform as a continuous signal, either electrical or mechanical (a stylus oscillating along a record groove). A digital system measures a series of sound samples and converts each value into a binary number.

37 An optical system is one that uses light. If you look up scanning in a large dictionary you get many choices. Our context is an electronic one so 'to move a beam of light in a predetermined pattern over a surface to obtain information' is probably what the author means. In other words, a laser beam will be moved along a spiral path from the centre to the edge of a CD.
   A stylus or pick-up is used with LPs.

38 (a) 1.6×10^{-6} m. (This could also be written 1.6 μm, as 1 μm $= 1 \times 10^{-6}$ m.)
   (b) In a perfect world the beam could have a diameter of 1.6×10^{-6} m but in practice it must be smaller to allow for wobbles and imperfections in the focusing of the light.

39 (a) The plastic coating must be transparent so that the light can reach the metallic layer.
   (b) The information is stored in the metallic layer as a spiral track of bumps.
   (c) The important reflection takes place at the metal surface to collect the information coded in its bumps.

40 The beam does not focus at the surface of the plastic but lower down on the metal layer. At the surface it is wide enough so that the amount of light blocked by a speck of dust is not critical (see Figure 80).

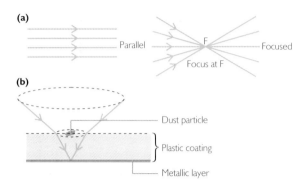

(a)

Parallel → Focused

Focus at F

(b)

Dust particle

Plastic coating

Metallic layer

Figure 80 *Diagram for the answer to question 40*

41 You should have drawn a diagram similar to Figure 81 illustrating which angles are equal when light rays change direction at a reflecting boundary. Reflection is not a property of light alone. Sounds, light and balls reflect from surfaces, often with some loss of energy.

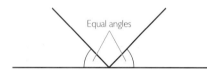

Equal angles

Figure 81 *Diagram for the answer to question 41*

42 The diode is a photodiode which absorbs light energy to produce an electrical signal. The tracking components control the movement of the laser light so that it keeps on the spiral track as the disc turns. A prism is a block of transparent material – glass or similar – with a triangular cross-section.

43 All resultant waves have period T, frequency f.
(a) (i) P amplitude $2.5a$, brighter than A or B individually.
   (ii) Q amplitude zero, totally dark.
(b) R amplitude $0.5a$, fainter than either A or B.
(c) S amplitude $2a$, brighter than either individually.

44 (a) Combination Q is 'off'. All the others are 'on'.
(b) They must have exactly the same frequency and amplitude and be $180°$ out of phase.

45 Now both Q and R count as 'off'.

46 (a) The smallest path difference between the two beams is half a wavelength. This gives a $180°$ phase difference.
(b) It must be zero or a whole number of wavelengths, i.e. $n\lambda$ where n is a whole number.
(c) 125 nm high since a half wavelength difference is achieved by an outward and return journey to make the 250 nm (half wavelength) difference.

47 (a) Material 1 is air, material 2 is glass. The turn towards the normal indicates that the second material is the denser (i greater than r).
(b) The ray would turn *away* from the normal as it emerged (r is greater than i). The path is the exact reverse of the one in the diagram. This an example of the so-called 'reversibility' of light. If you plot the path of light going one way through a block it will trace the identical path if the direction is reversed.
(c) It continues in the same direction.
(d) It gets larger.

48 A: $\sin 40° = 0.643$

$$\frac{0.643}{\sin r} = 1.33$$

$1.33 \sin r = 0.643$

$$\sin r = \frac{0.643}{1.33}$$

$\sin^{-1} 0.483 = 28.9°$, so $A \approx 29°$

$B = 47.3°$, $C = 1.53$

49 (a) [depends on your own results]
(b) $\mu = \dfrac{\text{speed in air}}{\text{speed in material}}$ (from equation 8) so

$$\text{speed in material} = \frac{\text{speed in air}}{\mu}$$

$$\text{speed in glass} = \frac{3.00 \times 10^8 \text{ m s}^{-1}}{1.47} = 2.04 \times 10^8 \text{ m s}^{-1}$$

similarly, speed in water $= 2.26 \times 10^8$ m s^{-1} and speed in polystyrene $= 1.88 \times 10^8$ m s^{-1}

50 (a) Equation (9): $P = \dfrac{1}{f} = \dfrac{1}{0.2 \text{ m}} = 5$ D
(b) $f = \dfrac{1}{P} = \dfrac{1}{4 \text{ D}} = \dfrac{1}{4 \text{ m}^{-1}} = 0.25 \text{ m} = 25 \text{ cm}$

51 (a) A circle of light with diameter less than 4 cm.
(b) A point of intense light – this is the principal focus.
(c) A circle of light.

52 See Figure 82.

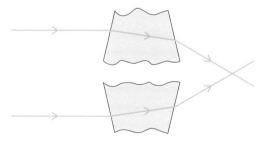

Figure 82 *The answer to question 52*

53 (a) The focal length $f = 2 \text{ mm} = 2 \times 10^{-3} \text{ m}$.
(b) $P = \dfrac{1}{f} = \dfrac{1}{2 \times 10^{-3} \text{ m}} = 5 \times 10^2 \text{ m}^{-1} = 500$ D

54 (a) 1 cm represents 10 cm for f, u and v. Object and image heights are shown actual size (1 cm to 1 cm).

(b) Magnification $= \dfrac{4 \text{ cm}}{2 \text{ cm}} = 2$.

55    $u = 30$ cm, $f = 20$ cm

Rearranging equation (10),

$$\frac{1}{v} = \frac{1}{f} - \frac{1}{u}$$

$$\frac{1}{v} = \frac{1}{20 \text{ cm}} - \frac{1}{30 \text{ cm}}$$

$$\frac{1}{v} = \frac{3}{60 \text{ cm}} - \frac{2}{60 \text{ cm}}$$

$$\frac{1}{v} = \frac{1}{60 \text{ cm}}$$

$v = 60$ cm – which *is* the same as found using the construction method.

56 (a) $v = 30$ cm, image 6 cm high, inverted, same size as object

(b) $v = 90$ cm, image 4 cm high, inverted, magnification = 2

(c) rays emerge parallel, no detectable image (v infinite)

(d) $v = 300$ cm, image 50 cm high, inverted, magnification = 5

(e) $v = 60$ cm, image 2 cm high, magnification = 0.2.

57   When the magnification is 1, $u = v = 2f$. (This is always true, and in such a situation the object and image are at their closest together.)

58   From equation (10), $\dfrac{1}{f} = \dfrac{1}{u} + \dfrac{1}{v}$

$$\frac{1}{f} = \frac{1}{2 \text{ mm}} + \frac{1}{15 \text{ mm}}$$

$$= \frac{15}{30 \text{ mm}} + \frac{2}{30 \text{ mm}} = \frac{17}{30 \text{ mm}}$$

so $f = \dfrac{30 \text{ mm}}{17} = 1.7$ mm.

(You could also have expressed u and v in cm to get f in cm, or expressed all the distances in m – it does not matter provided you are consistent.)

59   In Activity 24 you should have derived the relationship $\sin C = \dfrac{1}{\mu}$.

glass fibre: $\sin C = \dfrac{1}{1.55} = 0.645$

$C = \sin^{-1} 0.645 = 40.2°$.

Similarly for Perspex, $C = 42.5°$; water, $C = 48.8°$; flint glass, $C = 38.4°$.

TIR will occur when $42° > C$, which is the case for both types of glass. For water and Perspex, internal reflection will not be total and so the beam will split.

60   See Figure 83.

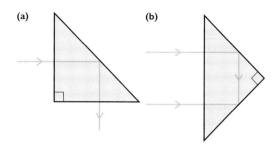

Figure 83   *The answers to question 60*

61 (a) See Table 7.

Colour	Wavelength λ/nm	frequency f/Hz	Photon energy E/J
infrared	775	3.87×10^{14}	2.57×10^{-19}
red	656	4.57×10^{14}	3.03×10^{-19}
green	486	6.17×10^{14}	4.09×10^{-19}
blue	434	6.91×10^{14}	4.58×10^{-19}
violet	410	7.32×10^{14}	4.85×10^{-19}
ultraviolet	389	7.71×10^{14}	5.11×10^{-19}

Table 7   *The answers to question 61(a)*

(b) Photons of ultraviolet radiation have more energy than those of visible or infrared radiation, so they can do more damage. Labels on barrier creams refer to their ability to absorb ultraviolet radiation.

62 (a) $f = \dfrac{c}{\lambda} = \dfrac{3.00 \times 10^8 \text{ m s}^{-1}}{775 \times 10^{-9} \text{ m}} = 3.87 \times 10^{14}$ Hz.

(b) Energy of single photon $E = hf$

$= 6.63 \times 10^{-34} \text{ J s} \times 3.87 \times 10^{14} \text{ Hz}$

$= 2.56 \times 10^{-19} \text{ J}$

No. of photons emitted per second =

total energy emitted per second / energy of each photon

$= \dfrac{0.2 \times 10^{-3} \text{ J s}^{-1}}{2.56 \times 10^{-19} \text{ J}} = 7.80 \times 10^{14} \text{ s}^{-1}$.

Note that we have included the units at each step, and this gives sensible units for the final answer, i.e. a number per second.

(c) The photon energy would be greater, so there would need to be fewer photons per second in order to deliver the same power.

63   Going from energy level 3 to level 2, the energy lost by the electron is $(1.94 - 1.63) \times 10^{-18} \text{ J} = 3.02 \times 10^{-19}$ J. From Table 7, this corresponds to the energy of a photon of red light (give or take a slight difference in the third figure due to rounding). Similarly, the transitions from level 4 to 2, 5 to 2 and 6 to 2 correspond, respectively, to the photon energies for the green, blue and violet light that you calculated for Table 7.

64 Even the smallest possible transition to the ground state (from level 2 to level 1) involves an electron losing 1.635×10^{-18} J, which is larger than any of the photon energies corresponding to visible light, so this radiation lies in the ultraviolet part of the spectrum.

65 (a) Refraction can best be explained using a wave model. A stream of particles will change direction when crossing a boundary, but when their speed is reduced they veer away from the normal, unlike what is observed for light.

(b) Line spectra can *only* be explained using the particle model.

(c) Many aspects of reflection can be explained using either model, but not the phase change – so the wave model is better.

66 (a) The speaker seems to mean that when a beam of light meets a surface it is absorbed in packets as photons.

(b) When light is emitted or absorbed it seems to behave as a particle, but on its travels it is behaving as a wave.

67 (a) Light undergoes total internal reflection at back surfaces. The angle between the light ray and the normal to the surface ($45°$) must therefore be greater than the critical angle C. Critical angle is related to the air–Perspex refractive index μ: i.e. $\sin C = \dfrac{1}{\mu}$.

(b) Using angles measured from Figure 67(b),

$$\mu = \frac{\sin 23°}{\sin 15°} = \frac{0.390}{0.258} \approx 1.5$$

$$\sin C = \frac{1}{1.5}, C \approx 41°.$$

The angle between ray and normal is less than $41°$ so some light will escape through the back of prism, i.e. it will not be a very good reflector.

68 Alice is wrong – light passes through the transparent glass. Oliver hasn't quite got a full explanation. The lens and object are too close together (the object distance is less than the focal length) so the rays emerging from the lens diverge rather than being brought together to form an image.

DIGGING UP THE PAST

Figure 1 *Archaeological artefacts*

Why a unit called Digging Up the Past?

Imagine the scene: It is a frosty Sunday morning in the middle of the English countryside. From a collection of parked cars and bikes emerge a group of people in warm clothing, their breaths dissipating as clouds through the grazing sunlight as they proceed to pace purposefully around a field of grass. This is an archaeological team at work. And who is that person in the middle? Well, believe it or not, it is a physicist! Modern physics now finds a place at the heart of historical research. This unit will reveal how archaeologists use physics to locate, date and investigate.

The story starts with some non-destructive investigations that use electrical measurements to locate likely areas with buried features. You will discover how the secrets of England's greatest battle, the Norman Invasion, are being revealed using physics in Sussex. Resistance, resistivity and electric potential can all be understood in the context of probing beneath the soil.

Figure 1 shows three artefacts from archaeological finds. Consider the recent history of each. How did anyone know it was under the ground and how did they know where to look? How can we be sure about its age? What about the structure and material composition? How could we answer these questions? These are the very questions that require an understanding of physics. History and physics meet in these three photographs.

The story continues with three techniques used to investigate and analyse artefacts that have emerged from an archaeological site. The passage of X-rays through objects will uncover secrets of material and hidden structure, and a technique that relies on the radiation emitted by heated objects – thermoluminescence – will be explained.

Overview of physics principles and techniques

In this unit you will build on earlier work to learn more about the physics of electromagnetic radiation, diffraction, radioactivity and photoelectrons. In doing so, you will be developing your skills in devising and carrying out experimental work, and in using mathematical techniques to display and analyse data. There are also opportunities to use spreadsheets and the Internet.

In this unit you will extend your knowledge of

- properties of waves, and photons and energy levels, from *The Sound of Music*;

- properties of materials, resistance and dc circuits from *Technology in Space*;

- energy and using graphs from *Higher, Faster, Stronger.*

In other units you will do more work on

- radioactivity in *Reach for the Stars*;

- diffraction in *Spare Part Surgery*;

- resistance and dc circuits in *Transport on Track*;

- photons and energy levels in *Probing the Heart of Matter*;

- properties of materials in *Spare Part Surgery* and *The Medium is the Message*;

- waves in *Build or Bust?*;

- using graphs in *The Medium is the Message* and *Probing the Heart of Matter*.

But back to the beginning. The interesting objects are under the soil somewhere, but where? Locating the correct site is the challenge ahead of us. You are now a geophysicist with an interest in archaeology – read on.

⬛ *The secrets of resistance*

The trained forensic scientist will look for clues at the scene of the crime, and these clues will be readily available on the surface. A hair on a table or a blood stain on a carpet might well be minute fragments of evidence but they are visible and they are accessible. The archaeologist has a much harder task. Time erases surface traces. The clues to the past often lie buried under layers of soil. The only indications that something interesting might lie below the surface are aerial photographs showing perhaps a hint of a ditch or a wall and of course historic records from the day.

When such historic research does hint that there might be something interesting below your feet, it is not a signal to grab your spades and dig. Careless digging may disturb valuable hidden artefacts and, anyway, all the land in the UK is owned by somebody. Your local Archaeological Society is your first port of call if you are interested in delving deeper.

1.1 *Resistive surveying*

Digging is an invasive activity. It changes the site permanently, rather like the destructive testing of a car just to test if the air bag works in the event of a crash. There are other preliminary techniques that archaeologists will use before picking up their spades and trowels. One of the most common is a resistive survey (Figure 2).

The water content of soil helps it to conduct an electric current. Rocks are poorer conductors (more resistive). By sinking two metal probes into the soil and measuring the resistance between them, archaeologists can make a tentative guess at where buried rocks and stones, and so walls, are likely to be. Later in this unit you will see just how this technique helped reveal the truth about the exact location of the landing site for William the Conqueror's invading army of 1066, perhaps the most important event in the history of England.

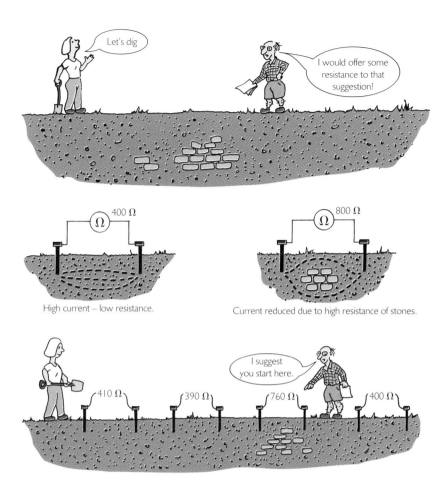

Figure 2 *A physicist advises an archaeologist where to dig*

ACTIVITY **1**   **Archaeology on the Internet**

Use the Internet to find out about archaeological survey techniques, and for background information on archaeology in general.

ACTIVITY **2**   **Probing resistance**

Use a resistance meter (an ohm meter), or an ammeter and voltmeter, to explore the resistance of various conducting objects. Include some non-uniform conductors such as that shown in Figure 3. Discuss your results in a group and make a summary describing how resistance depends on the length and cross-section of a conductor.

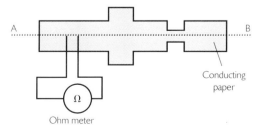

Figure 3 *Probing the resistance of a non-uniform conductor*

The search for the site of the Norman Invasion

Local Hastings historian Nick Austin has used soil resistance measurements to uncover what he believes to be the site of the first Norman encampment and landing site prior to the famous battle of Hastings. His survey was carried out between 1993 and 1994, and covered an area 560 m by 320 m that his research had led him to believe was the site of the main Norman fort. Aerial photographs of the area indicated a possible fort outline but gave no clue to subsoil details.

He used a resistance meter to measure soil resistance at 1 m spaces, and used a computer to display the results. Dark patches indicate areas of high resistance, i.e. the likely presence of walls, and light patches indicate low resistance, i.e. the likely presence of damp ditches. Figure 4 shows some of his results.

Nick Austin's interpretation of the results identifies a series of ditches and sections of the fort perimeter. The survey corroborates the aerial photographs and Nick's own dowsing results. However, the major finding was the square structure at the centre of the area. This is clearly a man-made structure and is most likely to be the keep of the original Norman fort.

Activity 3 uses a simple model to help you appreciate how resistance measurements can give information about hidden structures. In place of soil you will use conducting Teledeltos paper.

Figure 4   *Results of a resistance survey*

ACTIVITY **3**   **Modelling a resistive survey**

In each of two practical challenges you will be presented with the task of saying something about what lies below the surface by probing the resistance between pairs of points. The conducting paper has been shaped to represent places of lower and higher resistance. Your task is to locate the hidden structure simply by taking resistance measurements.

In real fieldwork a system of four probes is used. The outer two supply an emf to drive current through the soil and the inner two measure the potential difference across a standard distance. The measured pd depends on the resistance of the subsoil.

Resistance surveys can be seen in action on the *Time Team* videos (Channel 4). They help to confirm the speculation about subsoil structures that aerial surveys and historic document research indicate might be present. Only when these three, or more, indicators point towards a definite structure will the diggers start their work.

However, even if there is something hidden mysteriously below the topsoil, it is not always easy to predict its shape. As you saw in Activity 1, different shapes will give different resistances. Just how does shape affect resistance?

1.2   *Resistivity*

Activity 4 uses conducting putty as a material with a shape which can be easily changed. It will help you to focus your attention on the factors influencing the resistance of a conductor.

ACTIVITY 4 **Size and shape**

Investigate how the resistance of a piece of conducting putty with a fixed area of cross-section depends on its length. Combine your results with those of other students who have used a different area. Use a spreadsheet program to plot graphs showing how the resistance varies with length and with area of cross-section.

Resistivity defined

Gathering results from Activity 4 you can show that, for a piece of material of length ℓ and cross-sectional area A, resistance is directly proportional to the length of the conductor

$$R \propto \ell \tag{1}$$

and is inversely proportional to the cross-sectional area

$$R \propto \frac{1}{A} \tag{2}$$

Combining these two:

$$R \propto \frac{\ell}{A} \tag{3}$$

Provided we assume that temperature is constant, the only other variable is the type of material itself. For a given size and shape of sample, some materials have higher resistance than others. The number describing this property of the material is called its **resistivity**, and is given the symbol ρ (the Greek letter rho). Expression (3) then becomes

$$R = \rho \frac{\ell}{A} \tag{4}$$

If you rearrange equation (4), it becomes

$$\rho = \frac{RA}{\ell} \tag{4a}$$

Resistivity therefore has units of resistance × area ÷ length, in other words resistance × length, so its SI units are $\Omega\,\text{m}$. The numerical value of a material's resistivity is the same as the resistance of a 1 m long piece with a cross-sectional area of $1\,\text{m}^2$, i.e. a 1 metre cube.

Note that the resistivity of a material is a property of that type of material. It is a quantity like density in that it doesn't depend on the particular shape of material. It is pointless looking up the resistance of copper in a data book. You might as well look up the mass of copper. These answers will not be listed because the answer depends on the size and shape of the sample. However, it is quite likely that you will be able to look up a value for the resistivity of copper as well as its density. No other information is required, just the name of the material.

Maths reference

Inverse proportionality
See Maths note 5.4

The other side of the resistivity coin is the **conductivity**, symbolised σ (the Greek letter sigma). A good conductor will have a high conductivity and a low resistivity. Resistivity and conductivity are simply the reciprocals of one another:

$$\sigma = \frac{1}{\rho} \qquad (5)$$

The SI units of conductivity are $1/\Omega\,\text{m}$, or $\Omega^{-1}\,\text{m}^{-1}$.

Maths reference

Index notation and units
See Maths note 2.2

Reciprocals
See Maths note 3.3

Resistors in circuits

You have studied dc circuits and will know something about resistors connected together either in series or in parallel. We can relate an understanding of resistivity to such combinations.

Figure 5 shows how four blocks of conducting material (resistive putty, perhaps), each with resistance R, might be combined. In Figure 5(b) the four blocks are in series and can be considered as one long block. By increasing the length, we know the resistance increases, and this is in keeping with the resistor combination formula:

Study note

The unit *Technology in Space* included expressions for combinations of resistors.

$$R = R_1 + R_2 + R_3 + \dots \qquad (6)$$

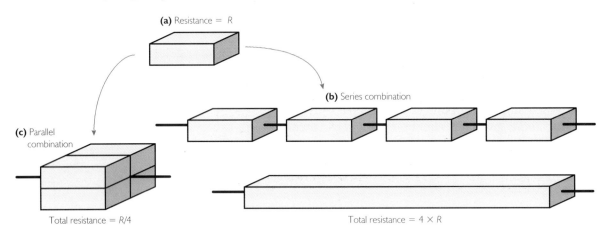

(a) Resistance = R

(b) Series combination

(c) Parallel combination

Total resistance = $R/4$

Total resistance = $4 \times R$

Figure 5   *Combining four blocks of resistive material*

Figure 5(c) shows how four blocks are equivalent to a single block with four times the cross-sectional area of the original. The four blocks are placed in parallel. We know from experience that the total resistance is reduced. We would expect the resistance to be divided by four, and this is in keeping with the parallel resistance formula:

$$\frac{1}{R} = \frac{1}{R_1} + \frac{1}{R_2} + \frac{1}{R_3} + \dots \qquad (7)$$

ACTIVITY **5**   **Measuring resistivity**

Your task is to determine an accurate value for the resistivity of a metal made into a wire, using a micrometer to measure its diameter and using electrical measurements when it is connected in a circuit.

QUESTIONS

1 A student found the resistance of a 20 cm length of cable to be 8 Ω. What would you expect the resistance of a metre of the cable to be? What assumption have you made?

2 An archaeologist found that two probes placed in soil 0.5 m apart showed a resistance of 300 Ω. What would you expect the resistance to be if the separation of the probes was increased to 5 m? The probe spacing in archaeology is typically 0.5 m rather than 5 m. Suggest a reason for this.

3 (**a**) The resistance of a 10 cm length of resistive putty was found to be 48 Ω. The putty was then rolled to twice its length. Suggest a value for the resistance between its ends and explain your answer.

(**b**) The original cross-sectional area of the putty in part (**a**) was 1 cm^2. Use this and the data from part (**a**) to calculate a value for the resistivity of the putty.

4 Derive an expression for the resistance R of a material sample in terms of its length, area of cross-section A and conductivity σ.

5 The resistance readings in Table 1 were taken from an archaeologist's notebook. She suspected that a salt water ditch and a stone wall crossed the path of her linear resistance readings but lie buried beneath the topsoil. Suggest a place for the location of each feature.

Distance from gate to probes/m	Ohm meter reading of resistance between probes/kΩ
1	0.35
2	0.33
3	0.35
4	0.37
5	0.22
6	0.34
7	0.35
8	0.36
9	0.77
10	0.80
11	0.34
12	0.30

Table 1   *Resistive survey data for question 5*

Comparing resistivities

Table 2 lists the resistivities of some materials, and Figure 6 is a partially completed bar chart displaying the data.

Material	Resistivity, $\rho/\Omega\,\text{m}$
copper	1.7×10^{-8}
glass	1.0×10^{12}
carbon	1.4×10^{-5}
Perspex	1.0×10^{16}
lead	2.1×10^{-7}

Table 2   *Resistivities of some materials*

QUESTION

6 The bar in Figure 6, for carbon, is 1.4 cm long. On the same scale, how long would be the bars representing glass and copper? Comment on your answers.

Maths reference

Combining powers
See Maths note 1.3

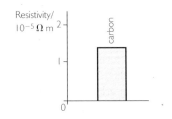

Figure 6   *A bar chart to display the data from Table 2*

As your answers to question 6 have shown, there are problems using a linear scale to represent data that range over several orders of magnitude. To compress the range of the numbers, such data are often plotted using a **logarithmic scale** (often shortened to log scale); the logarithm of the value is plotted rather than the value itself.

Maths reference

Logs and powers of 10
See Maths note 8.1

Logs on a calculator
See Maths note 8.2

ACTIVITY 6   **Plotting on a log scale**

Copy Table 2, and add another column headed 'log₁₀ of resistivity'. Use your calculator to find the values of $\log_{10}$ resistivity. Now display these values on a bar chart. Select your own scale factor so that the chart fits into a half page of your notes.

Explaining resistivity

A good electrical conductor like the metal wire you used in Activity 5 has a low resistivity. Electrical insulators have much higher resistivities. **Semiconductors**, as their name implies, are a group of materials in the middle of the resistivity spectrum. Table 3 lists some typical resistivities of each of these types of material.

	Material	Resistivity, $\rho/\Omega\,\text{m}$
good conductors	copper lead	1.7×10^{-8} 2.1×10^{-7}
semiconductors	silicon germanium	2.3×10^{3} 4.7×10^{-1}
insulators	glass Perspex	1.0×10^{12} 1.0×10^{16}

Table 3   *Conductors, semiconductors and insulators*

A simplified model enables us to explain these vast differences in resistivity. The model involves electrons being free from atoms and available to move through the lattice of atoms. Figure 7(a) illustrates the difference between conductors and insulators.

To explain why some electrons are free to move and others are bound in atoms demands a deep appreciation of the energetics of atoms and is beyond this course. However, it is not difficult to appreciate that, given enough extra energy, a bound electron can become a free electron. The most common example of this effect occurs in semiconductor materials, where a small increase in temperature can have the effect of releasing a large proportion of electrons and so reducing the resistivity of a material dramatically. Semiconductors are very temperature-sensitive and so find a use in thermistors and temperature-sensing circuits. LDRs (light-dependent resistors) free their electrons through energy supplied by light (Figure 7b). The result is the same: better conduction.

Study note

Electrical properties of materials are also discussed in the unit *Technology in Space*.

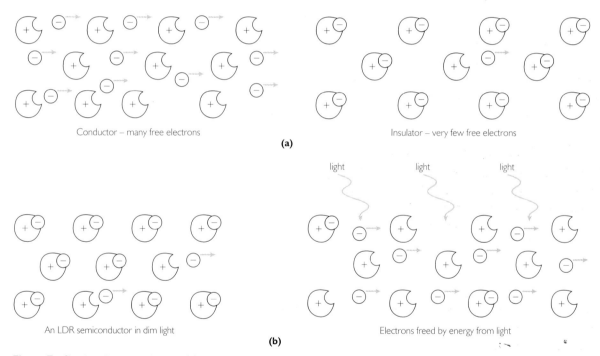

Figure 7   *Sketches illustrating electrons (a) in a conductor and in an insulator, and (b) in a semiconductor in dim and bright light*

1.3   *Potential difference, potentials and potential dividing*

This section looks more closely at the meaning of a voltage and involves estimating and calculating potential differences in simple circuits. By the end of the section you will be able to make predictions about changes in pd across components and be able to design simple resistor combinations to achieve a particular required potential difference.

Before starting, you would be advised to recall that voltmeters are connected 'across' components and that a voltage represents the energy transferred as electric charges pass through a component.

Study note

Ideas about energy, charge and potential difference should be familiar from *Technology in Space*.

ACTIVITY 7   Energy in circuits

Consider the two circuits shown in Figure 8. Discuss with a friend whether each circuit diagram makes sense. Consider in particular the conservation of energy.

Your discussion in Activity 7 ought to have identified that in the second circuit there appears to be more energy 'transformed' by the charges as they pass through the resistors than the cell could supply (remember that $1\,V = 1\,JC^{-1}$). If the cell supplies each coulomb of charge with 12 J of energy, then no more than 12 J can be transferred by each coulomb. A simple statement which summarises this conservation of energy is to say that, in such a circuit, the sum of pd values across the resistors in a series circuit must match the pd from the cell. Activity 8 explores this idea further.

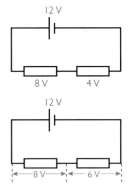

Figure 8   *Two circuit diagrams for Activity 7*

ACTIVITY 8   Splitting the potential difference

Use circuits like those in Figure 9 to explore the relationships between resistances and potential differences. Look in particular at the ratios of the resistances and of the potential differences.

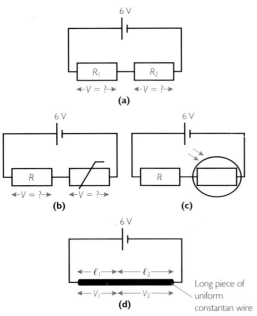

Figure 9   *Circuit diagrams for Activity 8*

The type of circuit you have used in Activity 8 is known as a **potential divider**: the terminal potential difference of a supply is divided between series resistors in the ratio of their resistances or, in the case of a uniform wire, the ratio of the distances from the contact point to the ends.

Archaeology fieldwork

Multi-probe techniques

To introduce you to the idea of a resistive survey, the earlier work in this section was restricted to the simple case of two resistance probes sunk into the soil. A more advanced technique, pioneered by Frank Wenner in 1916, uses a voltmeter to probe positions along a line of soil in which there are two *other* probes which are connected to a power supply. Figure 10 shows a simplified version of the arrangement.

Probes S1 and S2 are the electrodes connected to the supply. (In the field, an alternating supply is used to avoid problems of gaseous build-up at the electrodes due to electrolysis.) P1 and P2 are a second pair of probes at a fixed separation and which are connected to a voltmeter. By using the voltmeter probes along the line AB, a map of potential differences can be built up. As the pd between fixed points is related to the resistance between the points, the voltmeter readings indicate patches of high and low resistance.

The Wenner arrangement was used in 1971 to probe the site of a prehistoric ditch on the Hog's Back in Surrey. The results are shown schematically in Figure 11 together with a sketch of the ditch.

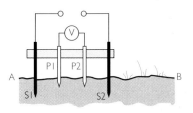

Figure 10   *Multi-probe resistance surveying*

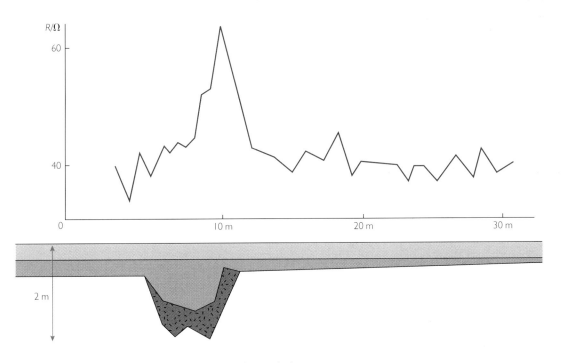

Figure 11   *A survey of the Hog's Back revealed a prehistoric ditch*

Resistive tomography

The availability of fast computer sampling has made possible a new technique in resistive surveying known as 'resistive **tomography**' (Figure 12). This uses a linear array of probes, 14 in this example, which are placed in location and the potential differences between

Study note

The word 'tomography' means 'drawing a slice' – the same word is used in some types of medical imaging, e.g. computerised tomography (CT) scanning.

all possible probe combinations is sampled using an interfaced field computer. The computer will then generate a resistive map of the ground in a vertical plane immediately below the row of probes. As the array of probes is advanced across a site, the computer can eventually generate a three-dimensional resistive image of the entire area to a depth of a few metres. This can be done 'live' on-site.

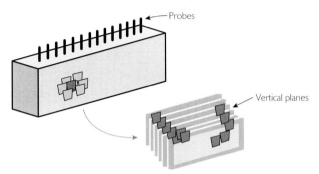

Figure 12 *Resistive tomography*

Potential and potential difference

Have you ever wondered why voltage is called potential difference? The difference between what and what? Consider the simple arrangement of two resistors in Figure 13. Without setting up the circuit you ought to be able to identify the value of the pd across each resistor.

The answer is 4 V and 8 V. The values 4 V and 8 V are potential differences. The word 'difference' implies a subtraction of two values. What two values could you use to produce 8 V? Obviously 8 V and 0 V come to mind. But also 9 V and 1 V, or 15 V and 7 V. They will each produce a difference of 8 V.

These pairs of numbers suggested are known as **potentials**. Their difference is naturally enough called a **potential difference**. It is conventional to label the negative terminal of a battery or cell as having a potential of zero. If the battery provides a potential difference of 12 V then the positive terminal will be labelled +12 V, hence a potential difference of 12 V.

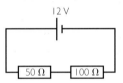

Figure 13 *Two resistors in a circuit*

ACTIVITY 9 **Potential**

Consider the two circuits shown in Figure 14. The circuit in Figure 14(a) has a number of places labelled with potentials. The potential differences are also shown. Look over this circuit so that you can follow the reason for the potential values.

Copy the circuit in Figure 14(b) and label the places marked X with suitable potentials. Take the cell negative terminal as zero. One of the potential differences is included as a clue.

In resistive surveying, the surveyor is mapping potential and potential differences in a three-dimensional object (the ground), so the situation is somewhat harder to analyse theoretically than that in Activity 9. Activity 10 is an extension activity in which you can explore variations of potential in two dimensions.

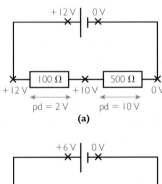

Figure 14 *Circuit diagrams for Activity 9*

ACTIVITY 10 **Potential in two dimensions**

Use an arrangement such as that shown in Figure 15 to explore the variation in potential in a two-dimensional object. Plot a 'map' of potential on a piece of graph paper. Look for points that have the same potential; you can link these with a line called an **equipotential** line.

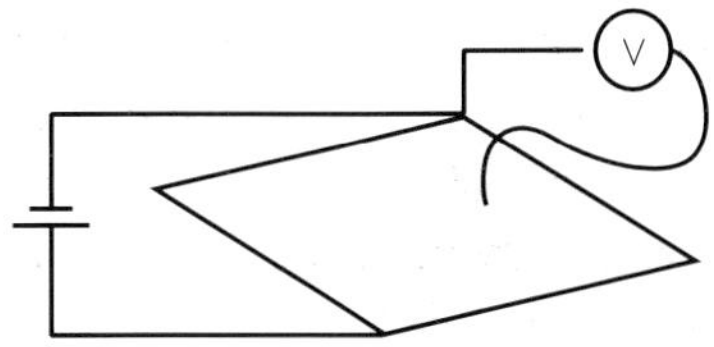

Figure 15 *Diagram for Activity 10*

1.4 Summing up part 1

In this section, you have reviewed and extended your knowledge of electric circuits and learned how the idea of resistivity is used in archaelogical surveys. Activity 11 is designed to help you to consolidate what you have learned and also develop your communication skills.

ACTIVITY 11 **Summing up part 1: surveying the field**

Imagine that you are a member of an archaeological team – perhaps a friend has dragged you along to a summer vacation 'holiday' site for company. The historical evidence suggests that a nearby field belonging to a local farmer, Mr Muncastle, is a likely site for the location of a Roman villa. The team you are working with want to carry out a resistive survey of the field. They have persuaded you to write to the farmer asking permission to gain access to his field for a survey, lasting about a day. (He will have to usher his bull into another field and is not too sure what damage you might do.)

Write a letter to Mr Muncastle explaining the non-destructive nature of the test in a language that he will appreciate and which explains what will happen during the day.

Prepare for a meeting with Mr Muncastle to do a deal with him in the event that the survey is positive and the team wants to spend four days excavating a corner of his field. What do you anticipate he will say? How will your team respond?

Further **investigations**

If you have an opportunity for further practical work, you might consider the following suggestions.

Make and test your own resistivity meter. Instructions are given in *Everyday Practical Electronics*, Jan, Feb 1997. (Before field testing, make sure you obtain permission from the land owner – it might be best to use it only within your school or college grounds, or at home.)

Use Teledeltos paper to explore the equipotentials and electric fields around conductors with a variety of shapes. In particular, look at the potential gradient around sharp points and think how this might relate to the operation of a lightning conductor, and to guidelines on safe behaviour during thunder storms.

7 For the circuits shown in Figure 16, (**a**) calculate the value of the pd when the voltmeter is attached as shown by the broken lines and (**b**) state the potential at each of the places marked X.

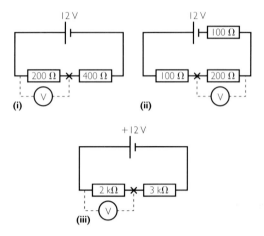

Figure 16 *Circuit diagrams for question 7*

8 Heavy vehicles can distort older steel and iron bridges. To monitor these distortions, scientists use an instrument called a strain gauge. A strain gauge is a thin strip of metal (Figure 17). When it stretches it gets longer and thinner and so its resistance changes. This change can be monitored using a potential divider circuit.

(**a**) If a strain gauge is stretched, in what way will its resistance change? Will it increase or decrease?

(**b**) If the length of a strain gauge increases by 10%, by what factor will the resistance change? Explain your answer.

The gauge shown in Figure 17 has a total uncoiled length of 28 cm. The thin strip is 0.6 mm wide and 0.002 mm thick. The resistivity of the metal used is $2.6 \times 10^{-6}\,\Omega\,\mathrm{m}$.

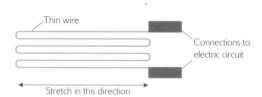

Figure 17 *Schematic diagram of a strain gauge*

(**c**) Calculate the resistance of the strain gauge.

In the potential divider circuit, the gauge is placed in series with a fixed resistor, R. They are connected to a 6 V supply and R must be chosen so that the pd across the strain gauge is 1.2 V.

(**d**) Calculate the value of the fixed resistor, R.

2 The inside story

2.1 X-rays

Once artefacts have been recovered then the real investigation begins. **X-rays** are invaluable in probing the finds both to discover what lies hidden within and to determine from what materials they are made and how best to conserve them.

ACTIVITY 12 **The electromagnetic spectrum**

Table 4 lists typical wavelengths of the radiation that makes up the electromagnetic spectrum. Use these values to produce a labelled 'number line' showing the various regions of the spectrum. First try plotting the wavelengths on a linear scale and note any problems this creates. Then copy Table 4 and add another column headed '$\log_{10}$ of wavelength'. Complete this column (you should be able to do most of this without using a calculator) and then plot the values of $\log_{10}$ wavelength on a number line. Choose a scale so that the entire spectrum fits across the page in your notes.

Type of radiation	Approximate wavelength range/m
gamma-rays	10^{-14} (or less) to 10^{-11}
X-rays	10^{-11} to 10^{-8}
ultraviolet	10^{-8} to 4×10^{-7}
visible	4×10^{-7} to 7×10^{-7}
infrared	7×10^{-7} to 10^{-3}
microwaves	10^{-3} to 10^{-1}
radio	10^{-1} to 10^{3} or more

Table 4 *The electromagnetic spectrum*

Maths reference

Logs and powers of 10
See Maths note 8.1

Logs on a calculator
See Maths note 8.2

ACTIVITY 13 **X-rays in archaeology**

When you have completed your work on this part of the unit, prepare a short information leaflet, aimed at the general public, giving a brief outline of how X-rays can be used in archaeology. Imagine that people might pick up this leaflet in passing an information desk, out of general interest, so it must be visually attractive and make them want to open it to see what's inside.

Such leaflets are often a single sheet of A4 folded into three (or A3 folded into four). Use diagrams and graphics to get your message across as well as text. As you work through this part of the unit, be thinking about what you will include in your leaflet.

2.2 What's inside?

Soon after Wilhelm Röntgen discovered X-rays in 1895, Sir Flinders Petrie obtained the first X-ray of a mummified leg (Figure 18) while Mr Elliot Smith and Mr Howard Carter tell of their experience transferring the rigid Pharaoh Tuthmosis VI by taxicab to a private X-ray unit in Cairo Hospital. Surprisingly almost no further use was made of X-rays by archaeologists until the 1960s. Now conservators consider X-rays an essential tool in probing archaeological finds to assess their condition and determine the best techniques of conservation.

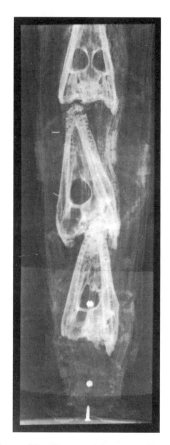

Figure 18   *A mummified leg*

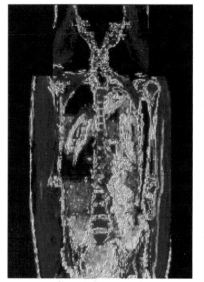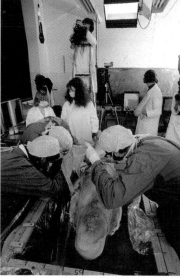

Figure 19   *X-radiography of an entire mummy can show the contents without the need to destroy or severely damage it*

The greatest benefit of X-radiography of archaeological artefacts is that it is a completely non-destructive technique. X-rays applied to intact mummies can identify the contents (Figures 19 and 20) through conventional transmission (shadow) radiographs, while a radiograph of bones can provide information on skeletal maturity, the effects of illness and nutrition, and injuries that may have been the cause of death. Generally such X-rays are undertaken in hospitals at night to avoid interfering with normal working procedures and alarming the patients!

Another technique, 'fluoroscopy', involves the transmission of X-rays on to a fluorescent screen and provides an instant dynamic view of the object. Since the apparatus allows the object to be moved during examination and viewed in real time, a three-dimensional effect is introduced as the object moves on the screen.

'Pete Marsh', the Iron Age human body found in Lindow Moss in Cheshire, was X-rayed using computer-aided tomography (CAT) scans whereby images of 'slices' of the body can be studied. The image is achieved by blurring out the unwanted shadows above and below the plane of interest. CAT scans have been invaluable in understanding pathological changes and mummification techniques.

Sometimes a group of archaeological objects, such as the contents of a grave, are lifted *en bloc*, then the components can be X-rayed *in situ*. This may reveal traces of former organic components related to the original metal objects for example.

Figure 20   *Mummy of three crocodile skulls*

X-rays will obviously show up the shape of metal objects but they can also show the extent of any deterioration, as the decorative metals that were used corrode differently from the base metal of the main object and may now appear 'suspended' in the surface corrosion products. The remains of a scabbard may also be preserved in the corrosion and will only be visible in the radiograph (Figure 21).

The radiographs also reveal a wealth of information about the technological skills that went in to the production of metal objects. Bronze Age castings of sword and daggers can be studied radiographically, and the distribution and orientation of the gas voids in the castings give an insight into the development of the casting process.

The conversion of iron into steel by carburisation is a means of improving the quality of the metal products. Anglo-Saxon smiths developed a range of techniques to make the most of the various properties of each metal, and the techniques they used to combine metals by 'pattern welding' can be seen radiographically on swords and other weapons (Figure 22).

The corrosion of iron was well understood, and in medieval times tin or copper plating was often used for its protection. Such non-ferrous platings are seen on radiographs as bright lines surrounding the object.

The construction techniques revealed through X-rays of artefacts can help in determining whether the artefact is genuinely of the period and whether there has been any attempts at repair or restoration in the past. Radiography was used in the authenticity studies of a pair of Egyptian bronze cats. They were shown to be made from copper filings and resin rather than cast bronze as would be expected of authentic articles from the period.

Radiography has thus become an essential tool for the study of a range of archaeological materials, and few conservators would risk conserving iron objects in particular and, increasingly, objects of other materials without the benefit of an X-ray to assess their condition.

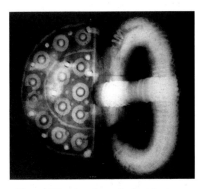

Figure 21 *A radiograph of an Anglo-Saxon buckle showing bands of silver 'floating' 2 mm above the surface*

Figure 22 *A pattern welded dagger*

ACTIVITY **14** **The Coppergate Helmet**

Read the following article, and then answer questions 9 to 13 that follow. Skim read the article first, look at the questions and then read more carefully to find the answers. Use a dictionary to look up any unfamiliar words.

In 1976 a major archaeological dig of a Viking settlement in the centre of York produced a wealth of finds that were so exciting that it was decided to build the Jorvik Viking Centre on the site. Now thousands of people visit the site every year and enjoy the re-creation of life in Viking times and of the excavations which were undertaken. However another amazing find came to light quite by accident – the Coppergate Helmet [Figure 23].

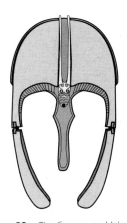

Figure 23 *The Coppergate Helmet*

In 1982 Andy Shaw was using a mechanical excavator to level the site ready for the construction of a large commercial centre when his supervisor, Chris Wade, noticed that the machine had struck something solid. Immediately archaeologists from the York Archaeological Trust were called in. It was apparent that the object was a helmet from the Anglo-Saxon period and of immense importance. It took archaeologists over five hours to excavate the area and record meticulously the precise location of the helmet and the surrounding features.

The helmet was lifted without removing the clay filling (Figure 24) in an attempt to prevent damage to any objects inside the helmet. This was finally accomplished at 9 o'clock in the evening of the day it was discovered.

To prevent corrosion of the copper alloy and iron the helmet and contents were transferred to a closed container to be stored in an atmosphere of nitrogen giving the conservators time to plan the conservation strategy and investigation of the helmet.

In order to see what was inside the helmet it was taken to York District Hospital and radiographed (X-rayed) with the help of hospital staff. They made a series of horizontal transmission shadow radiographs and the subsequent images were digitally enhanced. The horizontal radiographs revealed a substantial amount of chainmail and one of the cheekpieces inside the helmet.

The helmet was too fragile to be turned upright so to obtain vertical radiographs it was subjected to circular motion tomography using the sophisticated CAT (computer-aided tomography) scanner. Tomography is a means of generating images of 'slices' of the body by blurring out the unwanted shadows above and below the area of interest. This produced a series of vertical radiographs of the helmet fill at 10 mm intervals which gave information on the precise location of these objects.

Nothing of this nature had been attempted before as the machine was designed to cope with the human body and the helmet, being metal, had a density outside the scope of the scanner. However the images were successful [Figure 25] and armed with the X-ray sections the archaeologists excavated the interior of the helmet, knowing in advance exactly where the chainmail and cheekpiece lay.

Later high performance industrial radiography of the helmet and microfocus radiography of the chainmail rings enabled conservators to resolve the complex technology involved in the helmet's original construction. The manufacture of the chainmail was an incredible feat of skills on the part of the Anglo-Saxon metalworkers who must have taken many hundreds of hours to make it. It was surely one of the most costly components of the helmet.

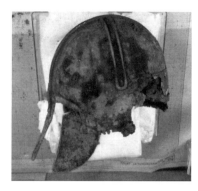

Figure 24 *The helmet shortly after excavation*

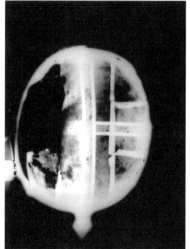

Figure 25 *Some of the original radiographs*

Evidence from the shape of the helmet, the inscriptions, the form of the animal ornaments and the methods of construction (compared with similar finds such as the Sutton Hoo Helmet from a royal grave in Suffolk and the Benty Grange Helmet from Derbyshire) led to the conclusion that it was made between AD 750 and 775 for a member of a noble family, possible named Oshere. It was probably in use for a number of years as it has been well polished and suffered some damage. The fact that it was not found in a burial site but had apparently been placed in the pit deliberately with the chainmail and cheek piece placed inside indicates that it may have been hidden with the intention of recovering it later. Perhaps the helmet was used and lost during the struggle for York between the Saxons and Vikings in AD 866.

An indication of when the helmet was placed in the pit may soon come from radiocarbon dating or from work on the tree rings of the timbers in the pit.

The spot where the Coppergate Helmet was found is marked by a plaque in the entrance of the Jorvik Centre in Coppergate, York. The helmet itself can be seen at the nearby Castle Museum.

QUESTIONS

9 Explain why the term 'shadow radiograph' is appropriate for a conventional X-ray image.

10 Explain the difference between conventional X-ray images and X-ray tomography.

11 Explain why there was concern that the hospital CAT scanner might not give satisfactory images of the helmet and its contents.

12 Explain, using diagrams if necessary, how taking both horizontal and vertical radiographs enabled the archaeologists to pinpoint the precise location of the items inside the helmet.

13 In addition to determining the nature and location of the contents of the helmet, what other information did archaeologists obtain through using X-rays?

2.3 X-ray diffraction

As well as using X-rays to probe the content of artefacts, another technique, X-ray diffraction, is a powerful tool in determining the precise composition of the materials that make up the object. This can lead archaeologists to a better understanding of the sources of the materials used, the methods used in manufacturing objects and how best to prevent further corrosion.

The archaeologist's view of X-ray diffraction

As well as using X-rays to 'see' what an artefact consists of, it is possible to use X-rays to analyse precisely what materials were used to create it. X-ray diffraction is a technique that uses **monochromatic** (i.e. single-wavelength) X-rays to identify which crystalline minerals are present, and it will reveal not only whether an element is present as an oxide or other compound but also the proportions of each mineral present and the phases of the minerals (i.e. the forms of crystal lattice, see Figure 26). It can be applied to metal, ceramic or stone artefacts and the pigments used to decorate them.

The use of X-ray diffraction to identify the minerals present in an object has a number of strengths:

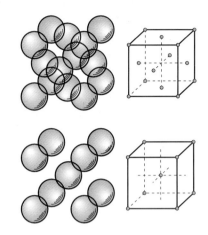

Figure 26 *Different phases of a mineral*

- First, conservators are interested in the corrosion products present. This allows them to know more about the burial history of the artefact – its exposure to water or oxides present in the soil surrounding it, for example. From this information conservators can determine the best conservation techniques to prevent further deterioration of the object.

- Archaeologists can determine the raw materials used to create the object. This may give an indication of the sources of these raw materials, which is helpful in determining ancient trade routes and other aspects of ancient economy and society. More importantly the precise composition of alloys, often determined by investigation of the slags and residues left in metal workshops, can indicate the techniques used to manufacture them, which then indicates the archaeological period and the economy of the site – was metal working undertaken only in the construction of the site or did the site include a metal workshop or even a mint where silver was extracted as coins were recycled, for example.

- X-ray diffraction analysis will provide information on the thermal treatments to which metal artefacts were subjected during their fabrication. For example, cold working a metal results in fragmentation and distortion of the crystal grains, whereas annealing results in the growth of large, undistorted crystal grains that give very distinctive X-ray diffraction patterns

- Study of the pigments used to decorate objects can provide an insight into the techniques of manufacture of the pigment and its application to the surface of the object. Different oxides were used to produce a particular colour in different places across the ancient world at different times. A study of similarities and differences in techniques for producing pigments can indicate whether groups were developing in isolation or influenced each other. The same technique can identify the true colours used in, for example, 17th century works of art (Figure 27) to aid accurate restoration.

Figure 27 *A 17th century work of art*

- X-ray diffraction can be used to estimate the firing temperatures used when making pottery because both the minerals present and their phases depend on the temperature to which the sample has been heated.

- Finally, the fluorine content of bones decreases with age, and thus X-ray diffraction techniques can be used to date bones by measuring their fluorine content – although the levels are dependent on the area in which the animal lived and therefore have to be calibrated accordingly.

How does X-ray diffraction work?

The simplest version of X-ray diffraction takes a thin slice of material and allows the X-rays to pass through it, or else passes the X-rays through a powdered sample of the material. You can simulate this using a low-power laser and some *Lycopodium* powder or talcum powder sandwiched between two microscope slides. Another simulation uses a diffraction grating (a regular array of very narrow lines ruled on transparent plastic or glass) in front of the laser – this produces a very different pattern.

ACTIVITY 15 **Simulating X-ray diffraction**

Observe the patterns produced on a screen when a laser shines through some fine powder and through one or more diffraction gratings (Figure 28). Try using two gratings together, crossed at various angles to one another. With other students, 'brainstorm' your ideas about how these different patterns are produced.

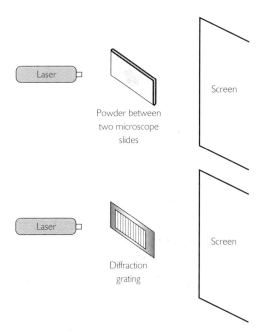

Figure 28 *Diagrams for Activity 15*

To explain the two effects you have just seen you will need to understand three phenomena: **diffraction**, **superposition** and **interference**.

Diffraction (the spreading of waves) and interference (when coherent waves undergo superposition and reinforce or cancel each other) combine to give the effects seen when a laser is shone through a single crystal or a powdered polycrystalline sample giving intense points of light at certain well-defined points as seen in Activity 15. If we know more about the precise mechanisms involved, we can use this phenomenon to find out more about the sample being used.

ACTIVITY 16 **Doing diffraction – investigating interference**

Explore the effects of diffraction and interference of different waves through a series of three experiments: a ripple tank, a laser and microwaves.

Activity 16 illustrates diffraction – the spreading of waves into unexpected areas. For significant diffraction to happen the gap or obstacle must be comparable in size to the wavelength of the waves used. If coherent waves travel through different distances and then meet up again, then superposition produces an interference pattern. If waves pass through a regular array of gaps or obstacles, such as a diffraction grating, then diffraction gives rise to many sets of overlapping waves that produce an interference pattern when they superpose.

Von Laue's experiment

The use of X-rays to analyse materials is based on an experiment performed early in the 20th century by the German physicist Max von Laue, though he himself had quite a different purpose in mind when he carried out the work.

After X-rays were discovered in 1896, their nature was the subject of much speculation and experiment. They were found *not* to be charged particles because they were not deflected by electric or magnetic fields, unlike electrons (whose deflection was discovered and explained by J.J. Thomson in 1897). In 1912 Max von Laue succeeded in showing that X-rays were electromagnetic waves by obtaining an interference effect. All attempts had so far failed as the gap size used was far greater that the wavelength of the X-rays. Von Laue realised that if the spacing between the regularly spaced atoms in a crystal were of the same size as the wavelength of X-rays, then the crystal could be used to diffract the X-rays and cause interference patterns. Figure 29 shows the basic set-up of his experiments.

The central bright spot surrounded by a fainter pattern of surrounding spots (Figure 30) confirmed that X-rays were waves, and measurements showed that their wavelength was of the order 10^{-10} m. It is precisely this effect that you saw with the laser shone through crossed gratings in Activity 15.

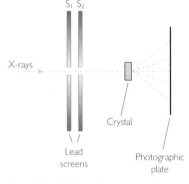

Figure 29 *Von Laue's experimental set-up*

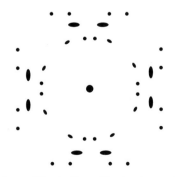

Figure 30 *An X-ray diffraction photograph*

Diffraction by crystals

Use a ripple tank to see the diffraction effects produced by a two-dimensional 'crystal', and use microwave apparatus to see the same effect in three dimensions.

Powder photos

Von Laue's experiments worked because the atomic spacing in crystals is similar in size to the wavelength of the X-rays. The precise pattern generated can be used to make measurements of the interatomic spacing in the crystal and this is is used to analyse the composition of materials. Broadly speaking, the smaller the interatomic spacing, and the shorter the wavelength, the more widely spaced the bright parts of the diffraction pattern.

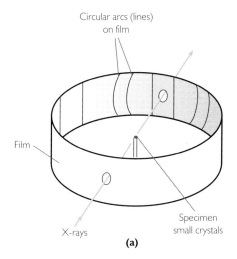

(a)

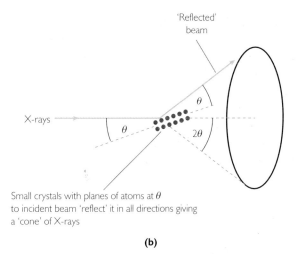

Small crystals with planes of atoms at θ to incident beam 'reflect' it in all directions giving a 'cone' of X-rays

(b)

Figure 31 *An X-ray powder camera*

Most X-ray diffraction analysis is carried out on a powdered sample, which is turned into a rod-shaped specimen either by mixing it with an adhesive or by sealing it in a glass capillary tube. The rod is placed in a cylindrical X-ray camera and illuminated with a beam of monochromatic X-rays (Figure 31). As the X-rays are reflected off successive layers of atoms, they undergo interference, and the film in the camera records a number of bright lines (areas of constructive interference) (Figure 32). The distances between these lines give information on the crystal lattice spacing of the crystals present, which then is used to identify the actual composition of the object by comparing the patterns of lines with the lines formed by known substances. (This powder technique cannot be used to determine the crystal form of metals as the powdering distorts the crystal lattice; instead a thin slice of the artefact has to be used.)

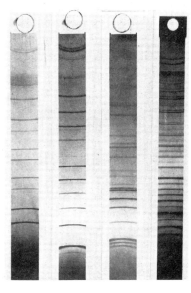

Figure 32 *Typical X-ray powder photos*

ACTIVITY **18** **Where has it been?**

The Coppergate Helmet was subjected to X-ray diffraction analysis in order to determine what it was made from and the likely conditions in which it was buried. Study the relevant X-ray diffraction spectra and write a short report on the deductions that can be made.

ACTIVITY **19** **Tales of the unexpected**

Write an essay entitled 'Diffraction – tales of the unexpected'. This should not only explain diffraction (briefly) but also discuss why diffraction can be associated with the phrase 'the unexpected'.

At the end of your essay note the points on which you would like feedback from your teacher.

2.4 Summing up part 2

In this part of the unit you have seen how the composition of artefacts can be analysed using X-rays. You have also had several opportunities to develop skills of communication.

ACTIVITY **20** **Summing up part 2**

Spend a few minutes checking through your notes and make sure you understand all the terms printed in bold. Then use what you have learned to complete your leaflet for Activity 13.

QUESTIONS

14 Explain why a sound from the far side of a doorway can be heard in all parts of a room but light passing through the same doorway casts a sharp shadow.

15 Steel components corrode (rust) in various ways when exposed to air, rain and heating. The compounds FeO (iron oxide), Fe_2O_3 (iron(III) oxide), Fe_3O_4 (tri-iron tetroxide) and $Fe_2O_3 \cdot H_2O$ (hydrated iron(III) oxide) can be formed, depending on the type of steel and its situation. Knowledge of which oxide(s) are present can help the manufacturer and the user of the steel.

X-ray diffraction is frequently used to analyse the corrosion products. The corroded surface layer of the steel component is scraped off, ground into a powder, placed in the X-ray camera and exposed to X-rays.

A drawing of an X-ray diffraction photograph for one particular sample is shown in Figure 33, together with those of pure iron and some known oxides. The original photographs were all negatives and so the dark lines indicate a high exposure to X-radiation.

Using the images in Figure 33, state which oxide was present in the corroded surface layer (in addition to iron itself).

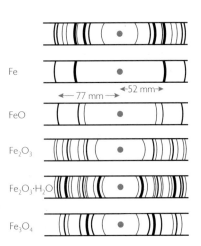

Figure 33 *X-ray diffraction images for question 15*

3 *The dating game*

In parts 1 and 2 of this unit you saw how archaeologists can locate ancient remains and how they can determine the composition of artefacts. But *when* they were made is also of vital concern. By dating artefacts, the archaeologist can begin to build up the time sequence of events which can then be used to provide an accurate analysis of the past.

3.1 *Scientific dating techniques*

Before the application of scientific methods and techniques, the dating of archaeological sites and artefacts was pretty much a hit-and-miss affair. For example, if one item was found at a deeper level in the dig than another, then it was assumed to be older; the Stone Age was supposed to be earlier than the Bronze Age, and this in turn preceded the Iron Age. There are hidden assumptions here: Has the site been disturbed, mixing up the artefacts? Were no stone articles produced in the Bronze Age?

Recently, archaeological dating has become more sophisticated. Measurements involving a deep understanding of nuclear physics, magnetism in materials and chemical analysis (amongst others) are now regularly used by archaeologists. As a result, a much greater understanding of the relationships between past events has emerged, though even these modern methods have their limitations.

One of the more sophisticated dating techniques uses **thermoluminescence** (TL), and that forms the subject of most of this part of the unit. But first, Activity 21 allows you to explore the basic principles behind two other important dating methods: dendrochronology and radiocarbon dating. See Figure 34.

Figure 34 *(a) A timber frame house can be dated by dendrochronology, (b) a skeleton can be dated by radiocarbon dating, and (c) pottery can be dated by thermoluminescence. (The hole in the top of the skull is evidence of surgery that probably killed the patient!)*

ACTIVITY 21	**Dating techniques**

Prepare a poster on a sheet of A3 paper that describes dendrochronology or radiocarbon dating.

ACTIVITY 22	**Why so many?**

What is the point of developing several methods of dating? Isn't just one sufficient?

In a group, spend a few minutes 'brainstorming' possible responses.

3.2 *Introducing thermoluminescence*

If a small sample of ancient pottery, roof tiles or brick is ground up to a powder and heated rapidly to about 500 °C, there is a weak but measurable emission of light in addition to the thermal radiation given out by warm objects. This extra light is **thermoluminescence** (literally, light produced by heating). If the sample is reheated then it will emit only 'ordinary' thermal radiation. See Figure 35. Not all substances behave like this; in general, only electrical insulators show thermoluminescence, while conductors do not.

Study note

You will learn more about radioactive decay in the unit *Reach for the Stars*.

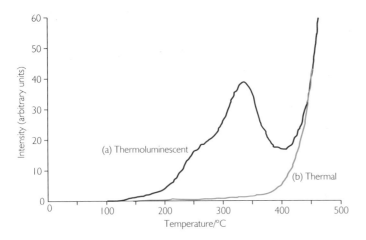

Figure 35 *Thermal and thermoluminescent radiation*

ACTIVITY **23** **Glowing reports**

Grind a small sample of the mineral fluorite – the grains need to be quite small, but not powdery. Heat a tin lid over a Bunsen flame so that it is hot but not glowing. Turn off the Bunsen. Sprinkle some of the fluorite on to the tin lid and record what you see. Let the grains cool, then repeat.

 Safety
Wear goggles

Thermoluminescence was first recorded by Robert Boyle in a paper dated 1663 where he describes how a diamond emitted a 'glimmering light' when heated by the warmth of his hand. However, in view of the relatively high temperatures needed in Activity 23 you might be somewhat sceptical of Boyle's reported sighting.

When archaeological artefacts exhibit thermoluminescence, the intensity of the glow is an indication of the age of the sample. The longer the sample has been buried in the ground, the more intense and longer lasting will be the glow. In real archaeological samples the thermoluminescence is much more feeble than that which you saw in Activity 23, and sensitive instruments are required in order to detect it. These will be discussed in section 3.4.

Why does it glow?

In the unit *The Sound of Music* you studied light that was given out as excited electrons moved from high to low energy levels within atoms. This process was described by the equation

$$E = hf \tag{8}$$

Use the following questions to check that you can remember what you learned earlier.

QUESTIONS

16 Say what each of the terms in equation (8) represents, and state their SI units.

17 Figure 36 shows some of the electron energy levels in a hydrogen atom.
(**a**) Calculate the energy of the photon emitted when an electron falls from level 4 to level 3, and calculate the corresponding frquency.
(**b**) Without doing a calculation, say whether the radiation emitted in a transition from level 3 to level 2 will have a higher or a lower frequency than your answer to part (**a**).

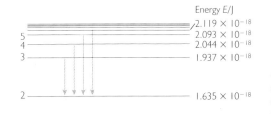

Figure 36 *Some of the electronic energy levels in hydrogen*

When you observe thermoluminescence, you are seeing light from electrons in the sample that are losing energy. But the work you have done so far has considered the behaviour of electrons in isolated atoms. Is this model of the atom appropriate for a solid material where atoms are not isolated? Can ideas about energy levels explain why the sample has to be heated to trigger the emission of light? And why does the age of the sample make a difference? The first two of those questions can be answered by considering the behaviour of electrons in solid materials that involves so-called **band theory**.

Band theory

In an isolated atom, the energy of an electron depends mainly on its distance from the nucleus. An electron has a negative charge and a nucleus has a positive charge, and as an electron 'falls' towards a nucleus it loses energy. The energy of one electron in an atom is also affected by the presence of all the other electrons within that atom, since they all have negative charge and so all repel one another.

If atoms are very close together, as in a solid, then the energy of each electron is affected by the nuclei and electrons of many nearby atoms. This has the effect of smearing out the energy levels into broad **bands**. The electrons are no longer restricted to certain well-defined energies; instead, there are broad ranges of allowed energy, and the higher energy band is 'shared' between atoms. If an electron has enough energy to be in this band, then it can break free of its parent atom and move through the solid, i.e. it can take part in conduction, so this upper band is called the **conduction band**. If, however, an electron is still bound to its parent atom then it cannot move around freely and it is said to be in the **valence band**. Between the two bands is a range of energies known as the **forbidden gap**. See Figure 37.

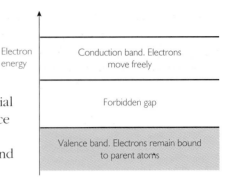

Figure 37 *The valence and conduction bands in a perfect crystalline solid*

The size of the forbidden gap determines whether a given material is a conductor or an insulator. In metals, the conduction and valence bands overlap, so the conduction band always contains electrons, and so metals are good conductors. In insulators, the conduction and valence bands are separated by a large forbidden gap, and the conduction band is virtually empty. To promote an electron from the valence band would require a large amount of energy. In a semiconductor, there is still a gap, but the range of forbidden energies is quite small. If energy is supplied, e.g. by heating, or by allowing the material to absorb photons, then some electrons gain enough energy to cross the gap and enter the conduction band. The more energy supplied, the more electrons are promoted; the resistance of many semiconductors falls with increasing temperature.

As you will see, thermoluminescence is a phenomenon associated only with insulating materials that have a distinct forbidden gap between valence and conduction bands. If there is no such forbidden gap (as is the case with metals), then there will be no thermoluminescence.

So far we have described the energy bands in a perfect crystal: between the valence and conduction bands there is a gap completely devoid of energy levels. However, in a real crystal there are imperfections (usually called **defects**). For example, there may be impurities – 'foreign' atoms, slightly bigger or smaller than the others – whose presence distorts the regular crystal structure (Figure 38a). Another possibility is that atoms of the crystal are simply missing, leaving a hole (see Figure 38b).

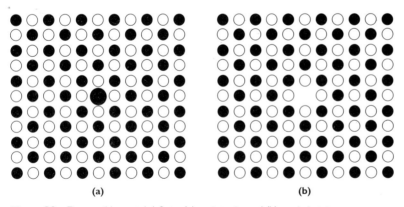

(a) **(b)**

Figure 38 *Two possible crystal defects: (a) an impurity and (b) a missing atom*

ACTIVITY **24** **Model crystals**

Use a ball-and-stick model and/or a bubble raft to illustrate how the presence of an impurity or a missing atom can distort the structure of a crystal. Record your observations using annotated sketches.

The presence of defects actually creates some additional energy levels within the forbidden gap, so it is possible for a few electrons to have energies intermediate between those of the valence and conduction bands. These **defect levels** are shown schematically in Figure 39; in a real crystal the gap is not so much forbidden as discouraged! Once an electron is in a defect level, it tends to stay there for quite a long time until something disturbs it and helps it to lose energy so that it can drop back into the valence band.

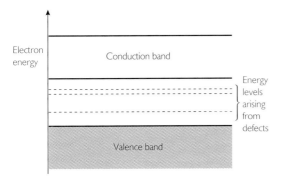

Figure 39 *Energy bands in a real crystal*

Defect levels are very important in thermoluminescence; the thermoluminescent glow is radiation emitted as electrons make transitions from the defect levels to the valence band. Heating the sample the first time provides the necessary disturbance to help the electrons undergo the transition, and once this has happened the defect levels are empty and so re-heating will not produce any theromoluminescent glow.

The longer a sample has been buried, the more electrons are trapped in defect levels, and hence the greater the thermoluminescent glow. The questions now are, how did the electrons get trapped there in the first place, and why does the time of burial affect the number of trapped electrons? The answer lies in the soil, and concerns radioactivity – the subject of the next section.

3.3 Radioactivity

Types and sources of radiation

Think of a piece of bone or pot buried undisturbed for hundreds of years. Almost imperceptibly, changes have been taking place within the material. Over the centuries, it has been subjected to the steady influence of ionising radiation, which has been gradually damaging the material to produce defects and, even more important, has been supplying energy to the electrons, raising them from the valence band to occupy some of the defect levels. The process is slow but remorseless, and, as time goes by, more and more of the defect levels are occupied by electrons.

As you probably remember from your earlier studies of radioactivity, there are three types of radiation from radioactive materials: **alpha** (α), **beta** (β) and **gamma** (γ) **radiation**. These three types differ in their nature and hence also in their ability to penetrate matter and to ionise (remove electrons from) atoms; both these properties are important in thermoluminescence. It is the ionisation that causes defects and also liberates electrons so that they can occupy defect levels. And the ability to penetrate determines whether the radiation can affect the whole of a sample or just parts near the surface.

ACTIVITY 25 α, β and γ radiation

Using your knowledge from GCSE work, or using information from textbooks, draw up a table to summarise the properties of α, β and γ radiation. Your table should include:

the nature of the radiation
the sign of any electric charge
the mass
the typical speed

ACTIVITY 26 **Penetration and ionisation**

Use a radioactivity kit and Geiger counter (Geiger–Müller tube) (Figure 40) to investigate the ability of α, β and γ radiation to travel through various materials, e.g. air, paper, aluminium and lead. Compare the ionising abilities of the three types of radiation. Do not attempt to make measurements – just make a qualitative comparison. Use your observations to add further rows to your table from Activity 25.

  Safety
If handling radioactive sources, always use tongs or other holder. Do not hold a source close to yourself or anyone else. Wash your hands afterwards.

Figure 40 *Exploring radioactivity*

If a radiation detector, such as a Geiger counter (Figure 41), is set up anywhere on Earth, it will detect some ionising radiation from a variety of sources, collectively known as **background radiation**. This radiation comes from space and from radioactive materials in the Earth itself. The radiation from space is known as **cosmic radiation**, and consists mainly of protons, along with some α particles and some electrons. Most of the lower-energy cosmic radiation probably originates from nearby regions of our own Galaxy, but some cosmic radiation probably originates in certain very distant galaxies where particles are accelerated to extremely high energies.

The backgound radiation that originates on Earth comes chiefly from radioactive elements such as uranium and potassium, which are found in the rocks and soil, and from carbon-14, which is found in rocks, the atmosphere and in living

Figure 41 *Measuring background radiation*

tissue. There is also a small contribution from medical equipment and from other sources such as nuclear power stations. The principal radioactive rock is granite, which is abundant in Scotland and the south-west of England. The radioactive **background count** (i.e. the number of 'clicks' per second, or per minute, registered by a detector) in these regions is significantly greater than elsewhere in the UK.

ACTIVITY **27** **Background radiation**

Set up a Geiger–Müller tube and counter to measure the background count in your laboratory. You could see whether the background count was greater inside the laboratory than outside, and try to explain any difference.

Use e-mail to contact physics students in other areas and compare measurements of background count. Consider how you will try to ensure that you are making a fair comparison, and try to make your contacts as widely dispersed as possible. If you can collect enough data, plot the background counts on a map – you will need to decide how best to display them.

Radiation dose

As we have seen, the thermoluminescence produced in an archaeological sample will depend on the number of electrons occupying defect energy levels. This in turn will depend on the extent to which the sample has been affected by ionising radiation; broadly speaking, the longer it has lain buried, the greater will be the effects of radiation. However, these effects also depend not only on the background count, but on the nature of the radiation – as you have seen, the different types of radiation are not all equally effective at penetrating or ionising. To quantify this, we need to use the idea of **radiation dose**.

We are mainly concerned here with the ability of radiation to produce ionisation within a material, which depends on the energy absorbed by the material. The dose is defined as the amount of energy absorbed by one kilogram of material, and the SI unit of radiation dose is the gray (Gy) where $1\,Gy = 1$ joule per kilogram ($1\,J\,kg^{-1}$). For archaeological samples, the dose is often described in terms of Gy per 1000 years. The actual dose received by a sample depends on where it has been buried and for how long.

By measuring the thermoluminescent light emitted from a sample, we can deduce the dose that it must have received. Using a knowledge of the soil in which it was buried, we can then work out how long such a dose would take to deliver – and this time gives an estimate of the sample's age.

QUESTION

18 Table 5 shows the radiation dose that would be received by a pottery sample buried in a typical soil containing 1% potassium, 10 parts per million (ppm) of thorium and 3 ppm of uranium as these elements go through successive stages of radioactive decay, emitting α, β or γ at each stage. Cosmic rays and traces of rubidium in the soil add a further 0.17 Gy.

(**a**) Calculate the total dose received by the pottery in 1000 years.
(**b**) Calculate the amount of energy absorbed by a 10 g piece of pottery buried for 500 years in the same location.

	Dose rate/Gy per 1000 years		
	α dose	**β dose**	**γ dose**
potassium	–	0.83	0.24
thorium	1.11	0.29	0.51
uranium	1.25	0.44	0.34

Table 5 Radiation dose data for question 18

ACTIVITY 28 **Thermoluminescent dating – the story**

Use a series of sketch diagrams or cartoons to show what happens to an archaeological artefact that is left in the ground for hundreds of years, and how this can be used to estimate the age of the artefact.

For example, you could start with an ancient Greek amphora (wine jar) (Figure 42) being buried in a grave or being covered by volcanic debris. The second frame might show a mineral crystal within the amphora and its detailed atomic structure with defects in the crystal lattice. Then, what . . . ? That's up to you, but your summary should be nice and colourful and have plenty of text boxes with appropriate explanations.

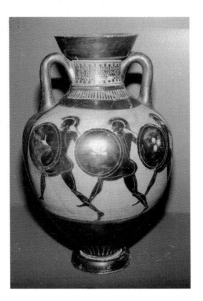

Figure 42 A Greek amphora

Further investigations

If you have an opportunity, you might like to investigate the absorption of α, β and γ radiation by different materials. See how the count rate varies with thickness of absorbing material and try to explain what you find.

3.4 Measuring faint light

The thermoluminescent light from a heated sample of pottery or bone is very weak and needs to be amplified in order to be measured accurately. This can be achieved using an instrument called, appropriately enough, a **photomultiplier**, which is able to detect a feeble light signal by using a single photon to produce a measurable electric current. This section introduces you to the physics behind this remarkable instrument.

Study note

The light can also be detected and measured using a CCD (charge-coupled device) imager, which also relies on the photoelectric effect. You will meet CCDs in the unit *The Medium is the Message*.

The photomultiplier

When electromagnetic radiation shines on a clean metal surface, electrons are sometimes given off. This is called the **photoelectric effect**, and the released electrons are called **photoelectrons**. Materials that readily release photoelectrons are said to be **photosensitive**.

Study note

You have already met a version of the photoelectric effect in the unit *Technology in Space*, where you used photovoltaic cells that rely on photons releasing electrons from semiconductors.

ACTIVITY **29** **Photoelectric effect**

Observe the photoelectric effect produced by ultraviolet radiation with zinc or magnesium. One way to do this is to use a zinc plate and a gold leaf electroscope or an electrometer (devices that detect the presence of electric charge – see Figure 43). Give the electroscope or electrometer a negative charge. Shine ultraviolet radiation on to the (very clean) zinc and explain what happens to the charge indicated by the electrometer or electroscope. (Think what will happen if electrons can escape from the metal.)

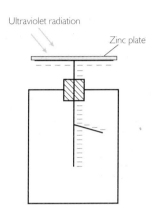

Figure 43   *A negatively charged electroscope*

Figure 44 shows how the photoelectric effect is exploited in a photomultiplier. A photon passes through the glass window and strikes a thin layer of photosensitive material, usually antimony–caesium, known as the photocathode. This causes the release of a photoelectron in about one in ten cases, and because the layer is very thin the photoelectron emerges from the underside of the antimony–caesium layer.

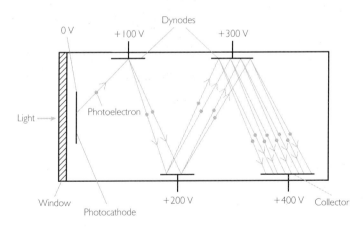

Figure 44   *Schematic diagram of a photomultiplier*

As soon as the photoelectron is free, it is accelerated towards the first 'dynode' through a potential difference of 100 V. The electron gains energy as it accelerates, and as it strikes the first dynode its energy is transferred, causing other electrons in the dynode to be released. On average, there are about four electrons released for every electron impacting on a dynode. These four new electrons are, in their turn, accelerated through a further 100 V to the next dynode and so on.

Photomultipliers usually contain about ten dynode stages and so by the end of the process there will be millions of electrons emerging to be collected at the anode. These electrons give a measurable current pulse that can be recorded on a suitably sensitive ammeter.

In order to understand how the measured current can be related to the incident radiation, and to explain why some materials are more photosensitive than others, we need to look in more detail at the photoelectric effect.

Explaining the photoelectric effect

Experiments show that:

- for any given metal, with radiation below a certain **threshold frequency** no electrons are released even if the radiation is very intense;

- provided the frequency is *above* the threshold, some electrons are released instantaneously, even if the radiation is very weak;

- the more intense the radiation, the more electrons are released;

- the kinetic energy of the individual photoelectrons depends only on the frequency of the radiation and not on its intensity.

These results can be explained using the photon model of light (see Figure 45). A wave model does not predict the observations correctly. In particular, the wave model would predict that weak radiation might eventually allow a large number of electrons to be released all with low energy, rather than the immediate release of a small number of electrons each with high kinetic energy (see Figure 46). The photoelectric effect gave one of the first indications, early in the 20th century, that the wave model of light is not always satisfactory. For explaining the photoelectric effect using a photon model, Einstein was awarded the Nobel Prize.

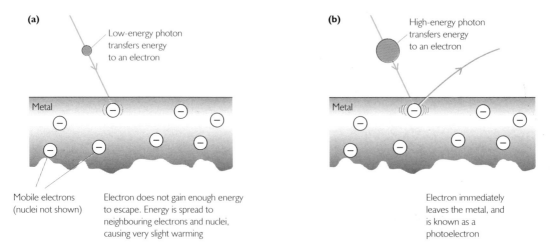

(a) Low-energy photon transfers energy to an electron

Metal

Mobile electrons (nuclei not shown)

Electron does not gain enough energy to escape. Energy is spread to neighbouring electrons and nuclei, causing very slight warming

(b) High-energy photon transfers energy to an electron

Metal

Electron immediately leaves the metal, and is known as a photoelectron

Figure 45 *The photoelectric effect can easily be explained using a photon model...*

(a)

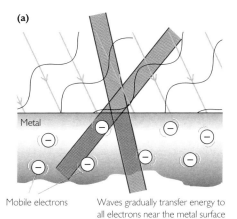

Mobile electrons   Waves gradually transfer energy to
                         all electrons near the metal surface

(b)

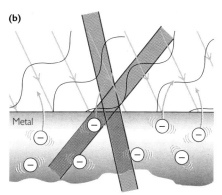

Eventually a large number of electrons gain enough
energy to leave the metal.
NB THIS IS NOT WHAT IS OBSERVED!

Figure 46   . . .but not using a wave model

The release of photoelectrons is initiated by the impact of photons on the target. The energy, E_{ph}, of each photon is related to the wave frequency, f, by

$$E_{ph} = hf \tag{8a}$$

An electron close to the surface of the target material absorbs the photon. In order to escape, the electron needs to do work against the electrical forces that bind it into the metal. The minimum amount of energy needed for this is called the **work function**, ϕ, of the material. In doing work the electron increases its potential energy by an amount ϕ. Any energy remaining is accounted for as the kinetic energy, E_k, of the escaped electron. Conservation of energy enables us to write the following expression:

$$E_{ph} = E_k + \phi \tag{9}$$

Equation (9) describes the following features of the photoelectric effect:

- If $E_{ph} < \phi$, then an electron is unable to do sufficient work and so cannot escape.

- If $E_{ph} = \phi$, then an electron may be released, but with no kinetic energy (i.e. it is free, but cannot move away of its own accord).

- If $E_{ph} > \phi$, then an electron can escape with a maximum kinetic energy of $E_{ph} - \phi$.

The smaller the work function, ϕ, of a material, the more photosensitive the material, i.e. the lower the photon energy needed to release photoelectrons – or, put another way, the lower the threshold frequency. If the threshold frequency is f_0, then

$$\phi = hf_0$$

Study note

We have labelled the photon energy E_{ph} here to distinguish from other energies also denoted by the letter E.

and equation (9) can be written in various ways, e.g.

$$hf = E_k + hf_0 \tag{10}$$

or

$$hf = \tfrac{1}{2}mv_{max}^2 + \phi \tag{10a}$$

where, as you saw in the unit *Higher, Faster, Stronger,*

$$E_k = \tfrac{1}{2}mv^2 \tag{10b}$$

is the kinetic energy of a particle mass m moving at speed v. The label 'max' is a reminder that this is the maximum kinetic energy that a photon can acquire; if it has to do more work than ϕ, then its kinetic energy will be less.

Measuring threshold frequency

The material for the target of a photomultiplier needs to be made from photosensitive material; if it is to detect visible radiation, its threshold frequency needs to be lower than that of zinc or magnesium – as you saw in Activity 29, these metals only release photoelectrons when illuminated with ultraviolet radiation. In principle, the threshold frequency can be determined in a single measurement: shine light of a known frequency on to a material, measure the maximum kinetic energy of the photoelectrons, and then use equation (10) to find f_0.

Figure 47 shows how, in principle, we can measure the electrons' kinetic energy using a **photocell** and an opposing potential difference that is adjustable by means of a potential divider. (See part 1 of this unit.) If photoelectrons are able to move across the gap in the photocell, then there will be a continuous flow of charge around the circuit and the electrometer/picoammeter registers a current; if the applied potential difference, V, is zero, this is what will happen. But if the photoelectrons have to travel towards the *negative* terminal of the power supply, then they lose kinetic energy, and the higher the potential difference, the greater the initial kinetic energy the electron will need to have if it is to reach the other side. If no electrons cross the gap, then the ammeter will read zero.

As you have seen in the unit *Technology in Space* and in part 1 of this unit, when charge moves through a potential difference, energy is transferred as described by the relationship

$$\Delta E = q\Delta V \tag{11}$$

where ΔE is the energy transferred, q the charge and ΔV the potential difference.

If an electron moved in the opposite direction across the gap, from negative to positive, then the power supply would be transferring energy to the electron; an electron starting from rest would gain kinetic energy

$$E_k = e\Delta V \tag{12}$$

where e is the electron's charge. Travelling in the opposite direction, an electron would lose this amount of kinetic energy. So

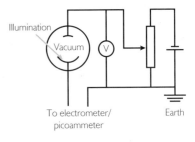

Figure 47 *Apparatus for determining the threshold frequency of a photosensitive material*

if the applied pd is adjusted so that it just stops the photoelectrons (i.e. so that the meter reading just becomes zero), then equation (11) can be used to calculate the electron's initial kinetic energy. The potential difference that just stops the photoelectrons crossing the gap is called, unsurprisingly, the **stopping potential**. Combining equations (10) and (12), with V now representing the stopping potential, gives

$$hf = eV + hf_0 \tag{13}$$

Rather than making just one single measurement to determine f_0, it is much better to use several different values of f and record the corresponding stopping potential V. A graph of f plotted against V, or V against f, can then be used to determine f_0.

Units: the electronvolt

When we are dealing with individual electrons moving through a potential difference of a few volts, the energies involved are extremely small because the magnitude of the electron charge is only 1.60×10^{-19} C. For example, if an electron moves through a pd of 1 V, the energy transferred is only 1.60×10^{-19} J (see equation 11). Rather than express such tiny energies in joules, we sometimes use an alternative unit, the **electronvolt** (eV), which is defined as the energy transferred when one electron moves through a pd of 1 V, so when an electron or a proton is accelerated through a potential difference of V, then the energy transferred is numerically the same as the pd measured in volts.

In other situations you might need to convert between joules and eV:

$$1\,\text{eV} = 1.60 \times 10^{-19}\,\text{J}$$

ACTIVITY 30 **Measuring threshold frequency**

Use a white light source and a set of coloured filters to find the threshold frequency, and hence the work function, of the photosensitive material in a photocell. Use a spreadsheet to plot and analyse a graph of your results.

QUESTIONS

magnitude of electron charge, $e = 1.60 \times 10^{-19}$ C
electron mass, $m_e = 9.1 \times 10^{-31}$ kg
proton mass, $m_p = 1.67 \times 10^{-27}$ kg

19 What is the the energy transferred when (**a**) an electron and (**b**) a proton is accelerated through a pd of 5000 V? Give your answers in joules and in eV.

20 Calculate the speeds of the electron and the proton in question 19, assuming that the transfer of energy from power supply to the particles is 100% efficient.

ACTIVITY **31** **Fast particles**

Use a spreadsheet to plot a graph to show how the speed of an electron changes with accelerating pd. Let the pd range between 0 and 10^4 V. At what pd does the electron reach $3 \times 10^7\,\text{m s}^{-1}$, i.e. one-tenth the speed of light?

Repeat using a proton accelerated through the same pd. Plot the speed on the same axes as the previous graph. Explain why the two graphs look different. What pd would be needed to accelerate a proton to one-tenth the speed of light?

The photomultiplier revisited

You are now in a position to explain how a photomultiplier can be used to measure the weak thermoluminescent radiation given off by an archaeological sample. Questions 21 to 25 illustrate this, and question 26 poses a challenge.

QUESTIONS

21 Suggest a reason why only one in ten of the photons from a heated sample might cause the release of a photoelectron.

22 If a photoelectron is released from the thin layer of photosensitive material with no kinetic energy, then accelerated through 100 V, what will be its energy when it reaches the first dynode? Give your answer in eV and in joules.

23 About four electrons are released for each electron that impacts on a dynode. Assuming that each electon is only *just* released, i.e. it has no initial kinetic energy, use your answer to question 22 to estimate the work function of the dynode material.

24 Assume we have a photomultiplier with ten dynode stages. If each electron that hits a dynode releases four further electrons, is it true to say that the thermoluminescent glow can result in 'millions of electrons' at the anode?

25 Suppose light produces produce a current of 6.5×10^{-11} A at the photocathode. How many electrons must come from the photocathode every second? What would be the final current from the anode of the photomultiplier?

Further investigations

Using light passing through coloured filters, investigate the frequency response of some photosensitive devices (e.g. photographers' light meters, or light-dependent resistors). Try to determine the lowest-frequency (longest-wavelength) radiation to which they respond.

3.5 Summing up part 3

In this part of the unit, you have seen how exposure to ionising radiation gives rise to electrons being trapped in defect levels in solid materials, and how thermoluminescence from artefacts (Figure 48) can be detected and measured using photomultipliers. You have revisited ideas about radioactivity from GCSE, been introduced to the idea of radiation dose, learned something about band theory that describes the energies of electrons in solids, and used the photon model of light to explain and analyse the photoelectric effect, thus revisiting ideas about electric charge, energy and potential difference.

Figure 48   *Some artefacts that can be dated using thermoluminescence*

ACTIVITY **32** **Summing up part 3**

Spend a few minutes checking through your notes, making sure you know the meaning of all the key terms printed in bold. If you are developing a summary of key terms, make sure it is up to date. In particular, look back at some of the terms that you met in earlier units and see whether you need to refine or extend your definitions.

Question 26 now challenges you to bring together all that you have learned abut thermoluminescent dating before we go on to make some general remarks about the technique.

┌ QUESTION ─────────────────────────────

26 Suppose that two similar pieces of pottery, A and B, are found at different sites, and that the background radiation in the soil at site A is twice that at site B. When both samples are heated to the same temperature, the thermoluminescence from Sample A produces a photomultiplier current that is one-third of that produced by B. What are the relative ages of the two samples? State any assumptions you have made.

└───────────────────────────────────────

How good is thermoluminescent dating?

In question 26 we used the proportionality:

$$\text{age} \propto \frac{I}{R}$$

where I is the photomultiplier current and R is the annual background radiation dose to which the sample has been subjected. The main assumption here is that R has been constant over archaeological time; this is not necessarily true.

For very old samples, all the defect energy levels may have become occupied. In other words the thermoluminescence has become saturated, and further exposure to radiation will not increase the number of filled defect levels. There is therefore a maximum age that can be measured for a particular type of material. For quartz crystals the maximum age of the sample, set by saturation, is about 70 000 years, and for feldspar (another natural mineral crystal) the limit is about one million years.

Many archaeological samples incorporate radioactive materials. The radiation from these materials is counted as part of the background radiation, but often they are not evenly distributed within the sample so the estimate of the radiation dose may be unreliable.

Provided all of these complications can be taken into account, the age estimates derived from the thermoluminescence method are accurate to around ±10%.

Other uses of thermoluminescence

Thermoluminescence is used in many situations when we need to know whether something has been subjected to ionising radiation – either due to natural background radiation, or because it has been deliberately or accidentally exposed to abnormally high radiation doses.

One area in which thermoluminescence has proved useful is in detecting forgeries of ancient pottery and other artefacts. A small sample can be tested for thermoluminescence. If none is visible, then the artefact is likely to be a modern forgery. However, some forgers are becoming very cunning and are irradiating their forgeries to produce artificial thermoluminescence.

In 1986 the unfortunate inhabitants of Chernobyl, in the Ukraine, were subjected to large doses of radiation when the local nuclear power station underwent meltdown. Everything, including the people, was exposed to large doses of radiation, and today they are experiencing many of the familiar symptoms of radioactive poisoning including a far higher than expected rate of childhood thyroid cancers. The effects of those dangerous levels of radioactivity are left etched in local tiles and bricks. The degree of thermoluminescence from these powdered and heated bricks and tiles gives an accurate measure of the radiation dose in the area at the time of the accident. This knowledge in turn will give more information about the immediate and long-term effects of radiation on the local people and their descendants.

4 Reconstruction

4.1 Putting the pieces together

An archaeologist collects and uses diverse pieces of evidence that provide information about a site – these might include survey results, physical objects (from walls to minute fragments of bone or pottery), and written historical evidence. These then need to be pieced together to construct a coherent and self-consistent story.

Rather in a similar way, this unit has contributed several pieces to your study of physics, some of which need to be brought together with things you have learned, or will be learning, in other units. In Activity 33, you will bring together some pieces from separate parts of *this* unit.

ACTIVITY **33** **Putting the pieces together**

You learned something about each of the following in at least two parts of this unit. Look back through your work and make brief notes under each heading, listing the examples that were used in different parts of the unit and noting any ways in which the ideas were developed or refined. You could also add cross-references to other units where you have studied these same areas.

- Dc circuits: resistance, resistivity, potential difference, potential divider, charge and energy

- Waves: electromagnetic spectrum, diffraction, superposition

- Models of solids: electrons in conductors, semiconductors and insulators

- Logarithmic scales

4.2 *Questions on the whole unit*

QUESTIONS

27 Scientists planned to use a length of steel wire, 12.35 m long, diameter 1.0 mm, stretched between two rocks either side of a geological fault line to detect small changes in movement of the Earth. As the fault moved, the wire would extend and its resistance change.

(**a**) The resistivity of the wire chosen was $1.5 \times 10^{-8} \, \Omega \, \text{m}$. Calculate the resistance of the length of wire used.

(**b**) The scientists were interested in changes in length greater than 5%. For such a change:

(**i**) What would be the new length of the stretched wire?
(**ii**) What would its new resistance be?

(**c**) In practice the 'noise' inherent in the experiment prevented meaningful results. Suggest what might be the cause of 'noise' in this case.

28 Some electronic devices need connections to −4.5 V, 0 V and +4.5 V. To achieve this, they are operated from so-called *split rail supplies*. Figure 49 shows how a 9 V battery can be used for such a supply.

(**a**) (**i**) Match the labels −4.5 V, 0 V and +4.5 V to the points A, B and C.

(**ii**) What name is given to this type of arrangement of resistors and battery?

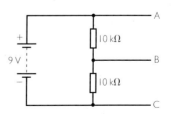

Figure 49 *A 9 V battery is used to provide a split rail supply*

(b) To check that the 25 kV overhead supply has been disconnected before starting work, railway engineers use a device consisting of a probe of resistance R_p and a voltage detector of resistance R_d. One end of the device is hooked on to the power line and the other end attached to Earth (usually the rail). See Figure 50. If the 25 kV supply is left on, then the detector registers a voltage of 25 V.

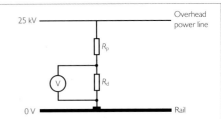

Figure 50 *A device for checking overhead power lines*

(i) If the resistance of the whole arrangement is 39 MΩ, what are the resistances of the detector, R_d, and the probe, R_p?

(ii) If there was poor contact with the rail or overhead cable (e.g. due to rust), explain the effect this would have on the voltage across the detector.

29 Figure 51 shows a *scintillation counter*, which is used to detect nuclear radiations. The *scintillator* is a material that gives out light when exposed to alpha, beta or gamma radiation. The light is incident on the *photocathode* of a photomultiplier, releasing photoelectrons. These electrons are accelerated and hit a surface called a *dynode*, from which they produce more electrons. The process continues through an array of dynodes and results in a large burst of electrons at the collector.

(a) One particular scintillator emits light with a wavelength of 413 nm. What is the energy of one photon of this radiation?

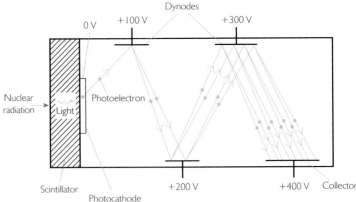

(b) If this photon is incident on a *photocathode* with a work function 1.2×10^{-19} J, what is the highest kinetic energy that the resulting photoelectron could have?

(c) In being accelerated from the photocathode to the first *dynode*, the electron passes through a potential difference of +100 V. What is the electron's kinetic energy when it reaches the dynode?

Figure 51 *A scintillation counter*

30 This poem was printed in *Punch* magazine in January 1896. Write a paragraph explaining what it is about.

> O Röntgen, then the news is true,
>   And not a trick of idle rumour,
> That bids us each beware of you,
>   And of your grim and graveyard humour.

We do not want, like Dr Swift,
    To take our flesh off and to pose in,
Our bones, or show each little rift,
    And joint for you to poke your nose in.

We only crave to contemplate,
    Each other's usual full-dress photo,
Your worse than 'altogether' state,
    Of portraiture we bar in toto!

31 Recently it has been discovered that, if certain foods are irradiated to kill harmful bacteria, they then have a longer shelf-life. Many people are suspicious of irradiated food, feeling that there may be harmful changes caused by ionising radiation to which the food is exposed. Food that has been irradiated must therefore be clearly labelled so that people can choose whether to eat it. To check that foods have been correctly labelled, samples (particularly of herbs and spices) are sometimes sent for thermoluminescent testing.

Write a short essay explaining how thermoluminescence could be used to detect whether food had been irradiated. Given two samples of the same food, one of which had been irradiated and the other not, which one would you expect to show the greater amount of thermoluminescence?

4.3 *Achievements*

Now you have studied this unit you should be able to:

- recall and use the relationship $R = \rho l/A$, and derive and use related expressions (e.g. $R = l/\sigma A$) (1.2)*;

- express quantities with a very large range, e.g. resistivities of materials, using $\log_{10}$ of those quantities (1.2, 2.1);

- explain how the potential along a uniform current-carrying wire varies with the distance along it and how use can be made of this variation in a potential divider (1.3);

- explain qualitatively how the potential varies with distance in a non-uniform current-carrying wire or other medium (1.3);

- recall that waves can be diffracted and that substantial diffraction occurs when the size of the gap or obstacle is comparable with the wavelength of the radiation (2.3);

- show an awareness of the existence and origin of background radiation, past and present (3.3);

- recognise nuclear radiations (alpha, beta and gamma) from their penetrating power and ionising ability (3.3);

- recall and use the fact that the amount of light emitted in thermoluminescence depends on the number of electrons trapped in 'defect energy levels' and hence on the nuclear radiation to which the material has been exposed (3.2, 3.3);

- recognise and use the expression $E = hf$ to calculate the highest frequency of radiation that could be emitted in a transition across a known energy band gap or between known energy levels (3.2);

- recall that the absorption of a photon can result in the emission of a photoelectron (3.4);

- understand and use the terms *threshold frequency* and *work function* and recognise and use the expression $hf = \phi + \frac{1}{2}mv_{max}^2$ (3.4);

- use the slope and intercept of a graph of a relationship of the form $y = mx + c$ to analyse a physical situation (3.4).

* Numbers indicate the section(s) that relate to each achievement.

Answers

1   A metre length would be five times longer, so its resistance is $5 \times 40\,\Omega$. This assumes that the cable cross-section is uniform throughout and so resistance is proportional to length.

2   The separation of 5 m is ten times greater, so you would expect a resistance about ten times greater, i.e. about $3000\,\Omega$. A 5 m separation would not detect small-scale structures such as a 1 m wide door opening, or a 0.5 m wall.

3 (a) If the length is doubled, then the area of cross-section is halved (to keep the same volume). On its own, doubling the length doubles the resistance, so does halving the area; both of these together multiply the resistance by four. $4 \times 48\,\Omega = 192\,\Omega$.

  (b) $\ell = 10\,\text{cm} = 0.1\,\text{m}$ and $A = 1\,\text{cm}^2 = (1 \times 10^{-2}\,\text{m})^2 = 1 \times 10^{-4}\,\text{m}^2$. Using equation (4):

$$\rho = \frac{RA}{\ell} = \frac{48\,\Omega \times 1.0 \times 10^{-4}\,\text{m}^2}{0.1\,\text{m}} = 4.8 \times 10^{-2}\,\Omega\,\text{m}$$

4   Combining equations (4) and (5):

$$R = \frac{\ell}{\sigma A}$$

5   The salty ditch was about 5 m from the gate (the resistance is lowest there) and the wall about 9 to 10 m from the gate where the resistance is highest.

6   On this scale, 1 cm represents $10^{-5}\,\Omega\,\text{m}$. $1.0 \times 10^{12} = 1.0 \times 10^{17} \times 10^{-5}$ so the bar for glass would be 1.0×10^{17} cm long (1.7×10^{15} m).

$1.7 \times 10^{-8} = 1.7 \times 10^{-3} \times 10^{-5}$, so the bar for copper would be 1.7×10^{-3} cm long (1.7×10^{-5} m).

The shortest bar would be too small to see, while the longest would not fit on the Earth (in fact, it would extend beyond the limits of the Solar System).

7 (a) (i) 4 V   (ii) 6 V   (iii) 4.8 V

  (b) (i) +8 V   (ii) +9 V   (iii) +7.2 V.

8 (a) The wire will get longer and thinner, and on both counts the resistance will increase.

  (b) If the length increases by 10%, then the area must decrease by 10% to keep the volume constant.

If $R_{\text{original}} = \dfrac{\rho\ell}{A}$

then $R_{\text{stretched}} = \dfrac{\rho(1.1\ell)}{(A \div 1.1)} = R_{\text{original}} \times (1.1)^2$

$$= 1.21\,R_{\text{original}}$$

i.e. the resistance increases by 21%.

  (c) Using equation (4):

$$R = \frac{\rho\ell}{A} = \frac{2.6 \times 10^{-6}\,\Omega\,\text{m} \times 28 \times 10^{-2}\,\text{m}}{0.6 \times 10^{-3}\,\text{m} \times 0.002 \times 10^{-3}\,\text{m}} = 606\,\Omega$$

  (d) See Figure 52. The pd across the fixed resistor is four times that across the gauge, so its resistance must be $4 \times 606\,\Omega = 2424\,\Omega$.

Figure 52   *Diagram for the answer to question 8*

9   The term 'shadow radiograph' is appropriate because the photographic film has a shadow cast upon it of the more dense parts of the object being X-rayed. The X-rays pass through the less dense materials and are absorbed by the more dense ones such as metals or bones. Thus the film is blackened except where the X-rays were prevented from getting to it. These shadow areas remain white on the film.

10   X-ray tomography is a technique whereby an image of a 'slice' of the body is acquired by blurring out the unwanted shadows below and above the plane of interest. A conventional X-ray image is a single 'shadow' produced by the transmission of X-rays through the thickness of the body and thus may result in certain elements being 'hidden' by those in front

11   There was concern that the CAT (computer-aided tomography) scanner might not give satisfactory images because the machine was calibrated for objects of the density of the human body. The helmet, being made of metal, had a density beyond the scope of the scanner. (The effect was to give images with less definition than might be required.)

12   The use of horizontal and vertical radiographs allowed the position of items within the helmet to be pinpointed as it provided two coordinates by which the position of the item was defined – much as two coordinates define the position of a point on a graph (see Figure 53).

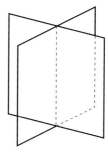

Figure 53   *Crossed 'slices' pinpoint location*

13 The high-performance industrial radiography of the helmet gave conservators information on the technology involved in the helmet's construction, while microfocus radiography of the chainmail provided information on its construction.

14 The typical width of a doorway is 1 m, which is comparable with the wavelength of sound. Thus the sound wave can be diffracted and spread out into the room. The wavelength of light is much much smaller, so the beam of light is not diffracted.

15 Fe_3O_4

16 E is the energy lost by the electron, and hence the energy of the photon that is emitted; it has SI units of joules (J). h is Planck's constant, and has SI units of joule seconds (J s). Equation (8) refers to two different ways of describing the light that is emitted. f is the frequency of the electromagnetic waves, and has SI units of hertz (Hz). $1\,Hz = 1\,s^{-1}$.

17 (a) Photon energy $E = (2.416 - 1.360) \times 10^{-19}\,J$
$$= 1.056 \times 10^{-19}\,J.$$

Frequency $f = \dfrac{E}{h} = \dfrac{1.056 \times 10^{-19}\,J}{6.63 \times 10^{-36}\,J s}$
$$= 1.593 \times 10^{14}\,Hz.$$

(b) The energy difference between levels 3 and 2 is greater than that between levels 4 and 3, so the emitted radiation will have a higher frequency.

18 (a) Adding up all the numbers in the table, and adding an extra 0.17 Gy, gives the total dose in 1000 years as 5.18 Gy.

(b) In 500 years, the dose will be $5.18\,J\,kg^{-1} \div 2 = 2.59\,J\,kg^{-1}$. The energy absorbed in this time by 10 g (0.010 kg) is therefore 0.0259 J.

19 (a) Energy transferred $= 5000\,eV$
$$= 5000 \times 1.60 \times 10^{-19}\,J$$
$$= 8.00 \times 10^{-16}\,J.$$

(b) The answers are the same as (a), because the same amount of charge has been accelerated through the same pd.

20 Rearranging equation (10b):

$$v = \sqrt{\frac{2E_k}{m}}$$

To be sure of getting speeds in $m\,s^{-1}$, you need to express the energies in joules, not eV.

Electron:

$$v = \sqrt{\frac{2E_k}{m_e}} = \sqrt{\left(\frac{2 \times 8.00 \times 10^{-16}\,J}{9.1 \times 10^{-31}\,kg}\right)}$$
$$= 4.19 \times 10^7\,m\,s^{-1}$$

Proton:

$$v = \sqrt{\frac{2E_k}{m_p}} = \sqrt{\left(\frac{2 \times 8.00 \times 10^{-16}\,J}{1.67 \times 10^{-27}\,kg}\right)}$$
$$= 9.79 \times 10^5\,m\,s^{-1}$$

21 Probably not all the photons will have enough energy to release a photoelectron.

22 Energy $= 100\,eV = 100 \times 1.60 \times 10^{-19}\,J$
$$= 1.60 \times 10^{-17}\,J.$$

23 The release of each electron requires 25 eV and so this must be the work function of the material. (In fact, most metals have work functions of only a few eV, and the material used in a dynode will probably be chosen so that it has a small work function, so the assumption of zero kinetic energy on release is almost certainly not valid.)

24 At each stage, the number of electrons increases by a factor 4, i.e. after one stage there are 4 electrons, after two stages there are 4×4, after three stages there are $4 \times 4 \times 4 = 4^3$, and so on. After 10 stages there are 4^{10} electrons, and $4^{10} \approx 10^6$ so the statement is correct.

Maths reference

Manipulating powers on a calculator
See Maths note 1.4

25 $6.5 \times 10^{-11}\,A = 6.5 \times 10^{-11}\,C\,s^{-1}$

No. of electrons per second $= \dfrac{6.5 \times 10^{-11}\,C\,s^{-1}}{1.60 \times 10^{-19}\,C}$
$$\approx 4 \times 10^8\,s^{-1}.$$

26 We assume that the two samples are affected in the same way by radiation, and that the number of electrons in a defect level is proportional to the radiation dose. If both were the same age, then A would produce twice as many photons as B when heated, and hence the photomultiplier current would also be twice that due to B. To make the currents equal, then A would need to be half as old as B. For A to produce only one-third the current, its age must be one-sixth that of B.

GOOD ENOUGH
TO EAT

Figure 1 *Confectionery products*

Why a unit called Good Enough to Eat?

Everyone has to eat and, for the most part, we enjoy the taste and textures of food as well as the social aspects of eating. Foods have to be manufactured and packaged so that they can be transported and stored safely and affordably, and labelled so that we know what we are eating.

The food production industry is enormous. In 1997, Nestlé, the world's largest food, drink and confectionery producer, was making over eight and a half thousand different products (Figure 1) to be sold in more than a hundred countries, and employing over two hundred thousand people directly. In the first six months of 1997 Nestlé's sales amounted to £18 thousand million.

Physicists have a part to play in most stages of food production. Physics principles are used to assess the raw materials' quality and condition. Ingredients must be weighed and mixed and brought together to form a homogeneous mass at a specified temperature. Food manufacture often involves the product flowing along pipes, being pushed through orifices or shaped in moulds, each of which is affected by the physical properties of the materials. The product must be tested to check that it has the desired properties. Finally the product needs to be packaged for safe storage and distribution, and so the physical nature of the packaging is important. Labelling, date stamping and detecting contaminants during processing all involve important elements of physics.

In this unit you will see how physics principles are used in the confectionery industry – in particular, the manufacture of biscuits and chocolates.

Overview of physics principles and techniques

In this unit you will see how the flow properties of liquids are affected by concentration and temperature, and how they can be measured or compared. Next you will see how to use light to measure the sugar content of raw materials, and so learn about refraction and polarisation of light. Products need to be tested (for example, to ensure that a biscuit provides a suitable 'crunch'), and in this part of the unit you will learn about materials testing and such factors as hardness, brittleness and toughness. Material properties feature again in the final part of the unit, on packaging, where you will also see how physics relates to aspects of health and safety.

During the course of this unit you will learn about instrumentation and calibration, and be introduced to some important techniques and measuring instruments; you will learn how to read a vernier scale, and how to use a micrometer screw gauge.

In this unit you will extend your knowledge of

- the behaviour of light from *The Sound of Music*;
- forces and motion and using graphs from *Higher, Faster, Stronger*.

In other units you will do more work on

- forces and motion in *Transport on Track*;

- refraction and reflection in *Spare Part Surgery* and *Build or Bust?*;

- polarisation of light in *The Medium is the Message*;

- bulk properties of materials in *Spare Part Surgery* and *Build or Bust?*.

⬛ *Physics in the food industry*

Stephen Beckett is a professional physicist working at the Nestlé Research and Development Centre in York. Here he provides an introduction to the place of physics in the food and confectionery industry.

1.1 Physics in the food and confectionery industry

Chocolate making, and indeed the food industry as a whole, is not at first sight an obvious place to need physics. Yet closer inspection shows that the industry needs and uses physics to an ever-increasing degree. Not only is food manufacture the UK's biggest industry, but it is also one that is currently in the middle of big changes from an essentially craft-based industry to a highly automated one requiring critical control. This makes the challenge and the opportunity for physicists even greater.

Food has the advantage over many industrial products in that if it is processed well, and to the customer's liking, then a repeat purchase is likely in the very short term, unlike other industries whose products may last for many years. It does however have an extra challenge in that the products must be absolutely safe to eat and obey the food laws. You cannot for instance help chocolate to melt in the mouth by something that tastes nasty or, even worse, makes the consumer ill. It is always worth remembering that food is bought because of how it looks and tastes, not because of the clever science that has been used to make it. Science can, however, help to manipulate the taste and texture of a product, ensure that it is relatively consistent from day to day (not an easy task when your raw ingredients are always varying) and indeed help to ensure a product's safety.

In addition, science can help to make the industry more efficient by optimising processing and other factors like extending shelf-life so that a product can be made all the year round, rather than having operators and expensive machinery employed only for a few weeks.

Further research
When a box of chocolate assortments becomes old, the centres containing nuts are usually the first ones to turn a white colour. This is known as 'bloom' and is when the fat from the sweet comes to the surface and sets there.

The reason why it is worse in the nut sweets is because the nuts contain a fat, which is mainly liquid at room temperature, whereas most of the fat within chocolate (cocoa butter) is solid. The soft nut fat reacts with the cocoa butter and softens it and also migrates through the sweet to the surface. In order to obtain more information about this process, magnetic resonance imaging (as used in body scanners) has been used at the University of Cambridge to monitor the changes in the position of the nut fat taking place within the sweets.

So, every time you buy a KitKat, Mars Bar or Crunchie it has been produced with the aid of physics. The chocolate industry, however, still has a lot of physics that remains to be done. Not only is a simple method required to detect plastic in chocolate, but other problems remain, such as the measurement of the three-dimensional contraction of chocolate as it sets in the mould, or of its stickiness as it melts in the hand. Perhaps you have the solution!

Stephen Beckett has written further comments to accompany some other sections as you progress through the unit.

ACTIVITY I **Food web**

Use the Internet to find some more background information about the food industry. If you want to find out more about the variety of food products, or if you are wondering whether your future might be in this field of employment, use the *Search* facility on your web browser to look up some famous names. Some relevant sites are listed below.

Oregon State University in the USA provides a food resource index that might prove useful. It is at

http://www.orst.edu/food-resource/index.html

If you would like to find out more about Nestlé, then go to their Japan website, which gives you an insight into the company, its research, products, sales, staffing and history:

http://www.nestle.co.jp/japan/index-e.htm

The Cadbury's website provides details of the company history and the history of chocolate:

http://www.cadbury.co.uk

If you have a particular interest in chocolate, then visit the Cadbury's page (Figure 2), which provides information on the history of chocolate and details of the production process:

Click first on 'Chocolate Encyclopaedia' and then on 'The production process'.

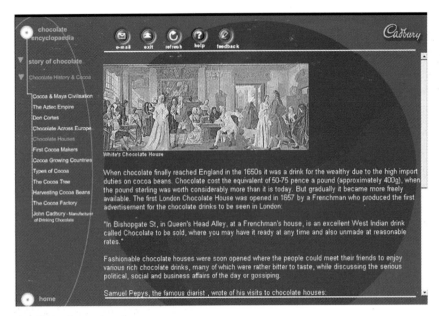

Figure 2 *Cadbury's web page*

2 *Going with the flow*

In many industrial processes it is essential to get liquids flowing at speeds to match the needs of the process. In the manufacture of chocolates or chocolate biscuits, the chocolate needs to flow at a rate that allows the correct thickness to be placed on a biscuit or soft centre, or to fill a mould, and to keep up the required rate of production. The description, understanding, measurement and control of the flow all involve physics.

2.1 *Flowing chocolate*

ACTIVITY 2 **Flowing chocolate**

Read the following short article in which Stephen Beckett describes aspects of chocolate manufacture. Then make notes on how physics is, or might be, used in the circumstances that he mentions. Expand on any points you can, suggesting techniques and equipment that might be used for sensing, testing or control.

Chocolate differs from most other foods in that it is solid at room temperature and yet easily melts in the mouth. This is because the fat it contains has a melting point below that of blood temperature. In confectionery manufacture, chocolate is produced as a liquid to pour into moulds, or to pour over (enrobe) a sweet centre, before being cooled to enable the fat to set (Figure 3). Incorrect flow properties will result in a poor-quality product. This may take the form of mis-shapes (Figure 4), where the chocolate runs down the sweet but, instead of flowing through the open grid on which the sweet is enrobed, it sticks to it, forming a sort of foot.

Figure 3 *The enrobing process*

Figure 4 *Mis-shapen chocolates*

Figure 5 *Incorrect aeration of an Aero bar*

In aerated products, such as an Aero bar, the flow properties of the chocolate will affect the size of the air bubbles (Figure 5). Weight control also becomes difficult, with thick chocolate sticking on top of the centre and sides and making it overweight. Too thin a chocolate may run off the centre altogether, allowing it to pick up or lose moisture and hence be more likely to deteriorate.

The flow property of chocolate is in fact very complex. Only about one-third is made up of fat which is capable of melting at moderate temperatures and helping chocolate to flow. The remainder consists of solid particles (sugar, cocoa and milk solids) that must be coated with fat for them to flow smoothly past one another when the chocolate is being processed or melted in the mouth. This high solids content makes the chocolate flow is what is known as a non-Newtonian manner. In other words its viscosity depends on how quickly it is moving. It is in fact a bit like tomato ketchup or non-drip paint, in that it becomes runnier when stirred or mixed quickly.

In addition, the more fine particles there are, the bigger is the surface to be coated by fat to enable it to flow and hence the thicker the chocolate becomes. Once again physics becomes important in that it is used to measure the size distribution of these solid particles. This is done by dispersing the chocolate in a liquid and then shining a laser through the dispersion. The distribution can be calculated from the relative intensity of the light scattered at different angles.

2.2 *Viscosity*

How fast liquids flow is partly dependent on their **viscosity**, a factor controlling their resistance to flow. Loosely speaking, the lower the viscosity of a fluid (a liquid or gas), the 'runnier' it is. Tar and treacle are very **viscous**, while water has low viscosity. Devices for comparing and measuring viscosity are called **viscometers**.

Comparing viscosities

One of the simplest tests for comparing viscosities is known as the line spread test and uses a device known as a consistometer (Figure 6). A fixed quantity of liquid is allowed to flow out of a container and spread out on a flat surface. How far or fast it spreads provides a measure of its viscosity. Another instrument, the Redwood viscometer (Figure 7), involves allowing the liquid to flow through a narrow tube driven by its own head of pressure. (This instrument was first developed by French physiologist and physicist Jean Léonard Poiseuille (1799–1869), who used it to study blood flow.) Both these tests are used in the food industry.

| ACTIVITY **3** | **Comparing viscosities** |

Use a model line spread test and Redwood viscometer to compare the viscosities of sugar solutions, syrups and honeys. Rank your samples in order of increasing viscosity. Comment on the reliability and ease of use of the two techniques.

Defining viscosity

The line spread and Redwood tests are useful for comparing the behaviour of fluids, but they do not give an absolute measurement of viscosity. For this we can use a falling ball viscometer. This instrument, developed by Irish physicist George Gabriel Stokes (1819–1903), involves timing a ball falling at constant speed through a fluid. The instrument has been adapted for use in the chocolate industry; as chocolate is opaque, a rod is attached to the ball so that its movement can be monitored (Figure 8).

Figure 6   *A consistometer used to perform a line spread test*

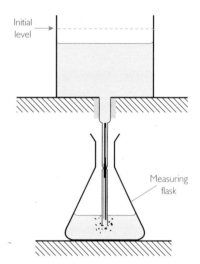

Figure 7   *Redwood viscometer*

Figure 8   *Chocolate falling ball viscometer*

Stokes was able to quantify viscosity by studying the force exerted on a spherical object as it moves through a fluid, or when a fluid flows past it. (There is an equivalence between a ball-bearing moving through a still fluid and a fluid moving past a stationary ball-bearing.) This **viscous drag** force is described by the relationship known as **Stokes' law**:

$$F = 6\pi r \eta v \qquad (1)$$

where r is the radius of the sphere, v the velocity of the fluid relative to the sphere and η the **coefficient of viscosity** of the fluid (or, commonly, just 'the viscosity'). The direction of the force is opposite to that of the velocity. Equation (1) can be rearranged to get an expression for η:

$$\eta = \frac{F}{6\pi r v} \qquad (1a)$$

From this we can see that the SI units of η are $\mathrm{N\,s\,m^{-2}}$. To give you an idea of typical values, the viscosity of water at 20 °C is $1.000 \times 10^{-3}\,\mathrm{N\,s\,m^{-2}}$ and that of air at 27 °C and a pressure of 1 atmosphere is $18.325 \times 10^{-6}\,\mathrm{N\,s\,m^{-2}}$. (Note that the temperatures are quoted – the viscosities of most fluids are highly dependent on temperature.)

Maths reference

Manipulating units
See Maths note 2.2

Archimedes in the balance

Figure 9 shows the forces acting on a sphere falling through a fluid. The sphere's weight acts downwards, and in addition to the viscous drag force there is another upwards force: the **upthrust** or **buoyancy force**. This force always acts on a object immersed in a fluid, and arises because the object displaces some of the fluid around it. When getting in to or out of a bath or swimming pool we feel lighter or heavier, and so become aware of the upthrust provided by the water. A similar force acts in air, too, and the weight we measure on bathroom scales is very slightly less than it would be in a vacuum. Indeed anything that is completely or partially immersed in a fluid will experience an upthrust or buoyancy force, be it a skydiver, a ship or a falling ball-bearing.

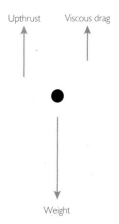

Figure 9 *Forces on a falling ball*

ACTIVITY 4 **Archimedes' principle**

Demonstrate Archimedes' principle by weighing an object in air and immersed in water.

The size of the upthrust is described by **Archimedes' principle**: 'When a body is partially or totally immersed in a fluid, the upthrust is equal to the weight of the fluid it displaces.'

Legend has it that Archimedes (*c.* 287–212 BC) discovered this whilst in his bathtub and then ran through the streets of Syracuse in Sicily where he lived shouting 'Eureka' (meaning 'I found it'). He was at the time trying to develop a method of checking that the King's crown really was made of pure gold as the maker had claimed.

A simple way of looking at upthrust is to consider a floating object. Its weight must still be acting downwards but, with an upthrust provided upwards, the forces are in equilibrium and the object remains at rest. Now think of an object fully immersed in fluid. If the upthrust exceeds the weight, there will be a net upward force, which will push the object upwards until it is only partially immersed and displaces exactly its own weight of fluid. If, on the other hand, the upthrust on the fully immersed object is less than the object's weight, there is a net downward force and so the object sinks.

When an object falls through a fluid, it first accelerates due to the net downward force (weight minus upthrust). But it also experiences a viscous drag force that increases with speed, so the net downward force is reduced as speed increases. When the net force reaches zero, the object can no longer accelerate and it falls with a constant downward velocity called its **terminal velocity**.

Questions 1 to 4 take you through some calculations of forces involved in a falling ball viscometer.

QUESTIONS

These questions refer to a ball-bearing of radius $r = 1.0 \times 10^{-3}$ m, made of steel with a density $\rho_{steel} = 7.8 \times 10^3$ kg m^{-3}, falling through oil with density $\rho_{oil} = 920$ kg m^{-3} and viscosity $\eta = 8.4 \times 10^{-2}$ N s m^{-2}.

The gravitational field strength, g, is 9.8 N kg^{-1}.

A sphere with radius r has volume $V = \dfrac{4\pi r^3}{3}$

1 Assuming that Stokes' law applies, calculate the viscous drag on the ball-bearing when it is travelling through the oil at a speed of 2.0×10^{-2} m s^{-1}.

2 Calculate (**a**) the volume of the ball-bearing, (**b**) its mass and (**c**) its weight.

3 When the ball-bearing is immersed in the oil, what are (**a**) the volume, (**b**) the mass and (**c**) the weight of the oil that it displaces?

4 Using your answers to questions 1 to 3: (**a**) state the size of the upthrust acting on the ball-bearing and hence (**b**) calculate the size and direction of the net force acting on the ball-bearing.

Measuring viscosity

In a falling ball viscometer, the ball-bearing is selected so that it reaches its terminal velocity after travelling only a short distance through the fluid.

Referring back to questions 1 to 4, we can then write down an expression for the forces acting on the ball-bearing, which must combine to give a resultant force of zero – in other words, the magnitudes of the forces must be related as follows:

upthrust + viscous drag = weight

or, in symbols:

$$\frac{4\pi r^3 \rho_{\text{fluid}}}{3} g + 6\pi r\eta v = \frac{4\pi r^3 \rho_{\text{steel}}}{3} g \qquad (2)$$

ACTIVITY 5 **Measuring viscosity**

Use a falling ball viscometer to determine the viscosity of honey or syrup at a particular temperature. Plan your experiment carefully and decide how best to analyse your measurements, taking account of any experimental uncertainties.

By comparing results with other students who have used different temperatures, explore the relationship between viscosity and temperature.

Calibration

A falling ball viscometer allows us to measure viscosities of fluids fairly directly. Once this has been done, then fluids of known viscosity can be used to **calibrate** other viscometers – that is, to establish a relationship between the performance of a particular viscometer and the actual viscosity of any fluids used. For example, your results from Activity 5 could be used to calibrate the consistometer or the Redwood viscometer that you used earlier; you could relate the flow of a fluid in a given time to its viscosity.

Figure 10 shows another type of viscometer popular in the food industry – the viscous drag viscometer. Here the liquid under test is contained within the outer cylinder, which is rotated at constant speed. As a result of the viscous properties of the liquid, this drags the inner cylinder round against the force of the spring S, moving a pointer over a scale. The position of the pointer indicates the liquid's viscosity, but there is not a simple relationship between the movement of the pointer and the viscosity of the liquid with the viscous drag viscometer.

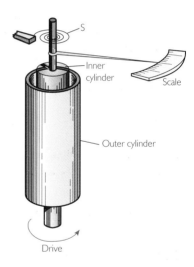

Figure 10   *A viscous drag viscometer*

ACTIVITY 6 **Calibration**

Discuss how you would go about calibrating a viscous drag viscometer. Suggest a value for the viscosity of the liquid which moved the pointer to the position shown in Figure 11.

QUESTIONS

5 If you were provided with a forcemeter, a measuring cylinder, some water, a piece of cotton and an object that could be immersed in the measuring cylinder, outline how you could check Archimedes' principle. (You will need to know that $g \approx 10\,\text{N}\,\text{kg}^{-1}$ and that the density of water is $1000\,\text{kg}\,\text{m}^{-3}$.)

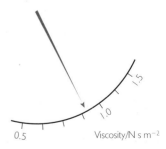

Figure 11   *Pointer on scale*

6 The pressure P at a depth h within a fluid is given by $P = h\rho g$, where ρ is the fluid's density and g is the gravitational field strength. By considering the pressures at the top and bottom surfaces of the rectangular object of area A shown in Figure 12, show that the upthrust must be equal to the weight of the fluid displaced.

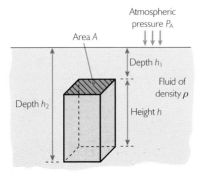

Atmospheric pressure P_A

Area A

Depth h_1

Fluid of density ρ

Depth h_2

Height h

Figure 12 *Rectangular block immersed in fluid*

7 Suppose that, when Archimedes compared the weight of the King's crown immersed in water with the same crown in air, the ratio came to 0.948. If the density of gold is 19.3 times that of water, was the crown solid gold?

8 Some motor oils are labelled 'viscostatic'. What behaviour might you expect these oils to have over a wide range of temperatures?

2.3 *More about flow*

Laminar/streamlined flow or turbulence?

Stokes' law relies on the flow of the liquid past the ball-bearing being streamlined or laminar and not turbulent. In **streamlined** or **laminar** flow the fluid does not make an abrupt change in direction or speed and adjacent layers within the fluid only mix on a molecular scale – the word 'laminar' means 'layered'. With **turbulent** flow there is a lot of mixing and a series of eddies (little whirlpools) are produced along the object's path. See Figure 13.

Turbulence is the unsteadiness that we observe with smoke billowing away from bonfires, the flapping of sails on yachts and of a flag on a flagpole, or the buffeting that one occasionally feels on an aeroplane. Turbulence gives rise to heating as energy is transferred to the fluid; this is usually unwanted and reduces the efficiency of a process.

Laminar or streamlined flow is what one hopes for around a vehicle as it lessens the fuel consumption. Similarly a professional speed skier will purchase clothing and adopt a posture that aims to achieve streamlined flow of air past the body and so allow him to go faster. Likewise less energy will be needed to move fluids in a factory if turbulence is avoided. The flow of chocolate on to centres needs to be as laminar as possible in order to produce a fairly even coating without air bubbles.

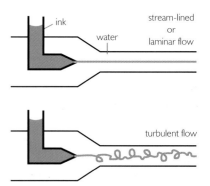

ink

water

stream-lined or laminar flow

turbulent flow

Figure 13 *Streamlined and turbulent flow patterns*

ACTIVITY 7 **Laminar and turbulent flow**

In this short activity you will be able to see the difference between laminar and turbulent flow.

Connect a piece of transparent plastic tubing to a laboratory water tap and arrange for a length of it to be horizontal before going into a sink. Fill a syringe with ink and pass the syringe needle into the tube just where it becomes horizontal. Turn the tap on slowly and squeeze some ink into the tube.

Compare, and comment on, the pattern of movement of the ink as the flow of the water is increased from slow to fast.

Thixotropy

A number of foods display the interesting property of thixotropy. Margarine in its container at normal temperatures will not flow. However, on exerting a force with a knife in order to spread it, the margarine's viscosity lessens and it flows. When that force is removed, the margarine's viscosity rises again and it acts like a solid on the bread. This behaviour identifies it as a thixotropic material. Similar effects are to be seen with chocolate spread, tomato ketchup and mayonnaise (Figure 14).

Figure 14 *Some thixotropic foods*

ACTIVITY 8 **Stirring custard**

In this activity you will be able to observe behaviour known as negative thixotropy.

Put two heaped teaspoonfuls of custard powder into a cup. Mix in up to two teaspoonfuls of water until, when the custard is stirred slowly, it is just runny. Now stir quickly and note what happens.

Further investigations

If you let honey or syrup pour from a spoon or jar it forms a small hill with a few spirals at the summit as shown in Figure 15. Might this perhaps provide a means of determining viscosity? What variables might be worth investigating?

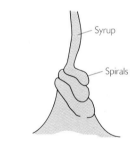

Syrup

Spirals

Figure 15 *Syrup hill*

2.4 *Measuring flow rates*

The measuring of flow rates is vital in the confectionery industry if one is to maintain consistency of the product – the same thickness of chocolate on the sweet's centre or in the mould for a chocolate rabbit or Easter egg (Figure 16). One way to do this would be to divert some of the fluid into a container and measure the mass or volume collected in a given time interval and hence determine the **mass flow rate** (the mass per unit time) or **volume flow rate** (the volume per unit time). However, this would interrupt the process, and it is preferable to use a flowmeter that can be left in position all the time.

Figure 16 *Chocolate moulds*

The light-gate flowmeter

One simple type of flowmeter is the light-gate flowmeter. When conducting experiments with dynamics trolleys you will probably have used light-gates to time the movement of a known length of card past a fixed point. The light-gate consists of a source of light (a bulb or a light-emitting diode (LED)), shining on to a photodiode. When the beam is interrupted, the change of illumination triggers an electronic timer, which is stopped when the illumination is restored.

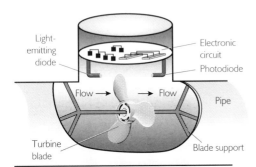

Figure 17 *Cutaway of light-gate flowmeter*

The same principle can be used in a flowmeter (Figure 17). Here, a rotating propeller blade, driven by the flowing liquid, repeatedly interrupts the illumination. The meter registers the frequency of interruptions, i.e. the number of 'darkenings' per second. To be useful, such a meter first has to be calibrated using known flow rates. When this has been done, a calibration certificate is attached to the instrument (see Figure 18).

You will calibrate a flowmeter in Activity 9. The following worked example and questions 9 and 10 illustrate what is involved.

While frequency can be measured directly on a frequency meter, you will often need to calculate it from an oscilloscope screen trace as shown in Figure 19.

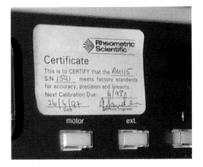

Figure 18 *Calibration certificate*

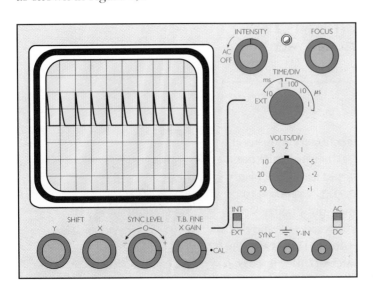

Figure 19 *Oscilloscope trace for the Worked example*

Worked example

Q Calculate the frequency of the output signal shown in Figure 19 if (a) the time-base setting was 10 ms/div and (b) 5.0 μs/div.

A The spacing between each repeated part of the trace is 1 division.

(a) With a time-base setting of 10 ms/div the time period of the signal is

$$T = 10\,\text{ms} = 10 \times 10^{-3}\,\text{s} = 1.0 \times 10^{-2}\,\text{s}.$$

Frequency $f = \dfrac{1}{T}$ so $f = \dfrac{1}{1.0 \times 10^{-2}\,\text{s}} = 100\,\text{Hz}.$

(b) With a time-base setting of 5.0 μs/div the time period is

$$T = 5.0\,\text{μs} = 5 \times 10^{-6}\,\text{s}$$

$$f = \frac{1}{T} = \frac{1}{5.0 \times 10^{-6}\,\text{s}} = 2.0 \times 10^{5}\,\text{Hz} = 200\,\text{kHz}.$$

Maths reference

SI prefixes
See Maths note 2.4

QUESTIONS

9 Calculate the frequency of the signal shown on the oscilloscope trace in Figure 20. The time-base setting was 10 ms/div.

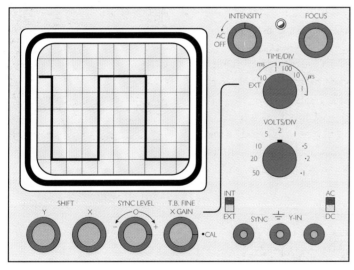

Figure 20 *Oscilloscope trace for question 9*

10 Figure 21 shows a calibration graph for an RS flowmeter.

(a) (i) When the output frequency was 400 Hz, what was the volume flow rate of the fluid (in litres per minute)?

(ii) If the fluid was water, with density 1 kg m^{-3}, what was the mass flow rate (in kilograms per second)?

(b) What would be the output frequency for a volume flow rate of 3 litres per minute?

(c) How would you describe the relationship between output frequency and flow rate for this particular flowmeter?

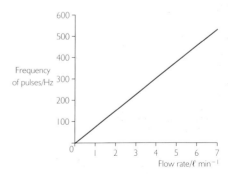

Figure 21 *Calibration graph from RS flow transducer*

ACTIVITY **9** **Calibrating a flowmeter**

Calibrate a light-gate flowmeter by investigating how its output frequency changes with volume flow rate. Compare your results with those shown in Figure 21.

Many types of flowmeter

Flowmeters are used widely in industry. For example, in the oil industry they monitor flow from oil fields to refineries or from storage depots into tankers; they measure milk flow from farms into collection tankers; and they are vital for process control in the brewing industry. If you visit any industry, look out for flowmeters in use.

There are many types of flowmeter, most of which make ingenious use of physics in their design. The names of some common types of meter give a clue to their diversity; there are the diaphragm meter, vortex meter, rotameter, hinged plate or gate meter, turbine meter, ultrasonic Doppler effect meter, Pitot tube, orifice meter, V-notch meter, and the electromagnetic meter, to mention but a few.

In Activity 10 you are asked to suggest an explanation of how one type of meter works. As an example, here is a description of a diaphragm meter, widely used to measure domestic gas consumption (Figures 22 and 23).

Figure 22 *Domestic gas meters*

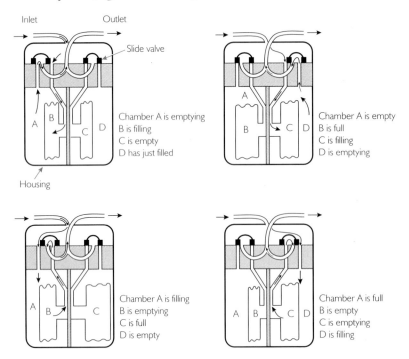

Figure 23 *Sequence of operations of a diaphragm meter*

As chamber B fills, the bellows expands and pushes gas out of A. With A empty, gas then flows into C and pushes out the gas already in D. Then gas flows back into A and pushes the gas out of B. Finally gas flows into D and pushes gas out of C. All of this is controlled by the slide valves shown in the diagrams. With the quantities of gas in each chamber known accurately, so the rate of flow can be calculated by knowing how many complete cycles of filling and emptying have been gone through each minute.

ACTIVITY 10 **How does it work?**

For either or both of the flowmeters shown in Figures 24 and 25, write a paragraph explaining how it works. Imagine you are writing for a book about how things work, suitable for readers about 15 years old who are studying science.

Study note

For Activity 10, you might find it useful to look back at the unit *Technology in Space*.

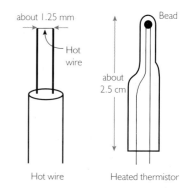

Figure 24   *A hot wire and hot thermistor flowmeter. The flow of fluid changes the temperature of the sensor*

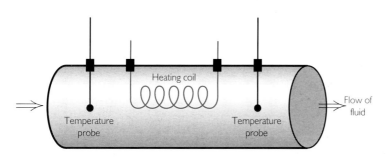

Figure 25   *Thermal flow meter. The heater warms the fluid*

2.5   *Controlling the flow*

Being able to measure rates of flow is not enough; their control is essential too. Mostly this is achieved using valves and pumps, but a rather more novel method is being considered at Michigan State University in the USA. In 1996 researchers in their Agricultural Engineering Department found molten chocolate to be an electro-rheological fluid, that is, one in which electric fields affect its viscous properties. The stronger the electric field, the more viscous the fluid. An extremely strong field can make the fluid solid.

An electric field is a region in which a charged object experiences a force. Electric fields are produced when objects become charged. You may have generated an electric field yourself by rubbing a comb on your clothes and seeing how it can then pick up small pieces of paper or make your hair stand up a little. More controllably, an electric field can be produced by connecting a potential difference between a pair of conducting plates.

The electro-rheological effect was first discovered in 1948. Since then a number of applications have been considered and developed. These include a clutch, for a motor vehicle in which the coupling between the engine, clutch and finally the wheels is controlled by the viscosity of the material in the clutch. The more viscous the fluid, the greater the coupling and the faster the vehicle will go. The viscosity is controlled by an electric field placed across the material.

┌─ QUESTION ──
│ **11** Suggest how you think electro-rheology might be used in the
│   making of a chocolate-coated product.
└──

2.6 Summing up part 2

This part of the unit should have given you some insight into the flow properties of materials and how they can be measured. Use Activities 11 ands 12, and questions 12 to 15, to check your progress and understanding.

ACTIVITY 11 **Summing up part 2**

Look back through your work and ensure that your notes include a clear definition, explanation or description of each of the terms printed in bold type.

ACTIVITY 12 **Going with the flow**

Draw a series of annotated sketches to illustrate the following:

(i) *very* viscous flow   (iv) streamlined flow
(ii) flow with little viscosity   (v) turbulent flow
(iii) a thixotropic material

In the cases of the first three, list some materials that would behave as described.

QUESTIONS

12 In a test of some motor oil, a ball-bearing of radius 0.5×10^{-3} m was dropped down the centre of a wide container of the oil and quickly reached a terminal velocity of $0.03 \, \mathrm{m \, s^{-1}}$.

(**a**) What is meant by *terminal velocity* and what can be said of the forces acting on the ball-bearing when it has reached its terminal velocity?

(**b**) Calculate the upthrust or buoyancy force on the ball-bearing. The density of this motor oil is $900 \, \mathrm{kg \, m^{-3}}$ at this temperature.

(**c**) Calculate the weight of the ball-bearing. The density of the steel from which it was made is $7860 \, \mathrm{kg \, m^{-3}}$ and g, the gravitational field strength, can be taken as $9.8 \, \mathrm{N \, kg^{-1}}$.

(**d**) The fall through the oil was such that Stokes' law could be applied. Calculate the viscosity η of the oil.

13 The data in Table 1 were collected from a flowmeter. Explain whether they indicate that output frequency is proportional to flow rate for this type of meter.

Mean output frequency/Hz	Mean flow rate/$\mathrm{l \, s^{-1}}$
12.5	0.15
13.9	0.17
16.0	0.20
18.9	0.23

Table 1   *Flowmeter data for question 13*

14 It is often more useful to measure mass flow rate than volume flow rate (for example, when charging customers for water or gas).
(**a**) Suggest a reason for this.
(**b**) Explain how mass flow rate can be calculated from volume flow rate.

15 Figure 26 shows a vortex-shedding flowmeter. When a non-streamlined obstruction is placed in a section of pipe, a series of vortices or eddies are produced non-symmetrically by the fluid flowing past. Mounted within the obstruction are two heated NTC thermistors, which are cooled by these eddies.

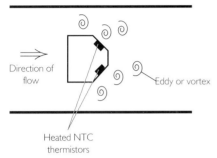

Figure 26 *Vortex-shedding flowmeter*

(**a**) How will the resistance of the thermistors change as each vortex goes past?

(**b**) Tables 2 and 3 show data collected for this type of meter for obstructions of diameters 10 mm and 5 mm.

Speed of flow/$m\,s^{-1}$	Time for 20 vortices to pass/s	Frequency of vortices/Hz
0.5	2.00	
1.0	0.95	
1.5	0.65	
2.0	0.48	
2.5	0.38	

Table 2 *Data for a vortex flowmeter: 10 mm obstruction*

Speed of flow/$m\,s^{-1}$	Time for 20 vortices to pass/s	Frequency of vortices/Hz
1.0	0.49	
1.5	0.32	
2.0	0.24	
2.5	0.19	

Table 3 *Data for a vortex flowmeter: 5 mm obstruction*

(**i**) Copy and complete the 'Frequency of vortices' column in each table.

(**ii**) What appears to be the relationship between the speed of flow and frequency of vortices for an obstruction of given size?

(**iii**) For any one speed of flow, what appears to be the relationship between the diameter of the obstruction and the frequency of the vortices?

(**c**) Suggest a problem that might occur with this type of meter if the vortex frequency became very high.

3 *Testing, testing…*

It is no use developing a product that no-one will buy. You are likely to try a new food or sweet just to see what it tastes like, and may purchase again if it is nice. But what makes a popular product, and how do manufacturers know this?

3.1 *Good enough to eat?*

What qualities do we look for in a chocolate, a biscuit or a sweet? The flavour is very important, and this will be determined by the chemical composition of the food. Another important factor is the texture, which, for some people, and especially young children, can make all the difference between liking and disliking the food.

Consider the texture of the food; when we put something in our mouth, a number of things can happen. To discuss this with others and explain what it is that we like or dislike, we need to be able to describe what happens so that others understand. We use a large number of words for this. A sweet manufacturer may employ tasting panels (Figure 27) to find out what the people like and dislike. Below, a member of a tasting panel talks about the need to agree on exactly what each word means.

Figure 27 *A tasting panel*

> The company has tasting panels to comment on texture, flavour and smell. When testing for flavour we have a number of reference flavours to compare with the test flavours, but we don't do that for texture. We were recruited through an advertisement in the local press and we spend one day a week testing. We did a lot of training and have regular retraining sessions. We have to discuss the product and come up with a description that we all agree with, although of course, no opinion is wrong and people do taste things very differently sometimes.
>
> When the panel formed we spent a long time defining different words. For example *chewy* means partly how much it sticks to your teeth – how flexible it is. Some sweets are *compact*, they go into a ball and move around your mouth more than others. *Brittle* means it breaks into shards, sharp edged pieces, easily and quickly when you bite it. *Crunchy* means it makes a noise when you chew it. A *sticky* sweet sticks to your teeth and leaves a residue. It might be *creamy* or *grainy* or something else – we have defined all these descriptions.
>
> When we do a profile for a product we start by saying what it looks like and what it feels like. Then we bite into it. Some products have a very different surface to the inside, so we comment on that, and on the initial bite. We time things like how long we suck before we bite, and how long the sweet lasts in the mouth. Finally we comment on the aftertaste.

Once tasters are experienced enough to give consistent descriptions, they can be employed in rating the attributes of various products. Frequently some 30 to 60 attributes will be judged on scales of 1–5, 1–7 or 1–9. These data are fed into a computer, which then constructs a star or spider diagram (Figure 28) to display the so-called sensory profile of the product.

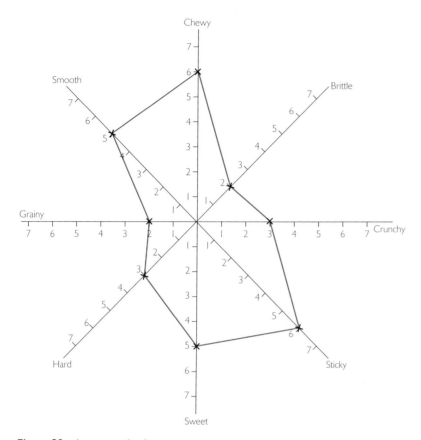

Figure 28   *A star or spider diagram*

ACTIVITY **13** **Describing food**

Make a list of the words you might use to describe the texture of some foods or confectionery. Combination products such as KitKat, Lion bar, Mars bar, Mint Crisp, Picnic and Snickers will give you opportunities to deal with a number of textures and tastes. Construct star/spider diagrams for your chosen products.

Human tasters give a subjective definition of what happens inside their mouth, described in words, with no measurement of how hard one has to chew to break a food. The taster speaking earlier does measure the time to suck a sweet, to melt it, and the time before it is soft enough to bite, but on the whole tasting panels are not concerned with measurement. However, research has been done to match sensory factors, such as chewiness, stickiness and hardness, to the muscle activity of the tester. Electrodes are attached to the tester (Figure 29), and the minute electrical signals are recorded as the product is eaten. These are then commented on.

Figure 29   *Recording electrical signals whilst eating*

The need for objective measurement arises when foods are to be produced on a large scale. The manufacturer must ensure that the product is always the same. You would be very surprised if you bought a food product one week and then the next week you bought the same product and found that the taste or texture was different. Is it possible to measure qualities like brittleness or chewiness? To describe behaviour quantitatively we need to be more definite about the meaning of the words, replacing verbal description with measurements. We must investigate and measure how the food responds to deformation, to force being applied to food.

Study note

The terms used to describe food are applied to other materials as well. You will meet them in the unit *Spare Part Surgery*.

3.2 *Hardness*

It is essential that sweets that are designed to be bitten can indeed be bitten without breaking your teeth – they must not be too **hard**. A hard material is one that is not readily scratched or indented. There is no absolute measure of hardness, but it is easy to rank samples in order of hardness according to whether they scratch, or can be scratched by, one another.

For minerals, an Austrian mineralogist Friedrich Mohs (1773–1839) devised the Mohs scale of hardness. He selected ten minerals and arranged them from the softest to the hardest. Talc (Figure 30) is 1 on the Mohs scale and diamond (Figure 31), the hardest known mineral, is 10. Any mineral will scratch all the minerals below it in the scale, and none of those above. The intervals on the Mohs scale are not regular; a fingernail has a hardness of about 2.5 and a copper coin has a hardness of about 3.5.

Figure 30 *Talc*

Figure 31 *Diamond*

ACTIVITY 14 **Sorting sweets**

Choose a variety of sweets and cut them so that each has a rough surface. Use a scratch test to put them in order of hardness, and record that order.

Another way to define hardness is to apply a known force to a surface and measure the indentation, but each test of this type defines its own scale. There is no such thing as *the* hardness of a material – the value is only defined for a particular test. One common test of this type is the Brinell hardness test in which a hardened steel ball is pressed into the surface of the material for 10 or 15 s, and the surface area of the indentation measured (Figure 32). A commercially made hardness-measuring machine is shown in Figure 33. You might see similar machines if you visit an industrial or research laboratory.

The Brinell hardness number (BHN) is defined as

BHN = mass of applied load in kg
          ÷ surface area of indentation in mm   (3)

The area of the curved surface can be calculated from the diameter, D, of the indenting ball and the diameter, d, of the indentation, which leads to

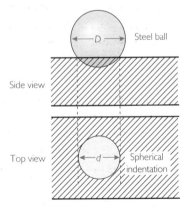

Figure 32 *Indentation produced by a steel ball*

$$\mathrm{BHN} = m \div \left\{ \left(\frac{\pi D}{2}\right) \times \left[D - \sqrt{(D^2 - d^2)} \right] \right\} \qquad (4)$$

where D is the diameter of the indenting ball in *millimetres*, d the diameter of the indentation in *millimetres*, and m the mass of the applied load in *kilograms*. An alternative expression is

$$\mathrm{BHN} = \frac{m}{\pi D h} \qquad (5)$$

where D is the diameter of the ball indenter in *millimetres*, h the depth of penetration in *millimetres* (not exceeding the diameter of the ball) and m the mass of the applied load in *kilograms*.

Expressions (3) to (5) are unlike most of the expressions you meet in physics; they are defined only for a particular situation and they only 'work' in specified units.

In the food industry, once a tasting panel has agreed on a product they like, the hardness can be measured to establish a standard. Quality control testing on each batch of the product can then ensure that the hardness falls within an accepted range. Compared with some other materials, such as metals and ceramics, foodstuffs are fairly soft. However, they tend to be referred to as 'hard' if they are made from compacted material that has little in the way of air- or liquid-filled gaps.

Figure 33 *A commercial hardness tester*

ACTIVITY 15 **Can you bite it?**

Use a Brinell hardness test to measure the BHN for a variety of mints. There are various questions that you could investigate.

- Are the mints in one packet as hard as those in another of the same type?
- Do you get the same hardness all over the mint? Does the hardness change if the mints are hot, cold or even frozen?
- Does the hardness change if the mints are heated or cooled and then returned to room temperature?
- Do you get the same Brinell hardness number regardless of the diameter of the indenter or the size of the load?

To carry out hardness tests on very soft materials, for example plastics, or very hard materials such as hard steel used to make tools, different indenters can be used. In commercial testing there are other hardness tests, for example the Vickers and the Rockwell. In the Rockwell hardness test there are different sizes of hardened steel ball which may be used to make the indentation, or various diamond indenters. The choice depends on the hardness of the material, and there are a number of scales, one for each indenter and the force used.

QUESTION

16 An extra strong mint was tested with a ball indenter of diameter 2.00 mm. An applied load of 5.3 kg produced an indentation of mean diameter 1.25 mm. What was the Brinell hardness number for this mint?

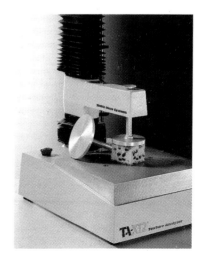

Figure 34 *Compression testing of a cake*

3.3 Crunching and chewing

Hardness is not the only property of interest to food and confectionery makers. The way foods deform, stretch or break under an applied force is related to the sensations we experience when eating them. Much of the testing in the food industry concerns the behaviour of foods under compression (Figure 34), because the manufacturers are interested in what happens to food when we chew or bite it, but tensile ('pulling') tests are also used (Figure 35). Some sweets, such as strawberry or cola laces (see Activity 16), are often gripped with the teeth and pulled to break them, so their tensile behaviour is of interest.

The results of tensile and compressive tests are often displayed as graphs. From a load–extension graph such as that in Figure 36, we can measure the stiffness of a material. As you saw in the earlier unit *Higher, Faster, Stronger*, the **stiffness** k is defined as

$$k = \frac{F}{x} \tag{6}$$

where F is the applied force and x the resulting extension. The stiffness depends on the size and shape of the sample, as well as on the material from which it is made. A thick sample will be stiffer than a thin one of the same material, and a long sample will be less stiff then a short one. However, provided the samples are all of a standard size and shape, graphs like that in Figure 36 provide a

Figure 35 *Tensile testing of pasta*

Study note

In the tests used to produce Figure 36, compressions were defined to be positive and extensions negative.

Figure 37 *Seaside rock, a stiff foodstuff*

Figure 38 *Jelly, an elastic foodstuff*

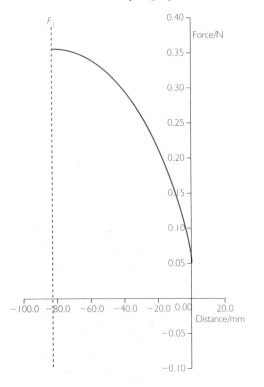

Figure 36 *Load–extension graph for noodles*

quick visual way to compare stiffness. A **stiff** material is one such as seaside rock (Figure 37) that does not easily change shape when a force is applied, so its force–extension (or force–compression) graph will be steep – a large load produces only a small deformation.

When the load is removed, some materials (such as jelly cubes or sweets, Figure 38) will spring back to their original shape; such materials are said to be **elastic**. Others, described as **plastic** materials, will remain deformed like well-chewed chewing-gum (Figure 39). Many materials are elastic under small loads, up to their **elastic limit**, but deform plastically when subjected to larger loads.

There are various ways in which a material can be deformed plastically. A **ductile** ('drawable') material is one that can readily be pulled out into a longer, thinner shape (like well chewed gum), and a **malleable** ('hammerable') material can be deformed under compression. All ductile materials are malleable, but not all malleable materials are ductile; some, like fudge (Figure 40) may tear apart under tension.

Tensile or compression testing can also measure the force needed to break a sample. Again, the actual force needed depends on the size and shape, but comparison of standard samples gives information about strength; a **strong** material is one that requires a large force to make it break.

The way in which foodstuffs break is of great interest to manufacturers and consumers. A **brittle** material is one that easily cracks, like a boiled sweet or hard toffee, or a biscuit; such foods might loosely be described as 'crunchy'. In brittle materials, an applied force is unable to deform the material; brittle materials are usually stiff, and show essentially no plastic deformation. Instead, the load causes any small cracks to spread rapidly. Sometimes, as in the case of wafers, this behaviour arises because there are many small air gaps within the structure which are unable to stop cracks spreading.

In contrast to brittle materials, a **tough** material deforms plastically and can withstand dynamic loads such as shock or impact. A tough material requires a large force to produce a small deformation – in other words, a large amount of **work** must be done on the material in order to produce a small plastic deformation. Few foodstuffs can be described as tough according to this definition (apart, perhaps, from some meats); it is a term more usually applied to materials such as Kevlar, which is used to make bullet-proof vests (Figure 41).

Figure 39   *Chewing gum, which is plastic when well chewed*

Figure 40   *Fudge, a malleable foodstuff that breaks apart under tension*

Study note

In the unit *Higher, Faster, Stronger*, you saw that work is defined as the product of the net force and the distance moved in the direction of the force.

Figure 41   *Bullet-proof vest made of Kevlar*

ACTIVITY 16   **Stretchy sweets**

Investigate the behaviour of strawberry or cola laces under tension. Display your results using graphs, and use some of the words printed above in bold type to describe the behaviour of your samples.

QUESTION

17 Table 4 lists some measurements obtained from hanging masses on a sweet called a Glow-worm. When the load is removed, the Glow-worm slowly goes back to its original length. It was 8.0 cm long at the start of the test, and its cross-section was an equilateral triangle with sides of 1 cm.

Load/g	Length/cm
20	8.6
30	8.8
40	9.1
50	9.5
60	9.9
70	10.0
90	10.6
150	11.6
200	12.6
250	13.4
300	14.2
400	15.0

Table 4 *Tensile tests on a Glow-worm*

(**a**) Plot a graph to display the data from Table 4.

(**b**) Use appropriate words to describe and explain what was happening to the Glow-worm during this test.

(**c**) Basing you answer on parts (**a**) and (**b**), describe what the texture of a Glow-worm would be like as you ate it.

More testing

Standard tests in industry are normally carried out by machines that automatically apply loads and record the resulting deformation. Figure 42 shows one widely used machine, the Instron Universal Testing Machine. The moving part of the machine is driven vertically to compress or stretch the sample, and drive is connected to a chart recorder so the force and distance can be recorded. It can perform tests in tension, compression or bending, and can be used for many materials including metal, wood, plastic and adhesives. There are different models, some developed specifically for the food industry, and accessories for performing different tests can be attached to the machine as required. The model shown here can apply a force in the range from 2 N to 5 kN and the speed of deformation can vary from 0.02 to 50 cm min^{-1}.

Food manufacturers use a variety of tests in addition to straightforward compressive and tensile testing. One common test is the three-point bend test, shown in Figure 43, testing the 'bendiness' of a wafer. This test is used in many industries – steel rails and PVC window frames, for example, are tested in this way.

Figure 42 *Instron Universal Testing Machine*

Figure 43 *Three-point bend test*

ACTIVITY 17 Bendy wafer

Devise and carry out a three-point bend test on a wafer.

Another test used to monitor the crispness of wafers is shown in Figure 44. A wafer is snapped in front of a microphone, and its waveform and frequency spectrum displayed – in this case, using *Multimedia Sound.* The sound produced, and hence the shape of the waveform and frequency spectrum, depends on the crispness or bendiness of the wafer.

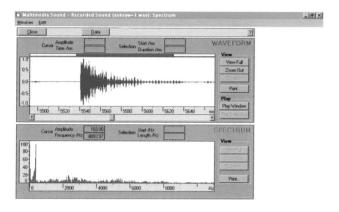

Figure 44 *Waveform and frequency spectrum of a breaking wafer*

In 1988 Michael McIntyre and James Woodhouse of Cambridge University suggested that Chladni figures, the patterns produced on resonant surfaces, might be used to analyse material properties. This was followed up for wafers by Simon Livings, now working at the Centre Recherche Nestlé in Switzerland, as part of his doctoral project. He placed glitter on the top surface of wafers, placed them near a loudspeaker and observed the patterns as the wafer resonated.

Further investigations

Materials testing provides scope for a variety of investigations, using foodstuffs or other materials. You could explore the sounds produced by snapping brittle foods, and try to relate the results to other properties of the materials such as stiffness and strength, or perhaps you could investigate Chladni figures on resonating wafers. Or you might like to devise a completely different 'crispness' test for wafers. You could investigate how the 'crispness' varied with water content of wafers left exposed to damp air.

You could try to devise tests to measure other physical aspects of food materials, such as 'stickiness'. A good test must be easy to use and should give reproducible results, i.e. the same test applied on different occasions to the same sample should give the same results within a relatively small range of uncertainty.

3.4 Summing up part 3

In this part of the unit, you have learned about so-called **mechanical properties** of materials. You have focused on the food industry, but the tests, and the terms used to describe the materials, are applicable wherever materials are tested and used.

Activity 18 and questions 18 to 21 are intended to help you look back though this part of the unit and check what you have learned.

ACTIVITY **18** **Pick and mix**

Select a variety of sweets or other foodstuffs, and use the words malleable, ductile, elastic, plastic and brittle, as appropriate, to describe their properties.

QUESTIONS

18 Why will the Brinell test not work for very hard or very soft materials?

19 In a Brinell hardness test of a sample of steel, a 3000 kg load produced an indentation of diameter 3.85 mm with an ball indenter of diameter 10.00 mm. Calculate the Brinell hardness number for this sample.

20 Figure 45 shows the results of compression tests on Gouda cheeses.

(**a**) Describe what happens to the stiffness of Gouda cheese as it ages.

(**b**) What happens to the strength of the cheese as it ages? (Strength as in physical property, not as in taste!)

(**c**) What effect do the cumin seeds have on the physical properties of the cheese? Suggest a reason for this effect.

21 Imagine that you are working in the quality control area of a textile factory. You are asked to select four threads from a large number to demonstrate to some visitors threads that are

(**a**) strong but not stiff

(**b**) stiff but not strong

(**c**) both strong and stiff

(**d**) neither strong nor stiff.

If you tested the threads by hand, what would you look for to identify each of (**a**) to (**d**)?

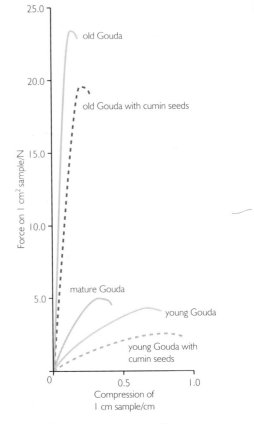

Figure 45 *Compression tests on Gouda cheeses*

4 Sweetness and light

The confectionery industry, and indeed the food industry in general, is a very large user of sugar. Sugar produced in the UK comes from sugar beet (Figure 46) and most imported sugar comes from sugar cane. In 1998, some ten thousand UK farmers were involved in growing sugar beet. A typical harvested beet contains 16.0% sugar, 75.9% water, 2.6% soluble non-sugar and 5.5% pulp, but both beet and cane can vary in quality. Beet samples are analysed for their sugar content, and farmers are paid according to the percentage of sugar in their beet.

In this part of the unit you will explore two techniques for analysing sugar content, both of which use light. The first, refractometry, involves ideas that you met in the unit *The Sound of Music*, while the second, polarimetry, introduces you to another aspect of the behaviour of light.

Figure 46 *Collecting sugar beet*

4.1 Refractometry

When light crosses a boundary between two materials, it is refracted – that it, it changes its speed and (unless it meets the boundary head-on) its direction (Figure 47). In the unit *The Sound of Music*, you used the **refractive index** and **Snell's law** to quantify this change of speed and direction. Table 5 shows how the refractive index of sugar solution changes with concentration. Refractometry is used in determining the payments to farmers dependent on the concentration of sugar in sugar beet and also in judging the ripeness of pineapples in the field.

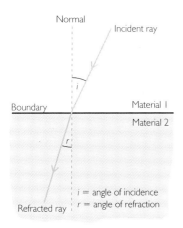

Figure 47 *Light crossing a boundary*

Concentration of sugar by mass/%	Refractive index
0	1.333
5	1.340
10	1.348
15	1.356
20	1.364
25	1.372
30	1.381
35	1.390
40	1.400
45	1.410
50	1.420
55	1.431
60	1.442
65	1.453
70	1.465
75	1.478
80	1.491
85	1.504

Table 5 *Refractive index of sugar solutions at 20 °C*

In principle, the concentration of a sugar solution can be determined from its refractive index. Figure 48 shows an Abbé refractometer, which can measure refractive index with a precision of ±0.001 or better. In Activity 19 you will use a model Pulfrich refractometer. Both of these instruments involve the measurement of **critical angle** to determine refractive index. Question 22 reminds you of some key ideas about refraction that you will need in order to do Activity 19.

Figure 48   *Abbé refractometer*

QUESTIONS

22 (**a**) Referring to Figure 47, write down the relationship(s) between the angles *i* and *r*, the speed of light v_1 and v_2 in the materials 1 and 2, and the refractive index, $_1\mu_2$.

(**b**) Say what is meant by *critical angle*, and write down the relationship(s) between critical angle, *C*, and refractive index.

23 (**a**) Plot a graph of the data in Table 5. (A spreadsheet with its graph plotting facility would be an ideal way of dealing with this.)

(**b**) Describe in words and, if appropriate, in mathematical terms the relationship between concentration and refractive index.

(**c**) What would be the percentage concentration of a sugar solution that had a refractive index of 1.470 at 20 °C?

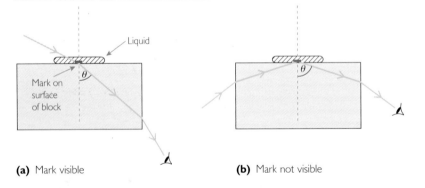

(**a**) Mark visible   (**b**) Mark not visible   (**c**) Mark *just* visible

Figure 49   *The principle of the Pulfrich refractometer*

The principle of the Pulfrich refractometer is shown in Figure 49. The idea is that you look though the glass block at a mark on its far edge, and trace the path of the light for which the mark *just* disappears – that is, the angle at the glass–liquid boundary is the critical angle for refraction *from the liquid to the glass*:

$$_1\mu_g = \frac{1}{\sin C} \tag{7}$$

Measurements of angles at the glass–air boundary give the refractive index *from air to glass*:

$$_a\mu_g = \frac{\sin i}{\sin r} \tag{8}$$

Study note

In interpreting Figure 49, it can be helpful to think of light travelling *from* the eye towards the mark on the surface of the block. It would follow a path exactly as shown in the diagram but with the arrows reversed.

Study note

You met refractive index and critical angle in the unit *The Sound of Music*.

But we are interested in the refractive index *from air to liquid*. We can use the answers to question 22 to see how to get this information from equations (7) and (8). We know that

$$_a\mu_g = \frac{v_a}{v_g} \qquad \text{and} \qquad _g\mu_l = \frac{v_g}{v_l} \qquad (9)$$

so we can write

$$_a\mu_l = \frac{v_a}{v_l} = \frac{v_a}{v_g} \times \frac{v_g}{v_l} = {_a\mu_g} \times {_g\mu_l} \qquad (10)$$

Also, since

$$_g\mu_l = \frac{v_g}{v_l} \qquad \text{and} \qquad _l\mu_g = \frac{v_l}{v_g} \qquad (11)$$

we can write

$$_g\mu_l = \frac{1}{_l\mu_g} \qquad (12)$$

From equations (7), (8), (10) and (12) we therefore have

$$_a\mu_l = \frac{\sin i}{\sin r} \times \sin C \qquad (13)$$

Finally, if the glass block has a right angled corner, we can also see from Figure 49(c) that

$$C = 90° - r \qquad (14)$$

and so

$$\sin C = \cos r \qquad (15)$$

and equation (13) can therefore be written as

$$_a\mu_l = \sin i \times \frac{\cos r}{\sin r} = \frac{\sin i}{\tan r} \qquad (16)$$

which gives a direct way to find the air–liquid refractive index from the experimental measurements.

ACTIVITY 19 **Refractometry**

Use a model Pulfrich refractometer to determine the refractive index of some sugar solutions. Use your results to plot a calibration graph and hence determine the concentration of an unknown sugar solution.

4.2 *Polarimetry*

You may already be familiar with **polarised light** through the use of polarising sunglasses, which reduce the intensity of light passing through them and are particularly effective at reducing glare from reflected surfaces. If you take two pieces of Polaroid from such sunglasses, and place one in front of the other and rotate it, you will notice that the brightness of the light changes with angle. At certain positions, the light is blocked completely; this arrangement is referred as 'crossed Polaroids' (see Figure 50).

Maths reference

Reciprocals
See Maths note 3.3

Sine, cosine and tangent of an angle
See Maths note 6.2

Figure 50 *View through crossed and uncrossed Polaroids*

Polaroid was first produced by George Wheelwright III, in the USA, in 1938. It is made by first stretching a piece of plastic to align its long chain molecules and then dipping it into iodine solution so that iodine atoms become attached to the chains and line up along them. Polaroid is a trade name; more correctly and generally, such a piece of plastic should be called a **polarising filter**.

To explain how polarising filters work – and to see what they have to do with the concentration of sugar solutions – we need to think about the behaviour of light waves.

Light waves, and all other electromagnetic waves, are **transverse** – that is, they involve oscillations at right angles to their direction of travel. What's actually oscillating is an electric and a magnetic field at right angles to each other and to the direction of travel, as shown in Figure 51.

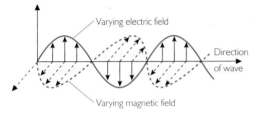

Figure 51   *An electromagnetic wave*

Study note

An electric field is a region in which a charged particle experiences a force. The direction of the electric field is defined as the direction of the force on a positive charge. A magnetic field is a region in which a magnet (e.g. a compass needle) experiences a force; its direction is defined as that in which the north-seeking pole of a compass needle would point.

Polarised waves

We can model the behaviour of light using transverse waves on a rope. If you shake the end of a rope up and down, you produce a travelling wave where the oscillations take place only in a vertical plane; the wave is said to be **polarised** or, more correctly, **plane polarised**. If you shake the rope in all transverse directions, you still produce a transverse travelling wave, but now the oscillations are no longer confined to a plane, and the wave is **unpolarised**. If the rope passes through a narrow slit as in Figure 52, only those oscillations parallel to the slit can get through, so the slit turns unpolarised into polarised waves – it acts as a polarising filter.

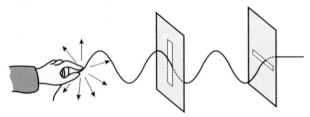

Figure 52   *Demonstrating polarised waves on a rope*

If polarised waves encounter a second polarising filter parallel to the first, they can travel through unimpeded, but if the slit is at 90° to the first, then it completely blocks their passage and the slits are behaving like crossed Polaroids. With the second filter at an intermediate angle, waves still emerge through it; their amplitude is reduced and the plane of polarisation is parallel to the second slit.

If you repeat this exercise with **longitudinal** waves (e.g. on a Slinky), then the slits have no effect on the passage of the waves –

they always get through the slits. Longitudinal waves cannot be plane polarised. The fact that electromagnetic waves *can* be plane polarised in fact shows that they *must* be transverse.

Rotating the plane of polarisation

Light is blocked by crossed Polaroids because the two filters are aligned at 90° to one another. However, there are some materials that rotate the plane of polarisation of light. Sugar solution is one such **optically active** material; others include turpentine and many plastics, particularly when stretched. If you place an optically active material between two crossed Polaroids, then some light can emerge, and you need to rotate one of the Polaroids to produce extinction.

Some materials, including most naturally occurring sugars, cause a clockwise rotation when you are looking at the light coming towards you; these materials are said to be **dextrorotatory**. Materials that cause an anticlockwise rotation are described as **laevorotatory**.

ACTIVITY 20 **Exploring polarisation**

Use a rope and a Slinky to demonstrate the polarisation of transverse waves, and to show that longitudinal waves cannot be plane polarised.

Use two polarising filters to observe the behaviour of some optically active materials. Look through a single polarising filter at light reflected at a shallow angle from a polished surface (e.g. a bench top) and hence explain why Polaroid sunglasses are particularly good at reducing glare.

Figure 53   *A polarimeter*

The rotation of the plane of polarisation can be measured with a polarimeter (Figure 53). In its simplest form, such an instrument for studying liquids consists of two polarising filters, one fixed and one that can be rotated against a protractor scale, with a tube of liquid placed between them.

ACTIVITY 21 **Polarimetry**

Use a polarimeter to measure the rotation of the plane of polarisation for some sugar solutions, and hence explain how polarimetry can be used to measure sugar concentration.

Further **investigations**

In Activity 20 you probably noticed colours produced by optically active materials between crossed Polaroids. You might like to devise a way to explore how the rotation of the plane of polarisation depends on wavelength. Or you might look into variations with temperature.

Engineers sometimes make plastic models of structures (such as bridges) and observe them through crossed Polaroids; the colour and intensity of light that emerges changes according to the load on the structure, indicating where the structure is under greatest stress. You might think of devising a way to explore this phenomenon.

QUESTION

24 The data in Table 6 were obtained using sugar solution of the same concentration throughout, but varying the length of the light path through the solution. Table 7 shows how the rotation of the plane of polarisation varied with concentration for a single light path length.

Rotation angle, θ/deg	Length of light path in solution, L/dm
7	0.2
14	0.4
20	0.6
27	0.8
34	1.0

Table 6 *Data for question 24: single concentration*

Rotation angle, θ/deg	Concentration of solution, c/g ml^{-1}
17	0.25
33	0.50
50	0.75

Table 7 *Data for question 24: single length of light path*

Plot graphs of the data in Tables 6 and 7 and hence describe, in mathematical terms, how the rotation angle θ depends on the concentration c and length L of the light path through the solution.

4.3 *Summing up part 4*

In this part of the unit you have used two aspects of the behaviour of light to measure sugar concentration. In doing so, you have reviewed and extended your knowledge of waves from the earlier unit *The Sound of Music*.

ACTIVITY 22 **Summing up part 4**

Spend a few minutes checking through your work on this part of the unit, and make sure you understand all the key terms printed in bold.

Look back at your work on *The Sound of Music*, and extend your table from Activity 31 in that unit by adding and completing a row at the bottom with 'can be plane polarised' in the left-hand column.

ACTIVITY 23 **Measuring concentration**

Compare and evaluate the two methods you have used to measure sugar concentration. Which method do you think is better? Take account of the following:

cost of equipment
amount of sugar solution needed
ease of use
reliability of results.

QUESTION
---

25 The specific rotation of an optically active solution is defined as:

$$\text{specific rotation} = \frac{\theta}{cL}$$

where θ is the rotation in degrees, c is the concentration in $g\,ml^{-1}$ for a substance in solution or its density in $g\,ml^{-1}$ for a pure substance, and L is the length of the light path (or depth of substance) in decimetres ($1\,dm = 10^{-1}\,m$).

(**a**) What is the specific rotation of a sugar solution that produced a rotation of the plane of polarisation of $33°$ with a concentration of $0.5\,g\,ml^{-1}$ and a light path of $1\,dm$?

(**b**) Some materials will, for a $1\,dm$ light path, rotate the plane of polarisation by many hundreds of degrees. Since it is not feasible to measure more than $360°$ directly, suggest how you might calculate their specific rotation.

5   *Wrapping up*

In this final part of the unit, you will look first at some other aspects of physics in the food industry and then review the work that you have done in earlier parts of the unit.

5.1   *Food quality and safety*

It is important to ensure that foods, including confectionery, are fit to eat. Government regulations have a role to play in this. The Food Safety Act 1990 and The Food Safety (Temperature Control) Regulations 1995 are two important pieces of legislation covering the food chain from the farm to the shop.

At each stage, the manufacture and processing of food must conform to high standards of quality. The relevant techniques, procedures and management systems are specified in 'British Standards'. The procedures for certification are independently inspected, and a company would lose its certificate if it failed to reach the required standards. Stephen Beckett of Nestlé Research and Development comments here on how physics is involved.

> The development and use of instrumentation is perhaps one of the most important areas for physicists in the food industry. Some of this is for safety and must be carried out on-line, e.g. foreign material detectors; other instruments are for quality control, e.g. temperature and humidity. Even these are not as simple as they may at first appear. An item containing a metal object must be detected and rejected when the product is passing at a rate of several hundred per minute, and a simple, robust device for detecting pieces of plastic within chocolate has still to be invented. In addition the chocolate's temperature must be monitored and controlled to within a fraction of a degree to ensure that it is glossy and has a good 'snap' when broken.

As you would expect, hygiene and safety are paramount. To ensure that any potential hazards are identified in a food production system, a Hazard and Critical Control Points (HACCP) system was developed. The first such system was designed in the USA in the 1960s to ensure the safety of food for astronauts (Figure 54) – getting food poisoning in space would be quite a problem! The key principles of HACCP involve:

- identifying steps in food production where significant hazards occur;

- identifying critical control points (CCPs) where it is essential that the hazards are removed;

- establishing critical limits which describe the difference between safe and unsafe;

- establishing the means of monitoring and controlling the hazards;

- keeping records;

- verifying that the system is working correctly.

Figure 54 *NASA Shuttle astronaut Rhea Seddon having a meal on the Space Shuttle*

The hazards could be biological ones, such as *Salmonella* in chicken, but they could also be chemical, related to the cleaning materials or lubricants used on the production line, or physical hazards, such as pieces of glass, metal, stones or wood getting into the food.

ACTIVITY **24** **Physical hazards in food**

In a small group, discuss your suggestions and ideas concerning the following:

- the types of physical hazards that could potentially contaminate food in the course of production;

- the possible source(s) of these contaminants;

- the techniques you might be able to use to detect such contaminants;

- the techniques you might use to keep out such contaminants.

Make notes on your discussions as you will need them for Activities 26 and 27.

If you have the opportunity to visit a food production company, you may be able to identify some of their critical control points, together with what is done to ensure monitoring and control at these points.

5.2 *Packaging*

Most confectionery products are wrapped to preserve them in good condition. There is a vast number of wrapping materials in use, mainly plastic-based, including cellulose acetate, polyester, polyethylene, polypropylene, polyvinyl chloride, nylon-6 and polyvinylidene chloride amongst others; the aluminium foil wrap of many chocolate bars is a good example of a non-plastic material. Stephen Beckett puts the final production stage (Figure 55) into perspective:

Packaging plays an important part in the chocolate confectionery industry, as it is often the only thing that a would-be purchaser sees. It is important to ensure therefore that the wrapper has been put on correctly. Major chocolate brands are produced at a rate of several million per day, and it is impossible to see the moving parts of the wrapping machines to determine what happens when something goes wrong. In such cases high-speed video cameras can be of great benefit in being able to slow down the motion and help determine the cause of the fault.

Figure 55 *A confectionery product going through a wrapping machine*

ACTIVITY 25 | **Which packaging?**

Your task here is to make a recommendation on the ideal wrapping material(s) for a white chocolate covered Crunchie bar which is wrapped at a speed of 1000–1500 bars each minute. Write a report giving reasons for your recommendations.

5.3 The final product

The following activities are designed to help you look back over your work in this unit; in doing so, make sure you have a full record of your work and that you are familiar with the key terms printed in bold earlier in the unit.

ACTIVITY 26 | **Coping with hazards**

Design a double page spread (perhaps using computer graphics) for a magazine showing how some physical hazards could be detected and coped with in the food industry. Accompany your diagrams by a short paragraph outlining the physics involved in the techniques employed. Use your discussion notes from Activity 24 to help you.

ACTIVITY 27 | **Sweet physics**

Write a short educational pamphlet 'Sweet physics' about physics in the confectionery industry, which might be useful for visitors to a confectionery company. Use your notes on the whole unit to help you with this.

5.4 *Questions on the whole unit*

QUESTIONS

26 When water vapour in the atmosphere cools, it condenses to form droplets of liquid water. This forms clouds. If the droplets cool further, they freeze to form ice pellets, which fall from the cloud. By the time they reach the ground they have usually melted again to form rain, but sometimes they reach the ground as hail. When the ice pellets melt, they break up into small water droplets, which reach their terminal velocity before they hit the ground. Hailstones can cause a lot of damage because they are larger and more massive and travel faster than raindrops.

(**a**) Explain, with the aid of a diagram, how the forces on an object falling through a viscous fluid bring it to a terminal velocity.

(**b**) Write down an expression for the forces on a raindrop of radius r and density ρ_{water} when it has reached a terminal velocity v while falling through air of density ρ_{air} and viscosity η.

(**c**) Given that $\rho_{air} \ll \rho_{water}$, rearrange your answer to (**b**) to obtain an expression for v.

(**d**) Given that $\rho_{ice} \approx \rho_{water}$, explain why hailstones reach the ground travelling faster than raindrops.

27 In 1809 Étienne Louis Malus (1775–1812) discovered that light can be partially or completely polarised by reflection from a shiny surface.

(**a**) Explain how you could use a polarising filter to demonstrate that light has become polarised on reflection.

(**b**) David Brewster (1781–1868) discovered that totally polarised light can be obtained on reflection when the refractive index μ of the reflecting material equals the tangent of the angle of incidence of the light, as shown in Figure 56. (The angle at which this happens is known as the Brewster angle.)

   (**i**) If the refractive index from air to glass is 1.5, what must be the angle of incidence in order to produce totally plane polarised light on reflection?

   (**ii**) What would be the angle of reflection of this polarised light from the glass surface?

(**c**) When light is polarised by reflection from glass, only about 8% of the light is reflected; the rest enters the glass. Suggest and explain how, using glass reflective surfaces *only*, you might boost this percentage.

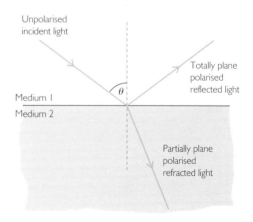

Figure 56 *Obtaining polarised light by reflection*

5.5 *Achievements*

Now you have studied this unit you should be able to:

- understand and use the terms *density, laminar flow, streamlined flow, terminal velocity, turbulent flow, upthrust* and *viscous drag* (2.2, 2.3)*;

- recall that the rate of flow of a fluid is related to its viscosity (2.2, 2.3, 2.5);

- recognise and use the expression for Stokes' law, $F = 6\pi r \eta v$ (2.2);

- recall that the viscosities of most fluids change with temperature (2.2);

- distinguish between elastic and plastic deformation of a material (3.3);

- explain what is meant by the terms *brittle, ductile, hard, malleable, stiff* and *tough*, use these terms, and give examples of materials exhibiting such behaviour (3.2, 3.3, 5.2);

- explain how to measure the refractive index of a liquid and how this can be used in comparing the concentrations of, for example, sugar solutions (4.1);

- recognise and use the expression for refractive index $\mu = \sin i / \sin r = v_1/v_2$ and predict whether total internal relection will occur at an interface (4.1);

- explain what is meant by *plane polarised light* (4.2);

- explain how to measure the rotation of the plane of polarisation by a liquid and how this can be used in comparing the concentrations of, for example, sugar solutions (4.2).

*Numbers indicate the section(s) that relate to each achievement.

Answers

1 Using equation (1), $F = 6\pi r \eta \dot{v}$ so
$$F = 6\pi \times 8.4 \times 1.0 \times 10^{-3}\,\text{m} \times 10^{-2}\,\text{N s m}^{-2}$$
$$\times 2.0 \times 10^{-2}\,\text{m s}^{-1}$$
$$= 3.2 \times 10^{-5}\,\text{N}$$

2 (a) $V = 4\pi \times \dfrac{(1.0 \times 10^{-3}\,\text{m})^3}{3} = 4.2 \times 10^{-9}\,\text{m}^3$

(b) Mass $m_{\text{steel}} = \rho_{\text{steel}}\,V$
$$= 7.8 \times 10^3\,\text{kg m}^{-3} \times 4.2 \times 10^{-9}\,\text{m}^3$$
$$= 3.3 \times 10^{-5}\,\text{kg}$$

(c) Weight of ball-bearing $= m_{\text{steel}}\,g$
$$= 3.3 \times 10^{-5}\,\text{kg} \times 9.8\,\text{N kg}^{-1} = 3.2 \times 10^{-4}\,\text{N}.$$

3 (a) Volume $= 4.2 \times 10^{-9}\,\text{m}^3$ as the ball-bearing will displace its own volume.

(b) Mass of oil $m_{\text{oil}} = \rho_{\text{oil}}\,V$
$$= 920\,\text{kg m}^{-3} \times 4.2 \times 10^{-9}\,\text{m}^3 = 3.9 \times 10^{-6}\,\text{kg}$$

(c) Weight of displaced oil $= m_{\text{oil}}\,g$
$$= 3.9 \times 10^{-6}\,\text{kg} \times 9.8\,\text{N kg}^{-1} = 3.8 \times 10^{-5}\,\text{N}$$

4 (a) Upthrust $=$ weight of displaced oil $= 3.8 \times 10^{-5}\,\text{N}.$

(b) Upward force $=$ upthrust $+$ viscous drag force
$$= 3.8 \times 10^{-5}\,\text{N} + 3.2 \times 10^{-5}\,\text{N} = 7.0 \times 10^{-5}\,\text{N}$$
Weight of ball-bearing $= 3.2 \times 10^{-4}\,\text{N}$ acting downwards.
There is therefore a net downwards force of magnitude F, where
$$F = 3.2 \times 10^{-4}\,\text{N} - 0.7 \times 10^{-4}\,\text{N} = 2.5 \times 10^{-4}\,\text{N}$$

5 Weigh the object in air by suspending it from the forcemeter by the cotton. Pour some water into the measuring cylinder to about half-way and note the volume. Lower the object, still attached to the forcemeter, completely into the water but don't let it touch the bottom. Note the new forcemeter reading and the new level of water in the measuring cylinder.

The difference between the two forcemeter readings gives the upthrust. The difference between the two levels in the measuring cylinder gives the volume of water displaced (which is also the volume of the object). Calculate the mass of water displaced and hence its weight, which should be equal to the upthrust.

6 See Figure 12.
Pressure exerted by water on top of
block $= P_A + h_1\rho g$
Downward force on top of block $= (P_A + h_1\rho g)A$
Pressure exerted by water at bottom of
block $= P_A + h_2\rho g$
Upward force on bottom of block $= (P_A + h_2\rho g)A$
So net upward force on block $= (h_2 - h_1)\rho g A = h\rho g A$

Volume of fluid displaced $=$ volume of block $= Ah$
Mass of fluid displaced $= \rho Ah$
Weight of fluid displaced $= \rho Ahg$, which is the same as the net upward force.

7 Using symbols:
$C_a =$ weight of crown in air
$C_w =$ weight of crown in water
$W_d =$ weight of water displaced
$\rho_w =$ density of water
$\rho_c =$ density of crown
$V =$ volume of crown $=$ volume of water displaced
By Archimedes' principle, we know that $C_w = C_a - W_d$ and we are told that
$$\frac{C_w}{C_a} = 0.948$$
so we can write
$$\frac{C_a - W_d}{C_a} = 0.948$$
and so
$$1 - \frac{W_d}{C_a} = 0.948$$
$$\frac{W_d}{C_a} = 1 - 0.948 = 0.052$$
But we can also say that
$$C_a = V\rho_c g$$
and
$$W_d = V\rho_w g$$
so
$$\frac{\rho_w}{\rho_c} = \frac{W_d}{C_a}$$
or
$$\frac{\rho_c}{\rho_w} = \frac{C_a}{W_d} = \frac{1}{0.52} = 19.3$$
This is the density ratio of pure gold to water, so the crown must be made of pure gold.

8 You might expect them to have the same coefficient of viscosity over a range of temperatures – visco (viscosity) and static (the same). (In reality this is not actually so, but the changes of viscosity are such as to enable the vehicle to function satisfactorily regardless of the temperature changes. For extremes of temperature, oils are specially formulated to provide suitable viscosity.)

9 With six divisions between repeated parts of the trace the time period is $T = 60\,\text{ms} = 60 \times 10^{-3}\,\text{s}$.
$$\text{Frequency } f = \frac{1}{T} = \frac{1}{6.0 \times 10^{-2}\,\text{s}} = 16.7\,\text{Hz}.$$

10 (a) (i) About 6 litre min^{-1}. (ii) 6 litre = 6×10^{-3} m^3. This volume of water has a mass of 6 kg. This gives a mass flow rate of 6 kg min^{-1}. 1 min = 60 s, so mass flow rate = 0.1 kg s^{-1}.

(b) About 200 Hz

(c) The graph is a straight line: output frequency is directly proportional to the volume flow rate.

11 By changing the electric field at certain points in the flow, the rate of flow of the chocolate could be changed in order to alter the thickness of a coating or take account of the change of speed of a production line.

12 (a) The terminal velocity is the greatest steady velocity reached by the falling ball-bearing. It is reached when the forces acting on the ball-bearing are balanced.

(b) Upthrust = $\dfrac{4\pi r^3 \rho_{oil} g}{3}$

$= \frac{4}{3}\pi \times (0.5 \times 10^{-3}$ m$)^3 \times 900$ kg m$^{-3} \times 9.8$ N kg^{-1}

$= 4.62 \times 10^{-6}$ N

(c) weight = $\dfrac{4\pi r^3 \rho_{steel} g}{3}$

$= \frac{4}{3}\pi \times (0.5 \times 10^{-3}$ m$)^3 \times 7860$ kg m$^{-3} \times 9.8$ N kg^{-1}

$= 4.03 \times 10^{-5}$ N

(d) From equation (2)

viscous drag force = weight − upthrust

$6\pi r \eta v = 4.03 \times 10^{-5}$ N $- 4.62 \times 10^{-6}$ N

$\eta = \dfrac{(4.03 \times 10^{-5}\text{ N}) - (4.62 \times 10^{-6}\text{ N})}{6\pi \times 0.5 \times 10^{-3}\text{ m} \times 0.03\text{ m s}^{-1}}$

$= 1.26 \times 10^{-1}$ N s m^{-2}.

13 If you plot the data on a graph, the points lie almost on a straight line, suggesting that the output frequency is proportional to the flow rate.

14 (a) The fluid will expand and contract as temperature changes, so customers would be charged incorrectly.

(b) Mass = density × volume, so

mass flow rate = density × volume flow rate.

(Some flowmeters incorporate densitometers which automatically measure the density and compensate for any changes.)

15 (a) The resistance of NTC thermistors will rise when they are cooled.

(b) (i) See Tables 8 and 9.

Speed of flow/m s^{-1}	Time for 20 vortices to pass/s	Frequency of vortices/Hz
0.5	2.00	10
1.0	0.98	20
1.5	0.66	30
2.0	0.50	40
2.5	0.40	50

Table 8 *Table 2 completed (10 mm obstacle)*

Speed of flow/m s^{-1}	Time for 20 vortices to pass/s	Frequency of vortices/Hz
1.0	0.50	40
1.5	0.33	61
2.0	0.25	80
2.5	0.20	100

Table 9 *Table 3 completed (5 mm obstacle)*

(ii) The speed of flow is directly proportional to the frequency of vortices. As one doubles, so the other also doubles. (iii) The diameter of the obstruction is inversely proportional to the frequency of vortices. As one doubles, the other halves; as one is reduced to a third, so the other triples.

(c) If the frequency of vortices was very high, there might not be enough time for the thermistors to heat up again before the next vortex cooled it. Then the vortices would not be detected.

16 Using equation (4):

BHN

$= 5.3 \div \left\{ \left(\dfrac{\pi \times 2.00}{2} \right) \times \left[2.00 - \sqrt{(2.00^2 - 1.25^2)} \right] \right\}$

$= 5.3 \div \{ \pi \times [2.00 - 1.56] \} = 3.84$

17 (a) See Figure 57. Notice that this graph is plotted using g and cm. If you worked out the load in newtons and the extension in m, your graph would have the same shape but the numbers on the axes would be different; a mass of 10 g has a weight of approximately 0.1 N, so when the mass is 20 g, the load is 0.2 N. You could also have plotted extension rather than total length, in which case your graph would start at the origin.

(b) The behaviour was elastic throughout (the Glow-worm returned to its original length when the load was removed). It was not very stiff (despite being quite thick, it doubled its length under a moderate load). As it extended it became slightly stiffer (the graph curves upwards, so load ÷ extension is greater when the extension is large).

(c) The Glow-worm would feel quite 'rubbery' and stretchy when chewed; it would deform and spring back.

18 For very hard materials the ball may make an indentation too small to measure. For very soft materials the ball will penetrate to a depth greater than the radius of the ball. The diameter of the indentation will then not increase any further and the indentation will just get deeper.

19 Using equation (4):

BHN

$= 3000 \div \left\{ \left(\dfrac{\pi \times 10.00}{2} \right) \right.$

$\left. \times \left[10.00 - \sqrt{(10.00^2 - 3.85^2)} \right] \right\}$

$= 3000 \div \{ 5.00\,\pi \times [10.00 - 9.23] \} = 248$

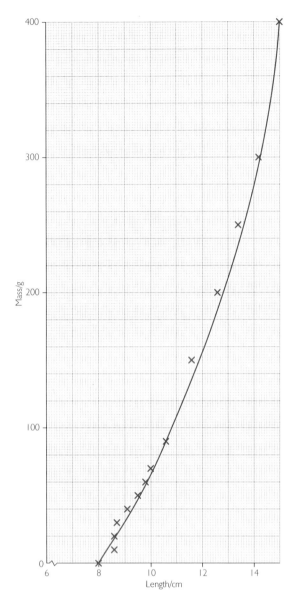

Figure 57   *The answer to question 17(a)*

(b) The critical angle, *C*, is the angle of refraction *r* that corresponds to *i* = 90°. If the light is travelling *from* material 2 *to* material 1, the critical angle is the largest angle that the ray can make with the normal in material 2 if is to emerge into material 1; at larger angles, the ray will undergo total internal reflection.

$$_1\mu_2 = \frac{1}{\sin C}$$

(See question 67 in *The Sound of Music*.)

23 (a) See Figure 58.

(b) Refractive index increases with concentration, but the relationship is not linear – the graph curves gently.

(c) About 72% (read from Figure 58).

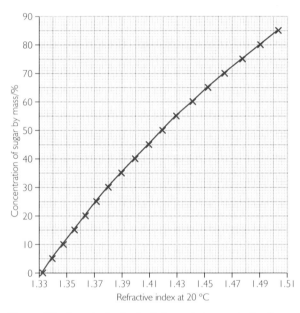

Figure 58   *A graph of refractive index against concentration for sugar solutions, question 23(a)*

20 (a) As it ages the cheese gets stiffer.

(b) It also becomes stronger with age.

(c) With cumin seeds, the cheese is less stiff and breaks more easily. Maybe the seeds act as small cracks, which spread when the cheese is deformed.

21 (a) Stretches easily, but requires a large force to break it.

(b) Does not stretch much, and breaks under a small force.

(c) Does not stretch much, and also does not break easily.

(d) Easily stretches and breaks.

22 (a) $_1\mu_2 = \dfrac{\sin i}{\sin r} = \dfrac{v_1}{v_2}$

(This is equation (8a) in *The Sound of Music*.)

24   See Figure 59. The graphs go through the origin and appear to be linear, suggesting that the angle is directly proportional to both concentration and path length: $\theta \propto cL$, i.e. $\theta = kcL$ where *k* is a constant.

25 (a) Specific rotation $= \dfrac{\theta}{cL} = \dfrac{33°}{0.5\,\text{g ml}^{-1} \times 1\,\text{dm}} = 66°$.

Note: The specific rotation is, by convention, expressed in degrees alone although it may appear more sensible to have used $°\,\text{ml g}^{-1}\,\text{dm}^{-1}$.

(b) Measure the rotation angle for a much smaller light path and multiply by a suitable factor (say 1 cm and multiply the rotation angle by 10). For even greater rotations light paths of millimetres could be used.

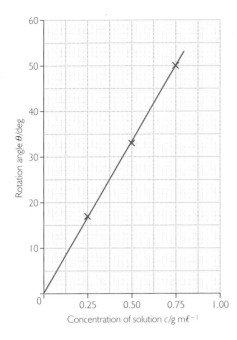

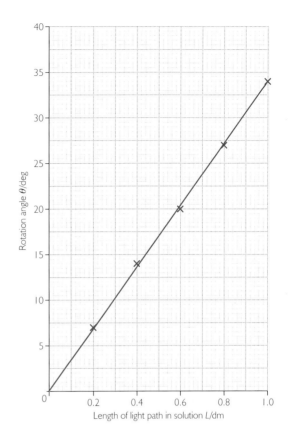

Figure 59 *Graphs of rotation angle against concentration and path length, question 24*

SPARE PART SURGERY

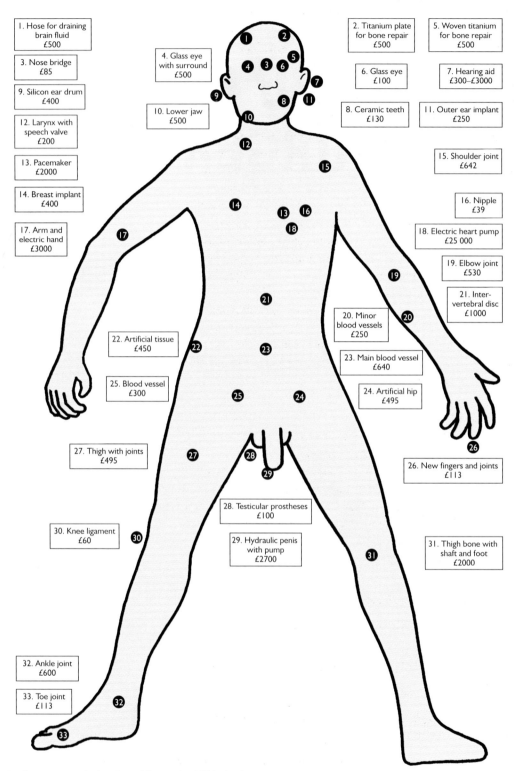

1. Hose for draining brain fluid £500

3. Nose bridge £85

9. Silicon ear drum £400

12. Larynx with speech valve £200

13. Pacemaker £2000

14. Breast implant £400

17. Arm and electric hand £3000

4. Glass eye with surround £500

10. Lower jaw £500

2. Titanium plate for bone repair £500

5. Woven titanium for bone repair £500

6. Glass eye £100

7. Hearing aid £300–£3000

8. Ceramic teeth £130

11. Outer ear implant £250

15. Shoulder joint £642

16. Nipple £39

18. Electric heart pump £25 000

19. Elbow joint £530

21. Inter-vertebral disc £1000

22. Artificial tissue £450

25. Blood vessel £300

20. Minor blood vessels £250

23. Main blood vessel £640

24. Artificial hip £495

27. Thigh with joints £495

28. Testicular prostheses £100

29. Hydraulic penis with pump £2700

26. New fingers and joints £113

31. Thigh bone with shaft and foot £2000

30. Knee ligament £60

32. Ankle joint £600

33. Toe joint £113

Figure 1 *Spare parts and what they might cost (at 1994 prices)*

274

Why a unit called Spare Part Surgery?

You probably know someone who has had spare part surgery. Perhaps an older relative or friend has a hip replacement, or a new heart valve or a pacemaker. You might know someone who has had an operation for cataracts, in which the eye lens has been replaced by an artificial implant. Not all spare parts involve surgery; you almost certainly know someone who wears contact lenses. Figure 1 shows some of the spare parts available nowadays, together with their approximate cost some years ago.

All of these spare parts help people to lead more pleasant and active lives, though there can be problems when a spare part wears out or is simply not as good as the original. Sometimes failures are dramatic and make the headline news. There have been cases involving heart valves that stick, and replacement hips that fail within months – unpleasant and possibly dangerous for the users, and expensive for the makers. Physics plays a key role in the development of good spare parts. To design a replacement joint you need to know about forces and the behaviour of materials in order to match the joint with natural bone. Lens implants and contact lenses involve optics and materials science. Physics is also used to diagnose a problem and to decide what sort of spare part is needed. The example that probably springs to mind is X-ray imaging, but for some examinations ultrasound is more useful – ultrasound imaging provides a quick and easy way to examine a beating heart.

Overview of physics principles and techniques

In this unit you will study the physics of materials, waves and light. Most of this work will build on and extend ideas that you have already met in earlier units, but you will also meet some new ideas – for example you will see that electrons can behave in unexpected ways, and will learn how large-scale properties of materials can be related to their small-scale structure. There are many opportunities in this unit for practical work, and to develop your skills in communication – both very important in medical uses of physics.

In this unit you will extend your knowledge of

- behaviour of waves from *The Sound of Music*;

- bulk properties of materials from *Higher, Faster, Stronger* and *Technology in Space*;

- microscopic properties of materials from *Technology in Space*.

In other units you will do more work on

- waves in *Good Enough to Eat*, *Digging Up the Past*, *Build or Bust?* and *Reach for the Stars*;

- bulk properties of materials in *Good Enough to Eat* and *Build or Bust?*;

- microscopic properties of materials in *Digging Up the Past* and *The Medium is the Message*.

1 *Spare parts*

Most people are somewhat nervous about any sort of hospital treatment, whether it is an operation or some kind of examination – they want to know what is involved, and how it will affect them. At the end of this unit, you will be asked to use what you have learned to produce some information for patients about one aspect of spare part surgery.

When deciding whether someone should have spare part surgery, several things need to be taken into account. One of these is the benefit to the patient, but there are other factors too, such as the cost of the operation, which need to be considered.

The following two activities provide a general introduction to this unit, and should also help you to plan what you would tell a patient.

ACTIVITY 1   The patient's view

Tape-record an interview with someone who has had some type of spare part surgery. Ask them how it has affected their life. Ask them about the advantages, and also ask if there have been any problems. Would they recommend it to someone else? Is there any information they would like to pass on to other people having a similar operation?

ACTIVITY 2   Spare parts

Study the information in Figure 1. Suggest reasons why some of the parts (e.g. an electric heart pump) are so much more expensive than others (e.g. a knee ligament). The actual cost of spare part surgery is much more than the cost of the part; suggest reasons for this. Choose one of the parts from Figure 1 and identify the aspects of physics that were probably involved in its development.

---

2 *Boning up*

As we age, our joints begin to wear out, making movement difficult and painful. Joints can also be affected by disease (such as arthritis), or may become injured. Nowadays, damaged or worn-out joints can be replaced relatively easily, and hip replacement is one of the commonest types of spare part surgery. This has become possible partly through the development of new materials and partly through improvements in surgical techniques.

In this part of the unit, you will study the properties of bones and the materials used to replace them. In doing so, you will advance your knowledge of the mechanical properties of materials.

2.1 *Bone and joint replacement*

In order to understand what is involved in making a good replacement joint, it is important first to know something about bones and joints and their function in our bodies. The article below outlines some key features of bones and joints, discusses some of the issues involved in bone replacement and then describes a recent development in artificial bone technology.

ACTIVITY **3** **Bone and joint replacement**

Read the following article about bones and joints and their replacement, and then answer questions 1 to 6.

Bones and joints

Imagine what we would look like without a skeleton [Figure 2] – we would certainly not be able to move! Our bony skeleton enables us to move against two important forces: weight (due to gravity) and the drag of the medium through which we are moving – this is usually air but may also be water. The cell is the basic building block of living material. Plants cells have rigid walls, so plants do not need skeletons, but animal cells are surrounded by a weak membrane that cannot be used for support. Our cells excrete materials to build up an internal skeleton (endoskeleton). Some animals have an external skeleton (exoskeleton).

Figure 2 *Artist's impression of a person without a skeleton*

Human skeletons are made of bone formed when proteins such as collagen are hardened by calcium and phosphorus salts excreted by cells. Bone is mainly crystalline calcium phosphate and calcium carbonate. About 20% of the bone is made up of living cells, which are fed with blood vessels through cavities in the bone.

The bones form levers in the body. They are held together by ligaments. Muscles are attached to bones by tendons. A place where two bones meet is called a joint. Joints which allow free movement are called synovial joints [Figure 3].

The capsule holds the joint together and the synovial fluid acts as a lubricant. The cartilage on the bone ends provides a smooth surface to allow the bones to move over each other with the minimum of friction. There are two main types of joint: ball-and-socket joints (such as the hip) and hinge joints (such as the knee). [See Figure 4.]

Replacement surgery

Like any mechanical device, joints undergo wear. Usually our body is able to repair any damage, but if the joint surfaces wear too quickly then osteoarthritis occurs. Disease can lead to a destruction of the surfaces; this is called rheumatoid arthritis. In severe cases replacement of the joint is necessary. The commonest joint that requires replacing is the hip joint.

Bone cancer used to require amputation but now the bone and joint can usually be replaced.

Replacement is rarely as a result of fracture since when this occurs blood vessels grow into the clot and a repair tissue develops which holds the bones together. This hardens and

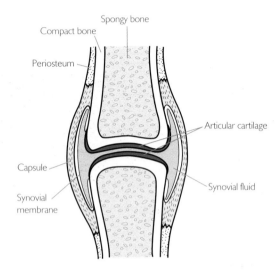

Figure 3 *Schematic diagram of a synovial joint*

(a) Ball-and-socket joint (hip)

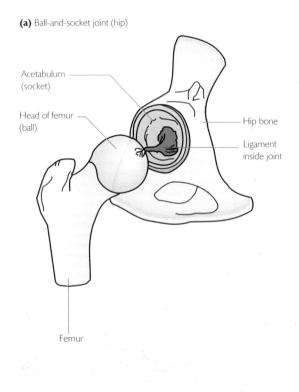

(b) Hinge joint (knee)

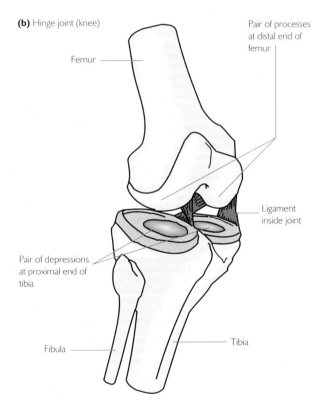

Figure 4 *Exploded sketches of knee and hip joints*

calcium salts are deposited to form bone. The role of an orthopaedic surgeon is normally to make sure the bones are aligned correctly. In the rare occasions that healing fails, then bone grafts from another part of the body can be used. This exposes the patient to the stress of two operations and an increased risk of complications and pain. It also costs a lot to perform a double operation and the long recovery time keeps the patient in an expensive hospital bed. Taking donor bone increases the risk of rejection or transmission of diseases such as hepatitis B or HIV.

New materials

Introducing new materials to the body can cause problems. Materials that are too weak may themselves break too easily. If the replacement material is much stiffer than the natural bone to which it is attached, then forces become concentrated in the replacement material. Bone regrows naturally when subjected to forces, but otherwise it wastes away – astronauts who live for long periods in weightless conditions can suffer problems with their bones if they do not undertake enough exercise. Not least, the new materials must be sterile and also must not cause the body's immune system to reject them.

Figure 5 *A coral reef*

'Of his bones are coral made'

Coral is a natural material, similar in many respects to bone. It is the subject of research to see whether it might make a good bone substitute. The title of this subsection comes from Shakespeare's '*The Tempest*', so even then the similarity between bone and coral was recognised.

Coral reefs are the largest structures on Earth. Tiny marine animals called corals feed off microscopic plankton and turn the consumed carbon into calcium carbonate. When they die their mineral skeletons become part of a reef, which we call coral [Figure 5]. It is similar in structure to bone, and a few species of coral have the necessary porous inner structure to allow new blood vessels to develop into the graft which will allow the body to start the growth of new bone and tissue around the coral.

Two researchers at the French Research Institute (CNRS) in Paris, Drs Patat and Guillemin, have pioneered the use of medical coral. They have mended shattered limbs, backbones and jaws with, they claim, 'as good as new' results [Figure 6].

Jonathan Knowles, a researcher at the Interdisciplinary Research Centre in Biomedical Materials, based at Queen Mary and Westfield College, London, believes that coral will be especially useful for treating more difficult fractures. 'When a bone breaks it normally heals within 8 weeks. But there are some cases where the two ends don't grow back together. If you put in a metal plate, it still doesn't heal. A stimulus is usually needed to get a new bone to grow. Coral actively promotes bone formation and healing in a way that materials like steel don't,' explains Knowles.

Figure 6 *A patient's shattered spine is repaired using coral*

As well as being tough and less likely to be rejected by the body's immune system, coral carries no risk of infection, unlike grafts of human bone. The only drawback is that coral has the potential to absorb toxic metals such as nickel, cadmium and mercury.

Medical coral is harvested from warm reefs in the South Pacific islands of New Caledonia, east of Australia, under strict rules that minimise environmental damage.

QUESTIONS

1 Name a common external skeleton (exoskeleton).

2 Write down at least two functions of a skeleton.

3 How might bone behave if it was without living fibres?

4 Describe the main difference in the movement of a hinge joint compared with that of a ball and socket.

5 List at least two advantages of using a bone substitute rather than using human bone.

6 What material is missing from coral that is present in bone?

2.2 The right stuff

To make a good bone substitute, a material must be strong enough to exert and withstand the forces involved in normal movement; if it is to be used in a hip replacement, it must support a person's weight. Its **mechanical properties** (the way it behaves when subjected to forces) must be similar to those of real bone. In this section you will see how materials are tested, described and compared.

If you have studied the unit *Good Enough to Eat*, you will have met several terms used to describe materials and their behaviour. Some of these are listed in Table 1, along with two extra terms (**smooth** and **durable**) not used in that unit. In the course of this unit, the meanings of some of these terms will be refined.

elastic	returns to its original size and shape when the load is removed
plastic	remains deformed when the load is removed
brittle	cracks and breaks without plastic deformation
ductile	can be pulled into a long thin shape
hard	not readily scratched or indented
stiff	requires a large force to produce a small deformation
tough	deforms plastically and can withstand dynamic loads such as shock or impact
smooth	low friction surface
durable	properties do not worsen with repeated loading and unloading

Table I *Terms used to describe the behaviour of materials*

QUESTION

7 Use terms from Table I to describe the ideal properties of the following spare parts: (**a**) blood vessel, (**b**) teeth and (**c**) thigh bone.

Stress and strain

In the unit *Higher, Faster, Stronger*, you saw that the extension of a rope or a cord under a given load depends on its length and thickness as well as on the material from which is made. One way to compare the behaviour of different materials is to use samples of a standard size. Another way is to define and measure properties in such a way that they depend only on the material and not on the size and shape of the sample; as bones do not come in standard sizes, it makes sense to compare their properties in this way.

Bones are normally subjected to compressive forces – that is, to forces that tend to squash them. Under a relatively small force, bone will deform slightly (though not much, because it is stiff), but if the force becomes large the bone may break. If two samples of different thickness are both subjected to compressive forces, the thinner one will break under a smaller force. If one sample has twice the cross-sectional area of the other, then it will withstand twice the force, but for each sample the force divided by the area is the same. Applied force, F, divided by area of cross-section, A, is called the **stress** and is represented by σ (the Greek letter sigma):

$$\sigma = \frac{F}{A} \qquad (1)$$

The same definition and symbols are used for **tensile stress** (when the sample is pulled) and for **compressive stress** (when the sample is squashed). The SI unit of stress is the pascal (Pa); $1\,\text{Pa} = 1\,\text{N m}^{-2}$. You have probably met the unit before – it is also used for pressure. 1 Pa is a very small stress; the SI prefixes kilo and mega are usually needed when measuring stresses in practical situations.

The stress needed to break a material is called its **ultimate compressive** (or **tensile**) **stress**, or simply the **breaking stress**, and is a measure of the **strength** of the material that does not depend on the size of the sample. The ultimate compressive stress of bone, or bone substitute, is clearly important to the user, as you will see in questions 8 and 9 and Activity 4.

QUESTIONS

8 Estimate the compressive stress in your leg bones when you are standing still. Explain why their ultimate compressive stress needs to be much greater than this.

9 A 70 kg man jumps from a wall 1.5 m high, lands on both feet together and takes 0.1 s to come to rest. The cross-sectional area of the bones in each of his lower legs is 30 cm².

Study note

If you have studied the unit *Good Enough to Eat*, you will have seen that many tests used by the food industry require samples of standard size.

Maths reference

SI prefixes
See Maths note 2.4

(a) How fast is he moving just as he reaches the ground?

(b) What is his average deceleration?

(c) What is the average force exerted as he comes to rest?

(d) What is the stress in his lower legs as he comes to rest?

Use $g = 9.8\,\mathrm{m\,s^{-2}} = 9.8\,\mathrm{N\,kg^{-1}}$. You might need to look back at the work you did in *Higher, Faster, Stronger*. Note that you need to express the areas in $\mathrm{m^2}$.

ACTIVITY 4   Crunchie bones?

The inside of a Crunchie bar is very similar to bone in structure and appearance. Measure the breaking stress for a piece of Crunchie bar, and hence decide whether it would make an acceptable bone substitute.

The amount by which a sample deforms also depends on the stress. In the unit *Higher, Faster, Stronger*, you learnt that, for a material that obey's **Hooke's law**, the extension is proportional to the applied force. Figure 7 shows two samples that obey Hooke's law. They are both made of the same material and are the same length but one has twice the cross-sectional area of the other. If the

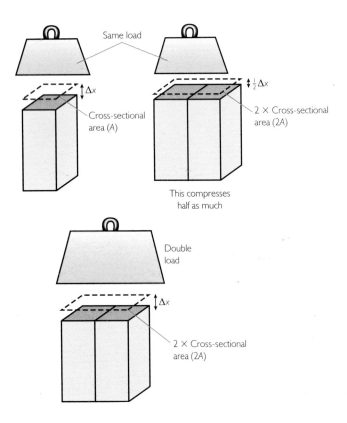

Figure 7   *Samples of different thickness being subjected to compression*

same force is applied to each, then the thicker sample is deformed by only half as much as the thinner one, but if they are both subject to the same stress, then they both suffer the same deformation. So, *for samples of the same length*, compression (or extension) Δx is proportional to stress, and Hooke's law can be expressed as

$$\Delta x \propto \sigma \tag{2}$$

The extension, or compression, of a sample, depends on its length as well as on its area of cross-section. As shown in Figure 8, doubling the length of the sample doubles the compression. For each sample, the ratio of compression, or extension, Δx to original length ℓ is the same. This ratio is defined as the **strain** and is represented by the symbol ε (the Greek letter epsilon):

$$\varepsilon = \frac{\Delta x}{\ell} \tag{3}$$

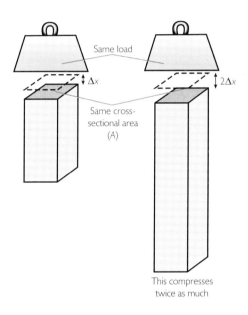

Figure 8 *Samples of different length being subjected to compression*

The same symbols are used for **compressive strain** and for **tensile strain**. Notice that strain is a ratio of two lengths and so it has *no units*. Strain is often expressed as a percentage – that is, the compression or extension as a percentage of the original length.

Maths reference

Fractions, decimals and percentages
See Maths note 3.1

QUESTIONS

10 In a test on a sample of possible bone substitute, a sample 40 cm long is compressed by 2.5 mm. What is the compressive strain expressed as a decimal and as a percentage?

11 A metal wire is given a tensile strain of 0.15%. If the original length of the wire was 50 cm, by how much did it extend? Express your answer in mm. If a 5 m wire is given the same strain, by how much will it extend?

Hooke's law and the Young modulus

In previous work, you have used force–extension graphs to show how a material sample deforms under a load. If, instead of force against extension, we plot stress against strain, then we get a graph that depends only on the nature of the material and not on the size and shape of the sample. Figure 9 shows such a **stress–strain graph** (b) plotted for a material sample, alongside two force–extension graphs (a) for different samples of the same material. Notice that all the graphs are the same shape, although they have different numbers on the axes.

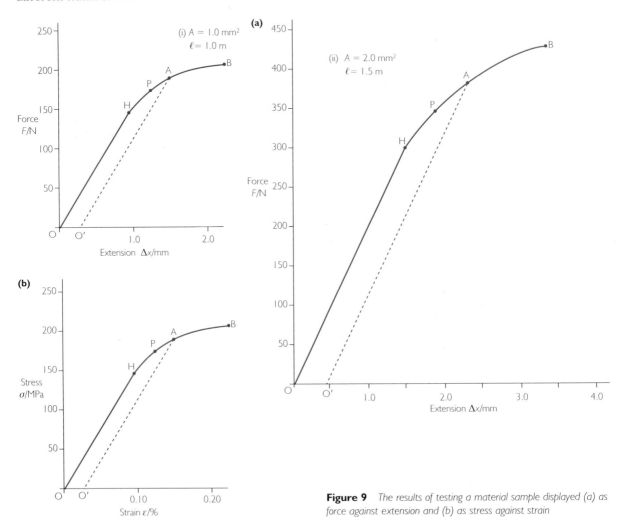

Figure 9 *The results of testing a material sample displayed (a) as force against extension and (b) as stress against strain*

The labels on the graphs in Figure 9 are related to the mechanical behaviour of the sample. In Figure 9(a), from O to H each graph is straight; H is the **limit of proportionality**. Force is proportional to extension, i.e. the sample obeys Hooke's law. In Figure 9(b), between O and H, stress is proportional to strain – which is another way of expressing Hooke's law.

Elastic deformation occurs up to P, the **elastic limit**. This means that the material returns to its original length when released.

Beyond P the material gains permanent extension and is therefore said to behave plastically. P is also known as the **yield point**. It is worth noting that if released at A (i.e. beyond P) the material recovers along AO', which is parallel to HO, giving it a permanent extension of OO'. If stress is reapplied then the curve O'AB is followed. At B the sample breaks. In Figure 9(b), the stress at B is the breaking stress or ultimate tensile stress.

In the unit *Higher, Faster, Stronger* we defined the stiffness, k, of a sample such that

$$k = \frac{\Delta F}{\Delta x} \tag{4}$$

k is equal to the gradient of the force–extension graph. Rather similarly, we can measure the gradient of the stress–strain graph. Now, though, we get a value that depends only on the material and not on the size or shape of the sample – it is a measure of the **stiffness of the material**. This value is known as the **Young modulus**, E, of the material:

$$E = \frac{\sigma}{\varepsilon} \tag{5}$$

Study note

The Young modulus is given the symbol E because it is a so-called 'elastic modulus'. There are other elastic moduli which you will meet in the unit *Build or Bust?*.

Since strain has no unit then the SI unit of the Young modulus is that of stress, i.e. pascals, Pa.

The Young modulus is important when designing materials for replacement joints. Figure 10 shows a typical hip replacement. Bone typically has a Young modulus of about 1×10^{10} Pa. If the

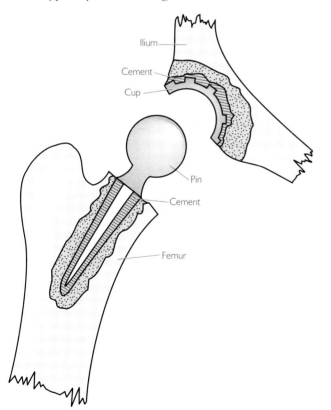

Figure 10   *A typical hip joint replacement*

replacement has a smaller Young modulus than the natural bone into which it is inserted, then most of the load will be supported by the natural bone, which might then be under too much stress and become damaged. (You can model this using two springs side by side, as in Figure 11. If one spring is stiffer than the other, then as you squash both springs you feel the stiffer spring exerting a greater force.) However, if the Young modulus of the replacement is too high, then it supports most of the load. Far from protecting the natural bone, this causes it to waste away because it is deprived of the stress that stimulates regrowth.

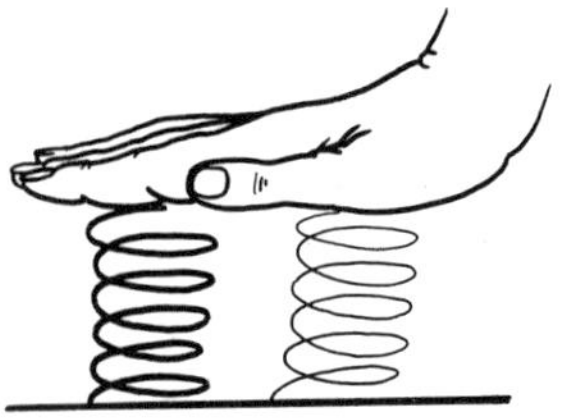

Figure 11 *Squashing two springs of different stiffness*

New materials

At the time of writing (1999) replacement hip joints are made of metal. These last for about ten years, after which time they need to be replaced. For this reason, hip replacements are not generally given to younger people, since they would need several operations in the course of a lifetime.

You have read of one possible substitute bone material: coral. The development of completely artificial bone materials is the subject of much current research. These have the advantage that they can be made to precise specifications in controlled sterile conditions. The most promising new materials are **polymers**, since these can be designed to have properties very similar to real bone and they are also very strong. One such material, HAPEX, has been developed at the Biomedical Materials Interdisciplinary Research Centre (IRC) at Queen Mary and Westfield College, London, under the leadership of Professor Bonfield. HAPEX is a composite material, consisting of a polymer (polyethylene) and a ceramic (hydroxyapatite), which is quite similar to natural bone in structure and chemical composition. (Coral, incidentally, is a natural hydroxyapatite.)

HAPEX has been used to replace the tiny bones in the middle ear which are responsible for the conduction of sound (Figure 12). Stronger versions of the material are being developed in collaboration with the Polymer IRC at Leeds, Bradford and Durham Universities and it is hoped to use it for hip replacements. As the material closely resembles real bone, the real bone will grow into it and attach the implant very firmly. It is anticipated that HAPEX implants will last about thirty years and will therefore be feasible for use with young sports-active people.

Figure 12 *A tiny HAPEX artificial bone for ear implants compared in size with a 5p coin*

As well as the replacement bone itself, the material to make the outer parts of the replacement joint must be carefully chosen to have suitable mechanical properties. Again, polymer materials are proving ideal. In Activity 5, you are asked to test a sample of UHMWPE (ultra-high-molecular-weight polyethylene) to check that its properties are suitable. This material is used to make the cup in replacement ball-and-socket joints. The main reason for its use is its low friction, but the material must also be able to withstand the large stresses exerted on the joint.

Polymers

Polymers consist of molecules that are long chains made up of fairly simple arrangements of carbon and other atoms repeated many times over. Polyethylene is a polymer whose molecules are long chains of C_2H_2 units joined together (Figure 13). Its official chemical name is poly(ethene) (C_2H_2 is ethene) and it is known colloquially as polythene. The length of the chains depends on how the polymer is made. UHMWPE has very long chains – 'ultra-high-molecular-weight' means that the (average) mass of each molecule is large.

UHMWPE has a very smooth surface, and is also very tough, so it is used for many other purposes as well as for replacement joints. These include:

- coating of hoppers in the steel industry to allow coke to flow easily
- rear of boring heads for tunnel building to allow earth and clay to fall off easily
- sliders in railway points so that ice will not stick to them
- harbour fenders
- rail guides for conveyor belts.

Perplas Medical Ltd in Lancashire specialise in the production of UHMWPE. They can produce rods, sheets and machined components using computer-aided design machining equipment and presses. Their machines work in an environment controlled by electrostatic filtration to submicrometre size to ensure that airborne contaminants are kept to an absolute minimum. Any material introduced into the body must be free of microbes. This medical-grade material is used in hip joints (Figure 14a), and is supplied with a certificate that allows total traceability and figures to show test results of its important mechanical properties to its user (Figure 14b).

Ethene

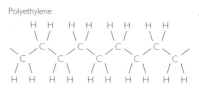

Polyethylene

Figure 13 *Ethene and polyethylene*

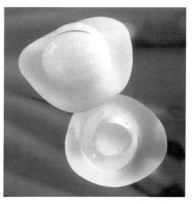

(a)

(b)

Figure 14 *(a) Hip joints made with UHMWPE. (b) A test certificate for medical-grade UHMWPE*

ACTIVITY 5 **Is it good enough?**

Test a sample of UHMWPE and see how well it compares with the medical-grade sample shown in Figure 14(b). Figure 15 shows two possible versions of the apparatus.

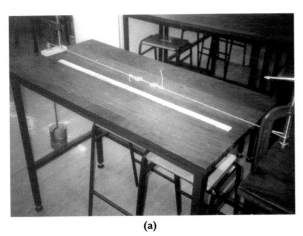

(a)

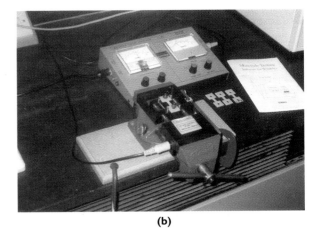

(b)

Figure 15 *Apparatus for Activity 5: (a) simple version and (b) materials testing kit*

Stress–strain graphs, and the Young modulus, are widely used in all areas of materials science, not just those concerned with medical applications, as questions 12 to 14 illustrate.

QUESTIONS

12 A steel wire of cross-sectional area $0.5\,mm^2$ and length $8.0\,m$ is found to stretch $6.0\,mm$ when the tension on it is increased by $75\,N$. It returned to its original length when the extra tension was released.

(**a**) What was its cross-sectional area in square metres?

(**b**) What stress had been applied?

(**c**) What was the resultant strain?

(**d**) What is the Young modulus for steel?

(**e**) Bone typically has a Young modulus of about $1 \times 10^{10}\,Pa$. What problems would there be in using steel as a replacement bone material?

(**f**) A lift cable consists of 100 strands of this wire. The lift is limited to 10 people of maximum mass $85\,kg$ each. When the lift is full, by how much will the $90\,m$ cable stretch? ($g = 9.8\,N\,kg^{-1}$.)

13 A steel rod was tested to destruction. It had a cross-sectional area of $1.30 \times 10^{-4}\,m^2$ and a length of $65 \times 10^{-3}\,m$. The results are listed in Table 2 in the order in which they were obtained.

(**a**) Use Table 2 to draw up a table of stress and strain and plot a stress–strain graph. Join the plotted points with a smooth curve, being careful to join them in the order in which they are listed. (You might need two graphs, one for small strains and one for large strains.)

(**b**) From your graph
  (**i**)   What was the yield stress of the steel?
  (**ii**) What was the ultimate tensile stress of the steel?
  (**iii**) What was the percentage strain when it broke?

14 A nylon guitar string has a diameter of $0.4\,mm$. The length of the string from its fixed point to the tension key is $840\,mm$. Turning the tension key once extends the string by $4.0\,mm$. Calculate the tension in the string when the key has been turned eight times. (Young modulus for nylon $= 3.0 \times 10^9\,Pa$.)

Tension /10^3 N	Extension /10^{-3} m
0.0	0.0
35.0	0.1
38.0	0.2
36.5	0.4
36.0	0.7
37.0	1.0
40.0	1.4
45.0	2.1
50.0	3.1
55.0	5.1
57.5	7.2
60.0	9.1
60.0	13.1
57.5	14.7
55.0	15.2
52.5	15.8 (broke)

Table 2 *Data for question 13*

Elastic energy

Look back at Figure 1, and think again about the different types of materials used to make spare parts such as bones, ligaments and blood vessels. Bone substitutes need to be strong and stiff, but other replacement parts need to be more elastic. In some cases, this is because they need to store and return energy. In the unit *Higher, Faster, Stronger*, you measured some of the energy transfers in sporting activities, and energies of a few hundred joules were common (for example, in jumping and weight-lifting). In Activity 5, you might have inadvertently experienced the elastic energy stored in stretched UHMWPE; this material's ability to store energy is not relevant to its use in hip joints, but it is important in some of its other uses (such as harbour fenders).

In *Higher, Faster, Stronger* you saw how to find elastic energy, ΔE_{el}, from a force–extension graph: it is equal to the area under the curve. If the sample obeys Hooke's law, then

$$\Delta E_{el} = \frac{F\Delta x}{2} = \tfrac{1}{2} k(\Delta x)^2 \qquad (6)$$

where F is the magnitude of the force needed to produce an extension Δx (see Figure 16a). If the sample does not obey Hooke's law, then the area can be found by counting squares (Figure 16b).

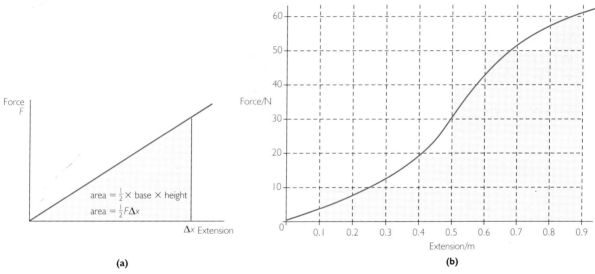

(a)

(b)

Figure 16 *Elastic energy is found from the area under a force–extension graph either (a) by calculation or (b) by counting squares*

What about stress–strain graphs? We have seen that the gradient of such a graph has a meaning (it is the Young modulus), but what about the area under the curve? Think of a material that obeys Hooke's law. At a given strain ε, the area under the stress–strain curve is $\sigma\varepsilon/2$ (Figure 17). Since (from equation 1)

$$F = \sigma A$$

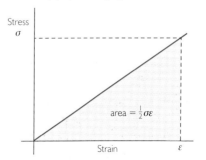

Figure 17 *The area under a stress–strain curve for a material that obeys Hooke's law*

and (from equation 3)

$$\Delta x = \varepsilon \ell$$

we can write equation (6) as

$$\Delta E_{el} = \frac{\sigma A \times \varepsilon \ell}{2} = A\ell \times \left(\frac{\sigma \varepsilon}{2}\right)$$

But ℓA is just the volume, V, of the sample, and so

$$\text{area under stress–strain curve} = \frac{\sigma \varepsilon}{2} = \frac{\Delta E_{el}}{V} \qquad (7)$$

In other words, the area under the curve is equal to the energy stored per unit volume, or the **energy density**, U.

For a material that obeys Hooke's law, we can rewrite equation (7) using the Young modulus, E (from equation 5):

$$\sigma = E\varepsilon$$

and so

$$U = \frac{\Delta E_{el}}{V} = \frac{E\varepsilon^2}{2} \qquad (8)$$

For a material that does not obey Hooke's law, equation (8) does not apply, but the area under a stress–strain curve is still equal to the stored energy density.

QUESTIONS

15 Suppose you want a material that is capable of storing a large amount of elastic energy per unit volume (e.g. to make an artificial tendon). What particular mechanical properties would you look for?

16 (a) Look back at your answer to question 13, and use your graph to find the energy density in steel when it breaks.

(b) Given that the density of steel is about $8 \times 10^3\,\mathrm{kg\,m^{-3}}$, estimate the speed of a steel wire when it breaks.

2.3 The inside story

As you saw in section 2.2, polymer materials are being developed to make substitute bones, and to make replacement ball-and-socket joints. These materials have mechanical properties (Young modulus, strength, smoothness) that enable them to match natural materials. Another recent development is artificial skin, which is particularly useful when treating people who have been badly burned or whose skin has become ulcerated. Artificial skin is much more elastic than artificial bone, to match natural skin. (You can demonstrate this elasticity by pinching a fold of skin on the back of your hand and noticing that it springs back. The elasticity of skin declines with age; ask an older or younger person to repeat the 'pinch test' and compare observations.)

A skin substitute called Dermagraft, made by Advanced Tissue Science Inc. in the USA, combines a bioengineered human dermal (skin) layer with a synthetic polymer covering. On being transplanted, the polymer covering dissolves and the patient's own cells start to grow.

Why do polymers play such a key role in spare part materials? The clue lies in their small-scale structure. Before discussing polymers, we will see how materials can be examined on a very small scale.

Diffraction patterns

The first materials to be investigated on a small scale were metals and minerals, in the early years of the 20th century. Many minerals form regular crystals, which suggests that there might be some underlying regular arrangement of their atoms. With the discovery of X-rays at the end of the 19th century, scientists had a tool with which to probe the structure of materials. If you shine a beam of visible light on to a screen through a regular array of obstacles whose size and separation are comparable to the wavelength, you produce a **diffraction pattern** on the screen – a regular array of bright spots of light whose separation and symmetry depend on the spacing and symmetry of the obstacles. You can demonstrate this by shining a laser through a fine gauze (Figure 18). The finer the gauze, the greater the spacing of the dots in the pattern. The spacing of the dots also depends on the wavelength of the light; the longer the wavelength, the greater the spacing – though this cannot be demonstrated with a laser, since it is monochromatic.

The same thing happens, on a much smaller scale, if you shine a beam of X-rays through a crystal (Figure 19). Analysis of X-ray diffraction patterns reveals that crystals do indeed consist of regular arrays of atoms – and so do metals. If you have studied the unit *Digging Up the Past*, you will have seen how X-ray diffraction can be used to identify minerals.

X-ray diffraction patterns rely on X-rays being scattered by relatively heavy atoms. For materials made up of light elements, such as carbon, nitrogen and hydrogen, another diffraction technique is used, involving beams of electrons. You probably find this quite surprising, since diffraction is something that waves do, whereas you have always thought of electrons as particles.

Electron waves

The wave-like side of the electron's character was discovered in the 1920s, and the discovery came about in two ways. First came a theoretical prediction by the French scientist Prince Louis de Broglie (1892–1987). Louis de Broglie knew that light can behave as either waves or 'particles' (photons), and in 1924, in his doctoral thesis, he

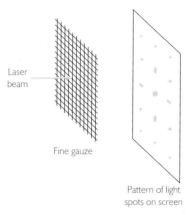

Figure 18   *Producing an optical diffraction pattern*

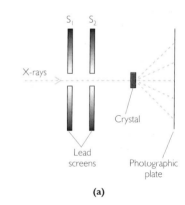

(a)

(b)

Figure 19   *An X-ray diffraction pattern like that drawn in (b) is produced by a crystal.*

put forward the idea that electrons (and other particles) might have a similar dual nature and sometimes behave as waves. He predicted that the wavelength, λ, of a particle of mass m moving at speed v would be given by

$$\lambda = \frac{h}{mv} \tag{9}$$

where h is Planck's constant. This wavelength is sometimes known as the **de Broglie wavelength** of a particle. Experimental support for this revolutionary idea was obtained within the next three years by American scientists Clinton Davisson and Lester Germer, and independently by British scientist George Thomson, who produced diffraction patterns using electron beams directed at metals and crystals. All these scientists received Nobel Prizes for their work. George Thomson was the son of J.J. (Joseph) Thomson who, a generation earlier, had received a Nobel Prize for demonstrating conclusively that electrons were particles.

Electron diffraction can be demonstrated using the apparatus shown in Figure 20. In the electron gun (Figure 21), electrons are 'boiled off' a heated filament by a process called **thermionic emission**. They are then attracted towards a positive anode, accelerated by a potential difference of a few hundred volts. The glass tube containing the gun and target has a near-vacuum inside, so there are few air molecules to impede the motion of the electrons. Most of the electrons pass straight through the anode and fly straight on to hit the graphite target. The electron beam passes through the thin layer of graphite and hits the fluorescent layer inside the rounded end of the tube, transferring energy to it and making it glow. Graphite consists of layers of carbon atoms arranged in regular hexagonal patterns (Figure 22), and so produces a diffraction pattern when waves pass through whose wavelength is comparable to the atomic spacing.

Study note

You will meet the de Broglie wavelength again in the unit *Probing the Heart of Matter*.

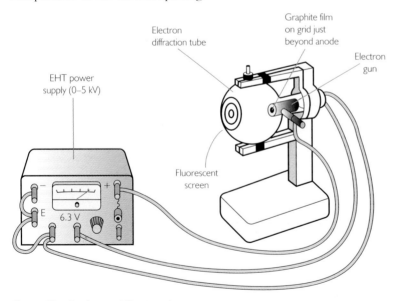

Figure 20 *An electron diffraction tube*

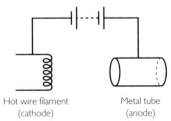

Figure 21 *An electron gun*

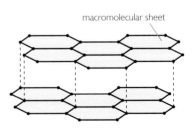

Figure 22 *The arrangement of carbon atoms in graphite*

ACTIVITY **6** **Electron diffraction**

Use the apparatus shown in Figure 20 to observe electron diffraction. Predict and observe what happens to the electrons' speed, and hence to their wavelength and to the spacing of the diffraction pattern, as the accelerating voltage is increased.

QUESTION

17 Electrons are accelerated in an electron gun by a potential difference, V, of 100 V. Calculate the speed of the electrons if each has a mass, m, of 9.1×10^{-31} kg and a charge, e, of 1.6×10^{-19} C. What is their de Broglie wavelength? ($h = 6.6 \times 10^{-34}$ J s)

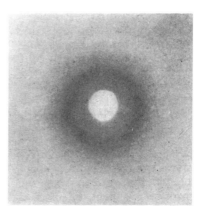

(a)

Polymer structures

Electron diffraction patterns reveal the crystal structure of graphite, but what about polymers? Figure 23 shows two electron diffraction patterns for rubber, a natural polymer. In Figure 23(b) there is evidence for a regular arrangement of atoms, but not in Figure 23(a). This shows that we are introducing some sort of structure as we stretch it. Unstretched polymers have no regular structure and are said to be **amorphous**: the long-chain polymer molecules are intertwined and jumbled up (Figure 24a). A stretching force tends to uncoil the chains and straighten them into orderly lines (Figure 24b), and so they can produce a regular diffraction pattern. When released, the molecules coil up again. When fully extended the chains are stiff because their interatomic bonds are then stretched directly. This explains why polymers have a Young modulus 10 000 times less than that of a metal but can be extended to perhaps ten times their original length (1000% strain).

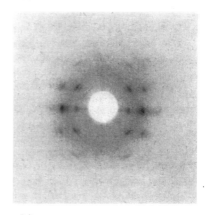

(b)

Figure 23 *Electron diffraction patterns for rubber: (a) unstretched and (b) stretched*

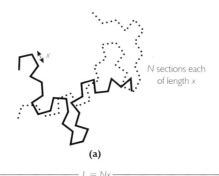

N sections each of length x

(a)

$$L = Nx$$

(b)

Figure 24 *Schematic diagrams of polymer chains: (a) in an unstretched polymer and (b) in a stretched polymer*

Low-density low-molecular-weight polyethylene is similar to rubber with lots of jumbled-up polymer chains. This is confirmed by the diffraction pattern in Figure 25(a). The pattern for high-density high-molecular-weight polyethylene (Figure 25b) must result from a more regular arrangement of the polymer molecules. In fact the very long molecules fold up as shown in Figure 26 and stack up in what is referred to as a lamella formation (lamella means 'little plate'). As can be seen, the vertical strands are parallel and regular and so resemble a crystalline structure.

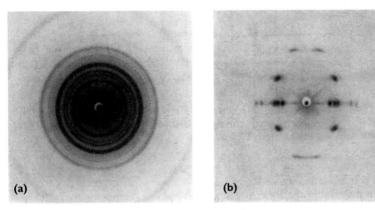

Figure 25　*Electron diffraction patterns for polyethylene with (a) low molecular weight and (b) high molecular weight*

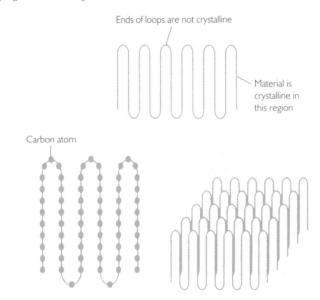

Figure 26　*Lamella formation in high-molecular-weight polyethylene*

When the material is unstretched, the lamellae are randomly orientated as shown in Figure 27. As the material is stretched, they start to align. This is a reversible effect, and so the material behaves elastically. It is quite stiff and so makes a good material for cups. Increased stress leads to a breakdown of the lamellae into fibrils (tiny fibres). The long polymer chains line up and then the material becomes strong as the carbon–carbon bonds are stretched.

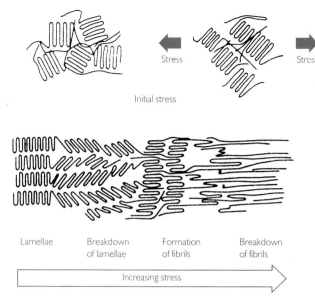

Initial stress

Stress

Stress

| Lamellae | Breakdown of lamellae | Formation of fibrils | Breakdown of fibrils |

Increasing stress

Figure 27   *Stretching UHMWPE*

Designer materials

Just as the Stone, Iron and Bronze Ages are so called because of the materials in common use at the time, perhaps the late 20th century will come to be called the 'Polymer Age'. Most of the man-made materials that we loosely call 'plastics' are in fact polymers. Polythene is one common example, and PVC (polyvinyl chloride) is another – you can probably think of others (having 'poly' in the name is a clue). Polymer materials such as PVC can be made relatively cheaply, can easily be shaped and coloured, and are also durable, hence their widespread use.

Polyethylene and PVC are man-made polymers, but there are also many natural polymers found in living things. Plant fibres such as cotton are made up of polymers, as are animal fibres such as hair and wool. It is because they can imitate natural materials that man-made polymers find a use in spare part surgery.

As you have seen, the mechanical properties of a polymer depend on the way its chain molecules arrange themselves, and this in turn depends on the length of the molecules and their chemical make-up. The disciplines of physics and chemistry come together in polymer science, enabling a vast range of polymers to be developed that have a very wide variety of properties.

2.4   Summing up part 2

In this part of the unit you have extended your knowledge of the physics of materials, and seen how a knowledge of the small-scale structure of a material can help explain its large-scale behaviour. This understanding can help materials scientists to develop materials with properties to suit a particular purpose.

ACTIVITY **7** **Summing up part 2**

Look back through your work and make sure you know the meanings of all the key terms printed in bold. Then write each term on a slip of paper (e.g. a 'Post-it' sticker) and arrange them on a large sheet of paper to make a concept map for this part of the unit. Link the slips of paper by writing a few words or an equation or by sketching a diagram.

When completed, your concept map should provide you with a summary of what you have learned about large-scale and small-scale properties of materials (particularly polymers) and how they are interrelated.

ACTIVITY **8** **Polymer science**

Write a short essay about polymers, using what you have learned in this section together with information obtained from one or more of the following websites, which are all related to the development of spare part materials and other current research:

- Advanced Tissue Science Inc. (developers of Dermagraft)
  http://www.advancedtissue.com/

- Smith and Nephew (suppliers of HAPEX and Dermagraft)
  http://www.smithnephew.com/

- IRC Research Programmes (includes HAPEX)
  http://www.qmw.ac.uk/~ugez027/irc.html

- Professor Paul Brown
  http://bioeng.psu.edu/brown.html

- Howmedica Products
  http://www.Howmedica.com/products/noframes/prod2p4.htm

QUESTION

18 Figure 28 shows a schematic stress–strain graph for a polymer material.

(**a**) How would a stress–strain graph for a metal differ from Figure 28?

(**b**) Suggest a physical interpretation for the area enclosed between the 'Loading' and 'Unloading' curves in Figure 28.

(**c**) Sketch (**i**) the arrangement of molecules and (**ii**) the electron diffraction pattern you would expect to obtain when the sample was at point A and at point C.

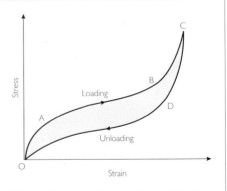

Figure 28   *Stress–strain graph for a polymer*

Further **investigations**

Explore the behaviour of various materials that appear 'bone-like', such as cuttle-fish bone (available from pet-shops), seaside rock and 'oasis' (used in flower-arranging). Try to measure the Young modulus and ultimate compressive strength. Observe the way they fracture. Comment on their resemblance (or otherwise) to real bone.

3 *A sight better*

3.1 *One in the eye*

Lens implants

Our eyes are our most important sense organs (Figure 29). They account for about 80% of our brains' sensory input which tells us what's going on around us. So if something goes wrong with our eyes, we're in trouble.

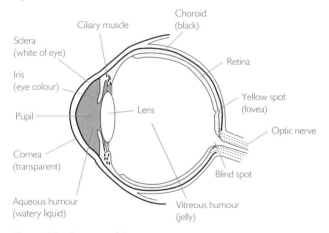

Figure 29 *Structure of the eye*

Study note

Note that Figure 29 is a horizontal section of the eye. You have to imagine that you are looking down on to the top of someone's head; this is a horizontal slice through their right eye.

For most people, the worst problem we are ever likely to have with our eyesight is cataracts. A cataract is a cloudy region within the lens of the eye, and seeing through a cataract-affected eye can be like looking through a steamed-up window.

Cataracts are common among elderly people. They may result from injuries, from disease or even from some medications. However, they can also occur simply as a result of the deterioration of the material of the lens as it ages. Some children are born with congenital cataracts. A small speck of cataract in the lens may have little effect on your vision, but a larger cataract in the centre of the lens can be very serious.

As a cataract develops, the sufferer is likely to notice two effects: their vision gets dimmer, and it gets more hazy – it's harder to see a clearly focused image. At first, spectacles can be prescribed to improve focusing, but eventually an operation may be necessary. In the past, it was common simply to remove the lens and provide the patient with spectacles with very strong lenses. This was a good solution at the time, but strong lenses tend to give you a clear view straight ahead but not to the sides, and what you see is 30% enlarged. Nowadays a different technique is available – lens implants.

Cataract surgery: a step-by-step guide
The lens of the eye is rather like a grape. The lens capsule is the grape's skin. Here's how to replace a faulty lens with an intra-ocular lens (an IOL). It only takes 20 to 30 minutes and can be done in the Outpatients' Department of a hospital. Don't try this at home!

- Make a tiny incision in the white of the eye, next to the cornea.
- Insert a fine tool and peel off the front of the lens capsule.
- Emulsify the material of the inside of the lens using ultrasound, to reduce it to tiny particles.
- Suck out this fluid using a tiny vacuum tube.
- Slide a substitute plastic lens into the lens capsule.
- Seal the incision.

Surgery is not appropriate for all patients with cataracts. There can be complications. Patients may be suffering from other complaints such as glaucoma or diabetic retinopathy (extra blood vessels in the retina resulting from diabetes), and these conditions may be worsened by cataract surgery. For the right patients, however, this operation can be very successful, greatly improving the brightness and clarity of their eyesight.

Contact lenses

A piece of grit in the eye is most uncomfortable. Your eye waters uncontrollably, and you have to stop what you are doing until you have got rid of the problem.

Our eyes are very sensitive to small particles of dirt, and no-one wants to be poked in the eye with a sharp stick. Even thinking about it can make us blink. So, at first, the idea of wearing contact lenses can seem pretty nasty. Who wants to have to put a piece of plastic in each eye, every day? Of course, most people quickly learn to manage with modern contact lenses, and their smoothness means that your eyes often don't even notice that you're wearing them.

The first contact lenses – over a century ago – were made of glass. They fitted right over the front of the eye (the cornea) and under both eyelids. They were very awkward to put in place, and so they were only used by a few people for whom spectacles were completely unsuitable. Nowadays, contact lenses are much smaller, and made of plastic. They cover the central part of the cornea and are precisely shaped to fit it. See Figure 30.

The cornea of the eye is an unusual part of the body. It consists of living tissue, but it has no blood supply. To get the oxygen supply needed for its cells to metabolise, it absorbs oxygen from the air and from the tears that keep it wet. Contact lenses are made from a type of plastic that contains moisture. Oxygen can diffuse

(a)

(b)

Figure 30 *(a) An early contact lens (b) Modern 'soft' contact lenses*

through the moisture to reach the cornea – some lenses are more permeable to oxygen than others (see Table 3). Carbon dioxide must be able to diffuse away in the opposite direction.

hard	Rigid plastic – impermeable to O_2 – small, so they don't cut out much O_2 – take time to get used to – least popular
soft	Contain moisture – permeable to O_2 – larger diameter than hard lenses – flexible – most popular
gas-permeable	Made from recently developed plastic – rigid, like hard lenses – allow some O_2 through
monthly/daily replacement	High-water-content plastic – disposable – sterile – no need for disinfectant or cleaning fluid – cost approximately £1 per pair

Table 3 *Contact lens types*

ACTIVITY **9** | **Vision on**

Who do you know who wears spectacles or contact lenses? When do they wear them? Do you know anyone with lens implants, or anyone who has had any other kind of eye surgery?

Compare notes with other members of the class. Estimate the proportion of people in your age group who need to wear spectacles or contact lenses. How does the proportion change as people get older?

3.2 Seeing eye to eye

Our eyes are complex organs, similar to the eyes of most other vertebrates. They have evolved to collect light from a wide angle in front of us, and to focus it into an image on the retina. Figure 31 shows how rays of light are bent (refracted) as they travel to the retina.

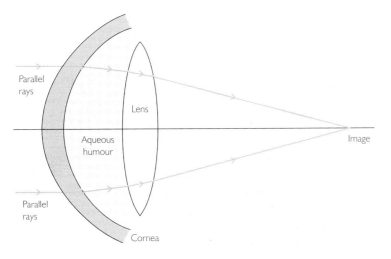

Figure 31 *Parallel rays of light from a distant object are made to converge on the retina*

You have already studied the refraction of light, in the unit *The Sound of Music*. You should recall that light changes speed and direction when it crosses a boundary between materials. Here's where a ray is bent as it passes into the eye:

- Entering the cornea: this is where most bending occurs; there is a big change in density on passing from air to corneal cells.

- Cornea/aqueous humour: small change in density, so just a small amount of bending.

- The lens: the ray bends as it enters the lens, and again as it leaves.

Because parallel rays of light are made to converge, we can regard the eye as a converging lens system. Its focal length is about 2.5 cm – roughly the distance from the front of the eye to the retina.

Seeing near and far

Look out of a window, into the distance. Now, hold a finger up in front of your eyes. You can't focus on both a distant object and a near object at the same time. You will probably feel your eyes adjusting as you focus first on one and then on the other. This adjustment is known as **accommodation**. What's going on?

To focus on objects at different distances, your eye must change its focal length. It does this by adjusting the lens in two ways:

- The ciliary muscles can relax. This pulls down on the ligaments and stretches the lens, making it thinner. When the muscles contract, the lens regains its fatter shape.

- The ciliary muscles can also pull the lens forward slightly, increasing the lens–retina distance.

At the same time, when you focus on a near object, your eyes rotate inwards slightly so that they are turned towards the object. If the object is too close, you may become cross-eyed.

Study note

Compare this with the focusing of a camera: the camera lens's focal length is fixed, and you focus simply by moving the lens back and forth, altering the lens–film distance.

QUESTIONS

19 At how many points does a ray of light bend between entering the eye and reaching the retina?

20 If you are suffering from eye strain, your ciliary muscles may be tired. Explain whether it is better to rest them by watching television or by looking at a distant view.

21 Does the focal length of the lens increase or decrease as it is stretched?

ACTIVITY 10 **Model eyes**

Use the models shown in Figure 32 to demonstrate the working of the eye. Compare the two models, and say which features of each best represent a real eye.

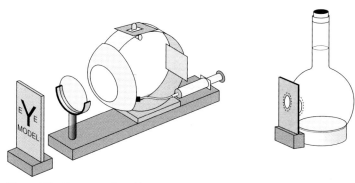

Figure 32 *Two types of model eye*

Young people are lucky – they generally have better eyesight than older people. In fact, our eyes are able to accommodate less and less as they age – that is, it gets harder and harder to focus on objects, particularly those close to us. The range over which we can focus is limited by the **near point**, usually about 20 cm for a teenager, but even closer for young children, and the **far point**, which is ideally at an infinite distance.

The decrease in the range of focusing with age is known as **presbyopia** and happens for a variety of reasons. The ciliary muscles become weaker. The lens becomes stiffer, so it is harder for the ligaments to pull on it and change its shape. Figure 33 shows how the average position of the near point changes with age. The solution is usually to wear spectacles or contact lenses.

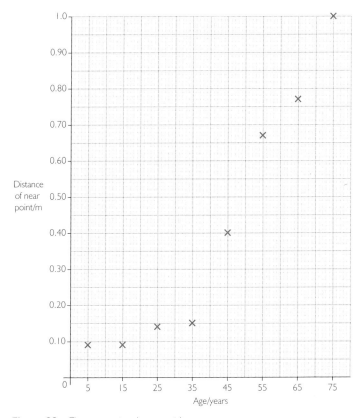

Figure 33 *The near point changes with age*

If you cannot see distant objects clearly, you are short-sighted and you are said to be suffering from **myopia**. The cause is a slightly elongated eyeball. As shown in Figure 34(a), parallel rays of light from a distant object are focused at a point in front of the retina. The lens of your eye cannot adjust its shape or position sufficiently to bring the focus on to the retina.

Long-sighted people find it impossible to focus on objects close to their eyes, and are said to suffer from **hypermetropia** or **hyperopia**. This is a problem particularly if you want to read. The focused image would only be produced behind the retina (Figure 34b) because the lens is too stiff to become fat enough to focus correctly. If you are long-sighted, your eyes can focus clearly on the horizon. In fact, your eyes can focus 'beyond the horizon', at a distance beyond infinity. This is a useless ability. You will still be able to focus on distant objects even when wearing spectacles that are intended to help you to read.

For all of these problems, an optician can prescribe spectacles or contact lenses. Figure 35 shows a typical prescription – in the rest of this section, you will learn the meaning of the hand-written numbers.

Study note

Figure 34 shows all the refraction taking place at the front of the eye, whereas in reality it takes place at several surfaces as shown in Figure 31.

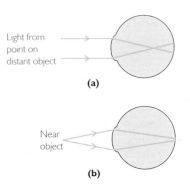

Light from point on distant object

(a)

Near object

(b)

Figure 34 (a) A short-sighted eye and (b) a long-sighted eye

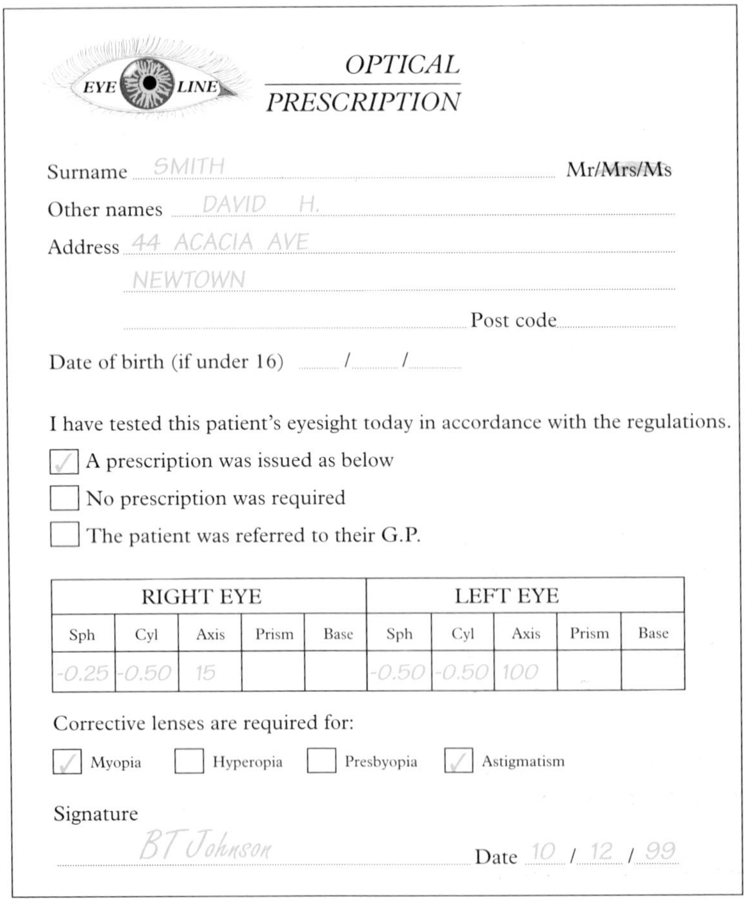

OPTICAL PRESCRIPTION

EYE ● LINE

Surname ___SMITH_____ Mr/Mrs/Ms

Other names ___DAVID   H.___

Address ___44 ACACIA AVE___

___NEWTOWN___

Post code_____

Date of birth (if under 16) ____/____/____

I have tested this patient's eyesight today in accordance with the regulations.

[✓] A prescription was issued as below

[ ] No prescription was required

[ ] The patient was referred to their G.P.

RIGHT EYE					LEFT EYE				
Sph	Cyl	Axis	Prism	Base	Sph	Cyl	Axis	Prism	Base
-0.25	-0.50	15			-0.50	-0.50	100		

Corrective lenses are required for:

[✓] Myopia   [ ] Hyperopia   [ ] Presbyopia   [✓] Astigmatism

Signature

BT Johnson

Date _10_ / _12_ / _99_

Figure 35 A typical optician's prescription might look like this

In the course of an eye test, the optician is also looking for evidence of **astigmatism**. If the eyeball is irregularly curved, the result can be blurred vision. Figure 36 shows an astigmatism chart. The lines in all directions on this chart should look equally dark. If not, you may be one of the many people whose eyes are astigmatic. (The person whose prescription is shown in Figure 35 suffers from mild astigmatism. When the number 11 bus was approaching, the number looked like 1111!) Astigmatism, too, can be corrected using spectacles.

Figure 36 *Astigmatism chart*

Lenses

Lenses come in two varieties, **converging** and **diverging**. They get their names from what they do to parallel rays of light, which depends on their shape (Figure 37).

- A converging lens makes parallel rays converge (come together).
- A diverging lens makes parallel rays diverge (spread out).
- A converging lens is thicker in the middle than at its edges.
- A diverging lens is thinner in the middle than at its edges.

(Note that it is not very helpful to categorise lenses as convex or concave, because this doesn't tell you what they do to light. Also, a lens may be convex on one side and concave on the other — most spectacle lenses are like this.)

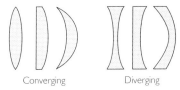

Figure 37 *Lens shapes*

ACTIVITY 11 **Looking through lenses**

Find some converging and diverging lenses. Check which is which by examining their shapes. Look through the lenses as follows, and try to summarise how they differ.

View a distant scene through each lens. Is the image that you see enlarged or reduced? Is it upside down (inverted) or the right way up (erect)?

Look through each lens at a nearby object – perhaps this page of text. What do you observe? Which type of lens can be used as a magnifying glass?

Which lenses can you use to make a **real image** on a screen? What effect does the curvature of the lens have on what you see?

ACTIVITY 12 Diverging lenses

Use a ray box to explore the effect of a diverging lens on parallel rays. Draw diagrams to show the incident and refracted rays. You should now recognise the ray diagram for a diverging lens, and be able to decide which diagram in Figure 38 is correct. Find the focal length of each lens you used.

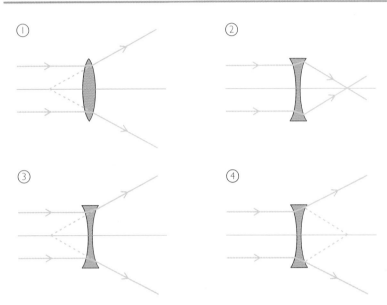

Figure 38 *Which diagram is correct?*

The correct diagram in Figure 38 shows how rays parallel to the **axis** of the lens are made to diverge. The dashed lines are known as construction lines. They show how the rays appear to diverge from a single point, the **principal focus** or **focal point** F of the lens. The **focal length** of a lens is the distance from its centre to F.

Ray diagrams

Now that you know how a diverging lens affects parallel rays of light, you can go on to draw ray diagrams which show how an image is formed by such a lens. The approach is the same as that used for converging lenses in *The Sound of Music*. We will construct ray diagrams for both types of lens, one above the other, to show the similarities.

For a converging lens, the ray diagram that results depends on the position of the object relative to the lens's principal focus F. Here we will consider an object closer to the lens than F. (This is the situation when a converging lens is used as a magnifying glass.) The situation is simpler for a diverging lens. Think back to Activity 11; no matter where you held the diverging lens relative to the object, the lens always made it look smaller.

In Figure 39, each lens is represented by a vertical line with a tiny sketch of the shape of the lens at the top. (Alternatively, you can draw a large lens in the centre, but this can be a distraction.) For the purposes of drawing ray diagrams, we show all the refraction taking place at the line.

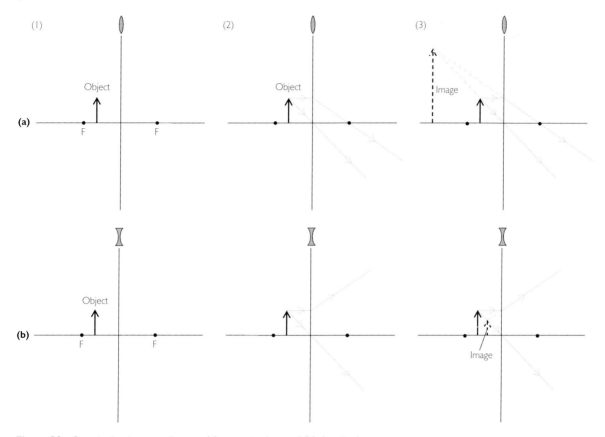

Figure 39 *Steps in drawing a ray diagram: (a) converging lens and (b) diverging lens*

1 Draw the lens, its axis, the principal focus on each side, and the object.

2 Draw two rays from the top of the object: one parallel to the axis, the other straight through the centre of the lens. For the converging lens, the horizontal ray is deflected down through F. For the diverging lens, the horizontal ray is deflected so that it appears to come from F.

3 Extend the rays back to find the point from which they *appear* to diverge. Draw in the virtual image.

As you saw in Activity 11, you cannot use a diverging lens on its own to make a real image. With a diverging lens, you produce a **virtual image** – the rays of light only *appear* to come from the image. As you can see in Figure 39(a), a converging lens also produces a virtual image of an object closer than F.

What else do the ray diagrams show us? For the converging lens, the image is beyond the object, magnified and the right way up (erect). For the diverging lens, the image is closer to the lens than the object, reduced in size (diminished) and erect. This should tie in with your observations in Activity 11.

QUESTION

22 Draw a ray diagram for a diverging lens where the object is beyond F.

The thin lens formula again

In *The Sound of Music* you learnt to recognise and use the thin lens formula with the **'real is positive' sign convention**, for converging lenses:

$$\frac{1}{u} + \frac{1}{v} = \frac{1}{f} \qquad (10)$$

Remind yourself: What do the three symbols u, v and f stand for in this formula? And what is the 'real is positive' sign convention? To see how to use the formula with a diverging lens, study the following worked example. Then test yourself with questions 23 to 25.

Worked example

Q   An object is placed at a distance of 20 cm from a diverging lens of focal length 10 cm. How far from the lens will the image be formed?
(Start by thinking: What answer would you expect? From the ray diagram in Figure 39, we would expect the image to be closer to the lens than the object, i.e. v should be less than 20 cm.)

A   We know two quantities, u and f, and we want to find v:

$$u = 20\,\text{cm}$$

$$f = -10\,\text{cm}$$

Note that, in the 'real is positive' sign convention, a diverging lens has a negative focal length. Rearranging the thin lens formula gives:

$$\frac{1}{v} = \frac{1}{f} - \frac{1}{u}$$

$$\frac{1}{v} = \frac{1}{-10\,\text{cm}} - \frac{1}{20\,\text{cm}} = \frac{-3}{20\,\text{cm}}$$

$$v = \frac{-20\,\text{cm}}{3} = -6.67\,\text{cm}$$

Maths reference

Adding and subtracting fractions
See Maths note 3.5

So the image is formed at 6.67 cm from the lens. This is, as we predicted, less than 20 cm. The minus sign tells us that the image is virtual.

QUESTIONS

23 An object is placed at the principal focus of a diverging lens. The lens's focal length is 10 cm. Where will the image be formed?

24 An object is placed at a distance of 6 cm from a lens. The image is found to be formed at a distance of 2 cm from the lens. What is the lens's focal length?

25 A ray diagram drawn accurately to scale should give the same answer to a problem as the lens formula.

An object 3 cm high is placed at a distance of 12 cm from a diverging lens. The lens's focal length is 6 cm.
(**a**) Draw an accurate ray diagram on a sheet of graph paper to deduce where the virtual image will be formed. (You can also deduce the size of the image.)
(**b**) Check your answer using the lens formula.

Prescribing lenses

The flask model of the eye that you used in Activity 10 can be used to show how lenses can correct long and short sight.

ACTIVITY 13 **Correcting long and short sight**

Use the flask model eye to demonstrate short and long sight. In each case, place various additional lenses in front of the eye such that the image is focused on the retina.

In Activity 13 you will have seen that the solution to short sight is to use a diverging spectacle or contact lens, as this deflects the rays outwards slightly, so that they focus further back in the eye (Figure 40a). Long sight can be corrected using a converging lens (Figure 40b).

If you look at an optician's prescription you will see a series of numbers that describe the lenses which have been prescribed as a result of an eye test. The patient whose prescription is shown in Figure 35 suffers from mild short sight (myopia) and needs to wear spectacles with diverging lenses in them.

The prescription gives several figures to specify each lens. The first figure for each lens (under the heading 'sphere' or 'sph') shows the **power** of the lens. You should recall from *The Sound of Music* that the power P of a lens is the reciprocal of its focal length f:

$$P = \frac{1}{f} \tag{11}$$

Power is measured in dioptres (D). From the equation relating P and f, you can see that $1\,D = 1\,m^{-1}$. For a converging lens, P and f are both positive, while for a diverging lens both are negative. A converging lens is sometimes known as a **positive lens**, and a diverging lens as a **negative lens**.

The right eye in the prescription in Figure 35 requires a lens of power $-0.25\,D$. The focal length of this lens will thus be

$$\frac{1}{-0.25\,D} = -4.0\,m$$

The left eye requires a lens of power $-0.50\,D$; this is twice the power of the right lens, and so its focal length is half of that of the right lens: $-2.0\,m$. Both lenses have negative values of P and f, so we know that they are both diverging lenses.

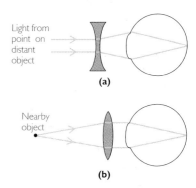

Light from point on distant object

(a)

Nearby object

(b)

Figure 40 *Using lenses to correct (a) short sight and (b) long sight*

Study note

Note that in reality refraction takes place at several surfaces in the eye, not just at the front as shown in Figure 40.

The problem of astigmatism is overcome by using lenses with a slight cylindrical curvature, as shown by the figures in the 'cylinder' (or 'cyl') and 'axis' columns.

When opticians test your eyes, they place lenses in front of your eyes until you see the clearest possible image. Rather than having a large number of lenses of all possible powers, they have a few which they can combine to give many different values. The optician determines which two or three lenses together give the clearest image. How do they then calculate the required lens to prescribe?

ACTIVITY 14 **Power puzzle**

Devise your own experiment to find out how powers combine. Use a ray box. Take two converging lenses and determine the power of each. Then find the power of the two together. What rule relates the combined power to the individual powers?

Test your answer using a different combination of lenses. Does the rule also work if one or more of the lenses is a diverging lens? For the rule to work, do the lenses need to be in contact?

Use your result from Activity 14 to answer questions 26 to 29. In *The Sound of Music* you found the focal length of a converging lens by producing a real image and measuring the object and image distances. Using your result from Activity 15, you can adapt the same method in order to find the focal length of a diverging lens. Questions 26 to 29 provide some hints.

QUESTIONS

26 If a patient has clearest vision when looking through three lenses of powers 1.0, 0.5 and 0.25 D, what power of lens should be prescribed? What is the focal length of the prescribed lens?

27 Calculate the power of the following combinations of lenses:

(**a**) two identical converging lenses of power 2.0 D, in contact;

(**b**) a 0.5 D converging lens in contact with a 1.5 D diverging lens;

(**c**) two converging lenses of focal lengths 10 cm and 25 cm, in contact.

28 Calculate the focal length of the following:

(**a**) two identical converging lenses of power 8.0 D, in contact;

(**b**) two diverging lenses of powers −5 D and −15 D in contact;

(**c**) two diverging lenses of focal lengths 10 cm and 5 cm, in contact.

29 This question describes an investigation carried out by a student. She wanted to see the effect of placing a diverging spectacle lens of power −1.0 D next to a converging lens.

First she focused a sharp image of a distant object onto a screen using a converging lens on its own. She measured the distance from the lens to the screen and found it to be 20.0 cm. Then she placed the diverging lens in contact with the converging lens. She predicted that she would have to move the screen further away to get a focused image. In fact, she had to move the screen a further 5.0 cm away from the lenses.

(**a**) What was the focal length of the converging lens? What was its power?

(**b**) Calculate the focal length of the combination of two lenses. Does your answer agree with the student's experimental findings?

The student then repeated her experiment using a converging lens of focal length 10.0 cm.

(**c**) What results would you predict for this part of her investigation?

(**d**) In which case did the image distance change the most when the diverging lens was added?

ACTIVITY 15 **Finding the focal length**

Devise and carry out a method to find the focal length of a diverging contact lens or spectacle lens. In addition to this lens, you may use a selection of other lenses (converging or diverging, as you choose), and a point source of light.

An easy life

When you go for an eye test, the optician will want to know about the lenses in your existing spectacles. They can take them away and measure the powers of the lenses in a matter of seconds. How do they do this? No setting up light sources and screens for opticians! They use the idea that the focal length of a lens depends on its curvature. A fat lens has a short focal length. Opticians have a machine that measures the curvature of the two sides of each lens. Then, knowing the refractive index of the glass or plastic used, they can deduce the prescription that was used to make them.

3.3 Lenses for all occasions

Materials for lenses

Spectacle lenses can be made from plastic or glass. Nowadays, plastic lenses are generally favoured because plastic has a lower density than glass, and so lightweight lenses can be manufactured. What other properties must lens materials have?

Mechanical properties

If you have already studied the unit *Good Enough to Eat*, and part 2 of this unit, you will have had some experience of thinking about the mechanical properties of materials – stiffness, strength, and so on. By thinking about the *uses* of materials – for example, the use of plastic and glass in lenses – you should be able to think about the desirable properties of these materials.

Spectacle lenses must be stiff and strong: stiff, because you wouldn't want your lenses to bend out of shape and change their focal length; and strong, because a broken lens could result in fragments of glass or plastic in your eye. A minimum thickness is specified: 2.2 mm for ordinary glasses, and 3.0 mm for industrial use. Strength is tested by dropping a steel ball onto the lens. Lenses must withstand a 15 g ball dropped from a height of 150 cm.

There are several ways of strengthening and toughening glass lenses. One technique is to heat them to a moderately high temperature, and then to cool them with a sudden blast of cool air. The surface is left in an expanded condition, and this helps to close any fine surface cracks. Alternatively, a thin film of plastic can be laminated between two layers of glass. The plastic holds the glass together if it cracks. (Both these techniques are also used to toughen car windscreens.)

Plastic is generally softer than glass – it scratches more easily – but this problem can be reduced by adding a thin film of quartz to the surfaces. One advantage of plastic over glass is that plastic lenses don't fog up as easily as glass ones.

QUESTION

30 Make a list of all the desirable properties of lens materials. For each property, say why it is desirable. (You may be able to think of some properties which are not mentioned here.)

Optical properties

Of course, it's essential that the materials which are chosen for lens manufacture are transparent. But just how transparent is glass?

Glass is very good at transmitting light; it absorbs very little. The problem, however, is that glass *reflects* a proportion of the light that falls on it. (You will have noticed that windows often reflect light, so that you can see yourself reflected in a shop window.) The proportion of light reflected depends on the refractive index of the glass, and is typically about 10%. This can be reduced by adding an anti-reflection coating to the lens (Figure 41). Such a coating often gives a coloured tint to the lens, which may then reflect 1% or less of the light that falls on it. Coatings are often used on the lenses of cameras and binoculars to maximise transmission and so to give the brightest possible view.

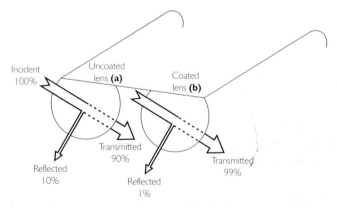

Figure 41 *Transmission and reflection of light by (a) uncoated and (b) coated lenses*

You can understand how an anti-reflection coating works if you think back to the ideas of the superposition and interference of waves, which you studied in connection with compact discs in *The Sound of Music*. The coating is a thin layer; its thickness is about one-quarter of the wavelength of light. A fraction of the light falling on the lens is reflected by the top surface of the coating, and more is reflected by the surface of the lens, after it has passed through the coating. Now we have two reflected waves, one of which has travelled half a wavelength further than the other. Their path difference is half a wavelength, and this is the condition needed for destructive interference. The two reflected waves cancel out, more or less.

QUESTION

31 Figure 42 shows an anti-reflection coating on a lens.

(**a**) Which is the incident ray, and which are the two reflected rays?

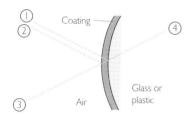

Figure 42 *Light is reflected at both surfaces of the anti-reflection coating layer*

(**b**) If the two reflected rays are to cancel out completely (interfere destructively), what can you say about their amplitudes?

(**c**) What can you say about the phase difference between them?

(**d**) If the thickness of the coating is 100 nm and its refractive index is 1.4, what wavelength of light will interfere most strongly? At what angle must it strike the lens if this is to happen? (You will need to recall how the refractive index of a material affects the wavelength of light passing through it. If you are not sure about this, look back to the end of section 2.3 in the unit *The Sound of Music*.)

(**e**) Visible light has wavelengths in the range 400 nm to 700 nm. Light strikes the lens at a range of angles. Use these ideas to help you explain why it is impossible to make a perfect anti-reflection coating for a lens, one which would prevent all reflection of light from the lens. Include diagrams in your answer, and suggest a suitable thickness for an effective coating.

The refractive index is important for another reason. The higher the refractive index, the thinner the lenses can be made. This is because a strong lens must have highly curved surfaces, and so it must be thick. A high refractive index material bends the light more, and so the surfaces can be less curved. Thick 'pebble' lenses are heavy and unattractive. Nowadays, high refractive index plastics have been devised, and so thin, high-power plastic lenses are possible.

Across the spectrum

Our eyes can only see visible light (by definition: that's what visible means!). But they also receive infrared and ultraviolet radiation.

Infrared (IR) radiation has longer wavelengths than visible light. The hotter an object, the more infrared it emits; you can feel it as heat on your skin. If you look at a hot object – an electric heater, or the Sun – some of this radiation will be absorbed by the cornea of your eye, and some by the lens. Much of it reaches your retina, and if it is very intense it may cause damage. There is some evidence that infrared exposure may contribute to the development of cataracts. However, infrared is much less of a problem than ultraviolet.

Ultraviolet (UV) radiation has shorter wavelengths than visible light. It is emitted by very hot objects, especially the Sun. Some ultraviolet reaches our eyes directly from the Sun; it can also reach us by reflection. Snow is an especially good reflector, reflecting up to 85% of the ultraviolet in sunlight. Excessive exposure can result in a form of snow-blindness, but this wears off with time. Some scientists believe that ultraviolet can cause premature ageing of the tissues of the eye. The lens and the retina contain cells which cannot regenerate, so any damage may be permanent.

Figure 43 shows some transmittance curves for various types of glass – the curves show the fraction of radiation transmitted at different wavelengths. Glass may transmit most of the visible light falling on it, but this doesn't mean that it lets through all of the invisible infrared and ultraviolet. Tinted lenses can help to cut out some of the harmful radiation.

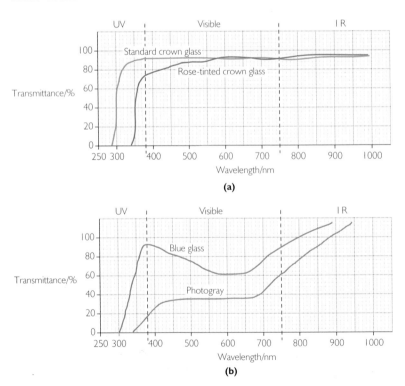

Figure 43 *Transmittance for (a) two types of crown glass and (b) two types of filter glass used for sunglasses*

QUESTION

32 **(a)** From the graphs in Figure 43, what is the wavelength range of visible light (the longest and shortest wavelengths of the visible part of the spectrum)?

(b) Which of the two types of crown glass shown in Figure 43(a) transmits the greater fraction of ultraviolet radiation? Which would be better for use in the manufacture of spectacle lenses?

(c) Look at the transmittance curve for 'Photogray' shown in Figure 43(b). This is often used for sunglasses. Why do objects seen through Photogray retain their natural colours? Why else is Photogray a good material for sunglasses?

(d) The blue glass whose transmittance curve is shown in Figure 43(b) is sometimes used in fashionable sunglasses. Explain why an optician might describe such sunglasses as 'for cosmetic use only'.

Figure 44 *This penguin needs to see under water in order to find its food*

Underwater eye

Penguins, crocodiles and whales – they can all do something you can't. They can all see clearly underwater (Figure 44). If you open your eyes underwater, everything looks blurred. The reason is that light is passing in to your eye from the water; your eye is designed to work in air. When light passes from water in to your eye, there is little change in refractive index and so the rays are bent very little. Your lens cannot bend them enough to focus a clear image.

Here are two solutions to this problem:

- Have a lens that is able to deform much more than the human lens, or can move back and forth in the eye to a greater extent. Many waterbirds can see underwater in this way.

- Have a flat-fronted eyeball. Some animals have eyes like this. Parallel rays remain parallel when they pass through a flat surface, and so if your cornea is flat, it does not contribute to the focusing of the eye. You will need a stronger lens instead. (You make use of this when you wear goggles or a mask for underwater viewing. A diving mask has a flat sheet of plastic through which you look, so light passes straight through.)

Figure 45 shows that a ray of light deflects more when there is a bigger change in the refractive index of the material it is passing through.

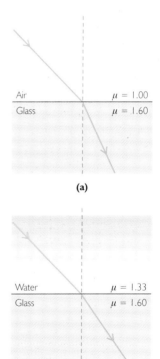

Figure 45 *Light being refracted as it travels (a) from air to glass and (b) from water to glass*

QUESTION

33 The refractive index of water is 1.33; the value for the cornea is 1.34. What can you say about the bending of a light ray as it passes from water into the cornea?

Study note

Refraction at a boundary between two materials is described in the unit *Good Enough to Eat*.

3.4 Eyes right – Summing up part 3

The following short passage uses ideas that you have studied in this part of the unit. Use it, and the questions and activities that follow, to remind you what you have done and to help you look back over your work.

Getting in shape with laser treatment

Many people are unhappy with their spectacles or contact lenses. This may be because they find them uncomfortable, or simply because they think they are unattractive. More seriously, some people have eye defects such as a deformed cornea which can cause very poor vision and which cannot be cured simply with a lens. For these people, the solution to their problem may lie in laser treatment.

Lasers have many uses in medicine. This is because they can provide a very fine beam or pulse of light which can be directed accurately at a point within the body. The light delivers a highly controlled amount of energy to the desired spot. This is made use of in delicate operations such as spinal injury repair, and in more mundane operations such as removing warts or sealing blood vessels. Today it is increasingly used by ophthalmic surgeons to improve eyesight.

The principle of laser treatment – or photorefractive keratectomy, PRK – is simple. Pulses of laser light are shone on to the cornea. Each pulse removes a thin layer of cells, perhaps 0.001 mm thick. The beam is directed over different areas of the cornea to achieve the desired reshaping. The surgeon looks down the binocular microscope to see the precise position of the laser beam as it removes cells from the cornea [Figure 46].

Figure 46 *Laser treatment in progress*

Before treatment, the patient's eyes are accurately tested to determine the amount of reshaping needed. Then the laser is programmed to deliver the correct amount of energy to the appropriate parts of the cornea. Treatment may take between 10 seconds and 3 minutes. For short treatments, the patient need only keep their eye still by staring at a light. For longer treatments, the surgeon holds the patient's eye still using a mask pressed into the eyesocket. The patient's vision is likely to be blurred for some time – perhaps several weeks – after the operation.

But what do the patients say afterwards? 'I didn't realise how bad my eyesight was.' 'It changed my life.' 'I feel young again.'

QUESTION

34 During laser treatment, the surgeon might burn away a greater thickness of cells at the centre of the cornea than around the edge; or more around the edge than at the centre. Which of these treatments would be appropriate for someone suffering from short sight? Draw a diagram to illustrate your answer.

Laser treatment

Laser treatment is increasing in popularity. Discuss the following points:

- What makes this treatment an attractive alternative for patients? What negative aspects can you identify?

- Why might it be attractive to surgeons?

- Are the benefits to the patient likely to be permanent? Might they need a further course of treatment later?

- Would you have this treatment, if it was offered to you?

Optical explanations

Find a cooperative individual who wears spectacles or contact lenses – it might be a fellow student (but not one who is following this course), or an adult in your family, or some other adult.

Prepare a report on your interviewee's eyesight. Use as many of the ideas from this unit as you can, including at least five of the terms printed in bold, to explain what you have found out. Present your report to the rest of the class.

Ask your interviewee about some or all of the following points:

- Do they wear glasses or contact lenses? When do they have to wear them?

- What changes have they noticed in their eyesight over the years?

- Examine their lenses. Try to estimate their powers – perhaps by comparing them with some standard lenses. Are they converging or diverging lenses?

- What are their lenses made of? Do they have coatings? Are they tinted? Why did they choose this type of lens?

- Do they have an optician's prescription which you can look at? What features of the prescription can you explain?

- What difference do the correct lenses make to their life? What would they be unable to do, without their lenses?

QUESTIONS

35 Explain why you may sometimes see an older person holding a book at arm's length in order to read it.

36 Why do older people often possess two or more pairs of spectacles? Might they be better off with a single pair of contact lenses?

37 If you suffer from long sight, is your eyeball too long or too short?

38 Patients who suffer from cataracts often have their lenses replaced with lens implants. Explain why they are likely to require spectacles both for distance viewing and for reading after their implants.

39 Figure 47 shows graph paper observed through three lenses.

(**a**) Which is a converging lens?

(**b**) Of the two diverging lenses, which has the greater power?

(**c**) Which diverging lens has the longer focal length?

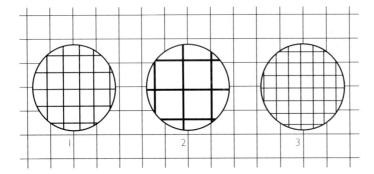

Figure 47   *Graph paper observed through three lenses*

40 A patient's closest distance of focusing (their near point) is at 50 cm. The image distance is then 2.5 cm.

(**a**) What is the effective focal length of the patient's eye?

(**b**) What power of lens is required to enable them to focus on a book at a distance of 20 cm? Is a converging or diverging lens needed?

41 Bifocals are spectacle lenses made in two parts, each having a different focal length. Benjamin Franklin, the American scientist, inventor and politician, is credited with making the first bifocals, in the 18th century. Nowadays, many people, particularly the elderly, wear bifocals.

(**a**) Which part of the lens, upper or lower, would you look through when reading?

(**b**) Would you expect this part of the lens to be converging or diverging?

(**c**) Would you expect the other part to be converging or diverging?

4 *Heartbeat*

4.1   Ultrasound imaging of the heart

Rest a finger lightly against the inside of your wrist and feel your pulse. Hold your hand against your chest and feel your heart beat. A healthy human heart beats about 70 times per minute, circulating blood to the lungs to pick up oxygen, and then to the other organs of the body (Figure 48). Blood enters the heart and is drawn into the lower chambers (the ventricles) when the upper chambers (the atria) contract, the bicuspid and tricuspid valves are open and the pocket valves closed. Then with the bicuspid and tricuspid valves closed and the pocket valves open, deoxygenated blood is pumped to the lungs, and oxygenated blood to the rest of the body. The rhythm of the heartbeat is controlled by a set of muscles known as the pacemaker, located in the atrium wall near the vena cava blood vessel.

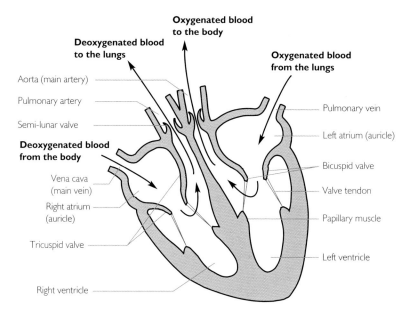

Figure 48 *Diagram of the human heart, showing the direction of blood flow*

Any interruption to the heart's action can have serious, even fatal, results. In this part of the unit, you will see how ultrasound can be used to help diagnose heart problems. The most common problem is coronary heart disease, which affects the blood supply to the heart muscle itself. Other problems can occur with the pacemaker, upsetting its rhythm, or with the valves, allowing blood to leak back into the atria when the ventricles contract. While complete replacement heart pumps (as shown in Figure 1) are very expensive and still at the developmental stage, the last two types of problem can readily be treated with 'spare parts': a battery-operated pacemaker (Figure 49) delivers a regular electrical pulse to control the heartbeat; and substitutes made from metal or plastic (Figure 50) can replace defective natural valves.

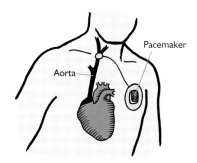

Figure 49 *A heart pacemaker*

Consultant cardiologist

Dr Roger Boyle, Consultant Cardiologist at York District Hospital, uses ultrasound imaging (a so-called echocardiogram) to help diagnose heart problems.

An ultrasound multiple transmitter–receiver is placed against the patient's chest, which has been smeared with 'ultrasound coupling gel'. The best subjects are young and slim, as too much fat or air (due to lung problems, for example) gets in the way. But with other patients, the probe can be lowered down the throat to examine the heart 'from behind'.

Figure 50 *Replacement heart valve*

Immediately, a fuzzy grey moving image of the heart appears on the monitor screen (Figure 51). You can see the muscles contract, and the valves open and close. The information can be displayed in various ways; for example, a small area of the image can be selected with an on-screen cursor and displayed as a colour-coded image to show blood flow. Changes in heart volume can be measured, and measurements of blood flow can indicate leaks and constrictions. There is also a small single probe that can be used to produce an audio signal related to blood flow (it sounds rather like a stethoscope).

The advantage of the ultrasound system is that it is very quick and simple to use – non-invasive and so non-threatening for the patient, and allowing the doctor to make a diagnosis in a matter of minutes.

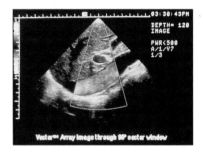

Figure 51   *An echocardiogram*

Hospital physicist

Hospital physicists are concerned with all aspects of medical imaging, including ultrasound, as this interview shows.

What is ultrasound used for in medicine?
The most common use for ultrasound in medicine is to examine the internal structure of the body and to study the movement of organs and blood.

X-rays are used for the same thing aren't they, so why is ultrasound used too?
Yes, X-rays are also used to obtain images of our bodies non-invasively, but they have limitations. If you look at X-ray plates you will notice that it is very difficult to see the structure of soft tissues. Bones are very clearly shown, but different soft tissues are hardly distinguishable at all from each other [see Figure 52]. Patients mustn't be given high doses of X-rays, so they cannot be used to look at the movement of organs.

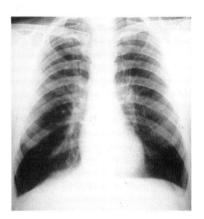

Figure 52   *An X-ray image shows bones clearly but not the soft tissues*

So ultrasound is safe for the patient?
Ultrasound is a pressure wave, much like audible sound. At the power levels used in medicine there are no harmful effects. The patient can be examined for quite long periods of time so that moving images can be built up. Even a foetus can be safely examined, which would be virtually out of the question with X-rays normally.

You said that the movement of blood can be studied too, how is that done?
Yes, we can use ultrasound to discover how quickly blood is moving through blood vessels. The ultrasound beam is reflected off the blood cells and the frequency of the ultrasound – remember it is like sound – changes due to the Doppler effect. This information reveals how well the heart is functioning and the state of the blood vessels themselves.

Study note

The Doppler effect is dealt with in section 4.3.

4.2 Ultrasound echoes

What is ultrasound?

In the unit *The Sound of Music,* you learned about sound. Sound is a longitudinal pressure wave which moves through material (it cannot travel through a vacuum) by making the particles oscillate parallel to the direction in which the wave is travelling. Generally we think of sound as something that we can hear. In fact we can only hear sounds in the frequency range of approximately 20 Hz to 20 kHz, which changes from individual to individual, with age and, of course, is different for other animals. Sound with a frequency above the upper limit of the human audible range, i.e. above 20 kHz, is known as **ultrasound**.

Figures 53 and 54 show various ways to depict sound, or ultrasound, waves. Figure 53 shows the particles of a material 'caught' during their oscillation. Where the particles are moving towards each other, the pressure is higher than the normal pressure; and where they are moving away from each other, the pressure is lower. The **frequency** of the wave determines the number of oscillations of the particles per second, and the **wavelength** of the wave is the distance between two pressure (or displacement) maxima or between two pressure (or displacement) minima (see Figure 54).

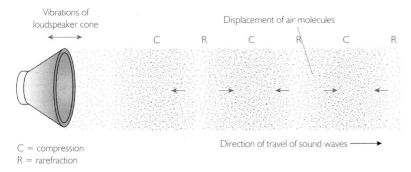

C = compression
R = rarefraction

Figure 53   *A 'snapshot' of a sound wave*

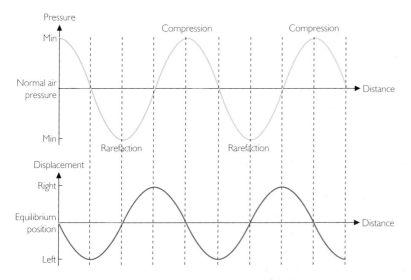

Figure 54   *Pressure–distance and displacement–distance graphs for a longitudinal wave*

Like audible sounds, ultrasound is produced by vibrations, but ultrasound frequencies are so high that devices such as loudspeakers are not able to produce the vibrations. Instead, ultrasound transducers (generators) make use of so-called piezoelectric crystals. A piezoelectric crystal is one that expands and contracts when an alternating potential difference is applied across it. A particular crystal will have a resonant frequency, at which the amplitude of oscillation is a maximum. This resonant frequency can be very high. As the crystal surface vibrates, it sets the surrounding air in motion and a wave of ultrasound travels outwards from the generator.

Figure 55 shows a piezoelectric crystal sandwiched between backing material, which damps the oscillation of the crystal so that it does not reverberate (continue to oscillate when the applied pd is switched off), and an **acoustic lens**, which protects the crystal and focuses the ultrasound beam.

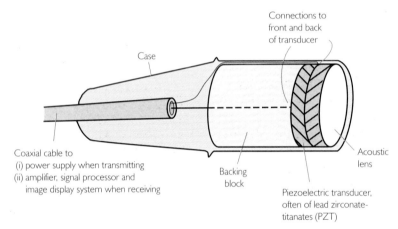

Figure 55 *Diagram of an ultrasound transducer*

The wavelength, λ, of the ultrasound depends on its frequency, f, and on the wave speed, v, in the material through which it is travelling. As with all waves, these quantities are related via the **wave equation**:

$$v = f\lambda \tag{12}$$

Ultrasound is often used in medicine in the same way that sonar is used by ships – knowing the speed and the time delay between sending a pulse and receiving it back again, a distance can be calculated.

We will start by measuring the speed of a sound that is very similar to ultrasound. In *The Sound of Music*, you measured the speed of sound in air using a recorder. In Activity 18 you will use a method that relates more directly to ultrasound imaging and also helps you to revise your knowledge of waves and the wave equation.

ACTIVITY 18 **Speed of sound**

Using the apparatus shown in Figure 56, move the microphone through a distance of one wavelength and hence calculate the speed of sound in air.

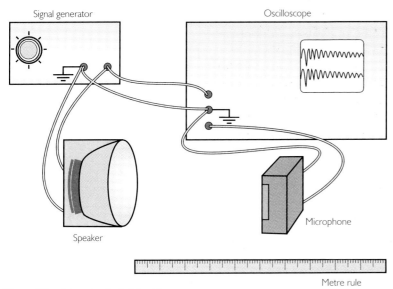

Figure 56 *Apparatus for Activity 18*

Why ultrasound?

You will have seen in Activity 18 that, in air, the wavelengths of fairly high-pitched audible sounds are typically a few tens of centimetres. In order to produce an image by reflection from an object, the wavelength of any radiation must be appreciably smaller than the size of the object. In order to produce images of structures within the body, wavelengths smaller than a few centimetres are needed – which, for sound waves, means frequencies above the audible range.

Study note

You have met this idea before, only from the opposite point of view, if you have studied diffraction of X-rays or electrons n *Digging Up the Past* or in part 2 of this unit: if waves meet an obstacle comparable in size to their wavelength, they are diffracted rather than simply being reflected or absorbed. The objects that we see by reflected light are much larger than the wavelength of the light.

Ultrasound in different materials

Sound, including ultrasound, travels at different speeds in different materials. This has several consequences:

- the time for an echo to return depends on the nature of the material as well as on the distance travelled;

- the wavelength of the ultrasound depends on the material as well as on the frequency;

- a beam of ultrasound is reflected and refracted at a boundary, rather than going straight on.

Question 42 illustrates the first of these, and Activities 19 and 20 the third.

QUESTION

42 Ultrasound has a speed of 1500 m s^{-1} in a sample of soft tissue and has a frequency of 10 MHz. What is the wavelength of the ultrasound wave in the soft tissue?

In your work in *The Sound of Music,* and in part 3 of this unit, you have used optical lenses to direct and control beams of light. You saw in *The Sound of Music* that light is refracted when it meets a boundary between materials – a lens makes use of this to change the direction of light. Exactly the same principle can be used with sound to make an acoustic lens such as the one on the front of an ultrasound transmitter–receiver. Activity 19 uses audible sound to make a simple large-scale acoustic lens.

ACTIVITY 19 **Acoustic lens**

Use the apparatus shown in Figure 57 to show that a balloon filled with carbon dioxide can act as a simple acoustic lens and focus a beam of sound. Make a rough measurement of the focal length of this lens. What can you deduce about the speed of sound in carbon dioxide compared with its speed in air?

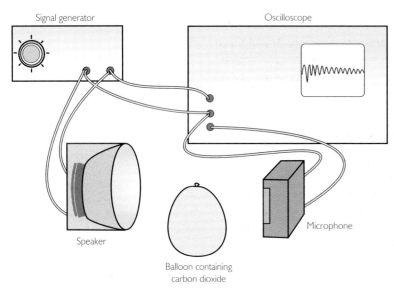

Figure 57 *A carbon dioxide acoustic lens*

In *The Sound of Music* you saw that light is partially (or totally) reflected at a boundary (it is this that enables you to see your reflection in shop windows). The same things happens to sound waves – and indeed to all types of waves, as you can demonstrate by fastening two different types of rope together and observing what happens when you send a wave pulse along the composite rope (Figure 58). The more similar the materials, the smaller the amplitude of the reflected wave compared to that of the transmitted wave.

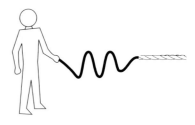

Figure 58 *Sending a wave pulse along a composite rope*

Table 4 lists the speed of ultrasound in various materials found inside the body. It also lists the density of the materials, because the amount of reflection at a boundary depends on the acoustic impedances, Z, of the two materials where

$$Z = \rho v \qquad (13)$$

The **intensity**, I_r, of the reflected beam of sound, as a fraction of the intensity of the incident beam, I_i, is given by

$$\frac{I_r}{I_i} = \frac{(Z_1 - Z_2)^2}{(Z_1 + Z_2)^2} \qquad (14)$$

The SI units of Z are kg m^{-2} s^{-1}.

Study note

Remember that in the unit *Technology in Space* you learned that intensity, or **flux**, of radiation is the power per unit area.

Table 4 *Sound speed and density for various materials*

Material	Speed of sound/$\mathrm{m\,s^{-1}}$	Density/$\mathrm{kg\,m^{-3}}$
air	330	1.3
water	1500	1000
blood	1570	1060
fat	1450	950
soft tissue (inc. skin)	1500	1050
muscle	1600	1080
bone	4000	1500

In section 4.1 you read that 'coupling gel' is smeared on the skin of a patient who is to have an ultrasound examination. This gel is a water-based jelly, whose density and sound speed are very similar to those of water. Activity 20 is a data-handling activity which will help you to understand the purpose of the gel.

ACTIVITY **20** **Ultrasound at the interface**

Use a spreadsheet to calculate the acoustic impedance of each of the materials in Table 4, and to calculate the ratio I_r/I_i for an interface between soft tissue and each of the other materials listed. Hence explain the purpose of ultrasound coupling gel, and why an ultrasound examination of the heart might be difficult if the patient had a large amount of air in the lungs.

Medical investigations using ultrasound

Now consider a pulse of ultrasound which is directed through a patient's body so that it reaches the heart, as in Figure 59.

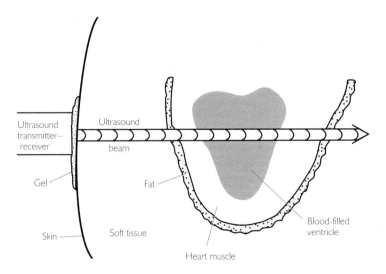

Figure 59 *Sketch showing ultrasound travelling from the transducer into a patient and through the heart*

Only small proportions of the ultrasound are reflected by interfaces met on the way to the heart, provided there is no bone or air in the way. Some of the ultrasound will then be reflected by the interfaces associated with the heart – soft tissue/fat outside the heart, fat/heart muscle, heart muscle/blood and so on.

Once the ultrasound transducer has produced the pulse of ultrasound, its function can be reversed from transmitter to receiver. When a sound wave makes a piezoelectric crystal vibrate, it produces an alternating pd imitating the pressure variations in the wave.

The signal from the transducer as it receives the reflected ultrasound can be amplified and displayed on an oscilloscope as in Figure 60. The horizontal axis is time. The delays between the various peaks can be used to calculate distances if the tissues between the peaks can be identified, which an experienced user is able to do.

The time between any two peaks is the time taken for the ultrasound pulse to travel between the interfaces they represent. The time t and the distance s are related to the velocity v by the expression:

$$s = vt \tag{15}$$

Questions 43 and 44 illustrate this pulse–echo technique. It is a safe, non-invasive, way to measure distances inside the body and is applied to many medical investigations including those of eyes and foetuses.

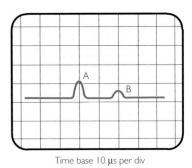

Time base 10 μs per div

Figure 60   *Oscilloscope display of reflected ultrasound detected by a transducer*

QUESTIONS

Use data from Table 4 to answer these questions.

43 On leaving the transmitter–receiver, a pulse of ultrasound travels 5 cm through soft tissue and is then reflected back. How long is the time delay between sending and receiving the pulse? What is the greatest number of pulses that could be transmitted per second if each echo is to return before the next pulse is sent?

44 Calculate the thickness of the heart wall from the delay between the two peaks labelled A and B in Figure 60.

Moving images

Real-time moving images can be produced using ultrasound. These are particularly appropriate for images of the heart, which is always moving: a still image that took more than a fraction of a second to obtain would be blurred and useless anyway.

Figure 61 shows how an ultrasound scanner is used to obtain the moving images. Basically it is an array of a number of piezoelectric transducers. Each of the transducers sends out a pulse of ultrasound slightly after the previous one. To get a focusing and scanning effect, pulses to each transducer are arranged to arrive at slightly different times. The signals received back by the transducers are processed by a computer to produce the image. The array can cover an arc of 90° and the firing of the transducers in the array can be done as frequently as 150 times per second. Still images produced with this type of scanner appear quite fuzzy (see Figure 51), but the apparent quality is much higher when a full sequence is viewed as each frame adds a little more detail. Even slowed down by a factor of three or more, a scan can be viewed as a flicker-free film, as Activity 21 illustrates.

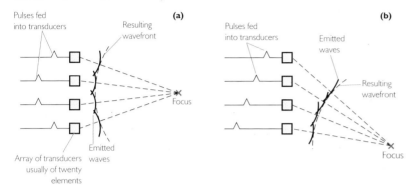

Figure 61 *A phased array scanner*

ACTIVITY **21** **Flicker fusion**

Use a signal generator and light-emitting diode (LED) to find the lowest frequency at which your eyes can detect the flickering of a light source. Write an account of your findings, explaining their importance for ultrasound imaging and for other moving images.

4.3 *Doppler ultrasound*

As you read in section 4.1, ultrasound examinations can reveal the speed, as well as the location, of objects within the body. This aspect of the technique uses the **Doppler effect**. You have probably experienced the Doppler effect yourself. If an ambulance or police car has passed you with its siren sounding, you will have noticed that the pitch of the sound changed. It was higher as the siren approached you and lower when it was going away, and just as it passed you it was the same as it would have been if the siren had been stationary. The change in pitch is most noticeable if the source of the sound is moving at high speed directly towards or away from you.

ACTIVITY **22** **The Doppler effect**

The Doppler effect can be demonstated by whirling a small loudspeaker, or a whistle, in a large horizontal circle (Figure 62). Listen for the change in frequency as the source of sound moves towards/away from you.

 Safety
This should be done outside, and make sure that the listeners stand well away from the whirling object.

Use the *Multimedia Sound* CD-ROM to record and display sounds that illustrate the Doppler effect.

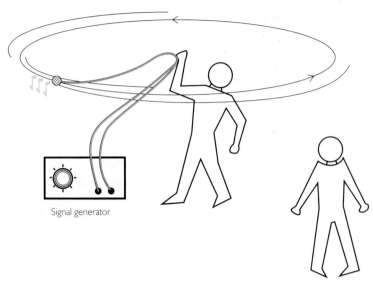

Figure 62 *Demonstrating the Doppler effect*

The Doppler effect

When a moving object emits or reflects waves, the frequency of the waves received by a stationary detector differs from the frequency at which they were produced. Figure 63 shows how this comes about. When the source is at rest, the wavelength and therefore the detected frequency are the same for the detectors placed each side of the source. With the source moving towards one detector and away from the other, the waves are squashed up on one side (decreased wavelength, increased frequency) and spread out on the other (increased wavelength, decreased frequency). This is because the source has moved to a new position by the time it produces each subsequent wave, but the waves themselves always travel at the same speed.

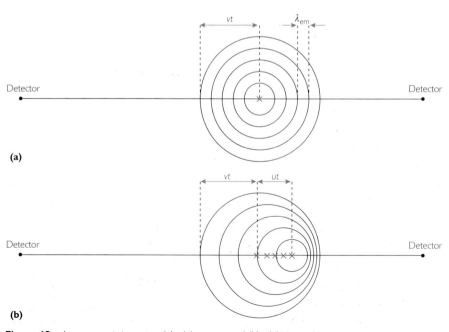

Figure 63 *A source emitting waves (a) while at rest and (b) while in motion*

The Doppler effect also occurs when a detector moves towards or away from a source of waves. Imagine one of the detectors in Figure 63(a) moving towards the source; it would encounter more waves per second than if it were at rest, so it would measure a higher frequency (shorter apparent wavelength) than that of the source. Similarly if a detector is moving away from the source it measures a lower frequency (longer wavelength). Provided the speed, u, of the source or detector is much less than the wave speed, v, the **Doppler shift**, Δf, in the received frequency is given by

$$\frac{\Delta f}{f_{em}} \approx \frac{u}{v} \qquad (16)$$

where f_{em} is the frequency emitted by the source, f_{rec} is the frequency of waves received by the detector, and

$$\Delta f = f_{em} - f_{rec} \qquad (17)$$

The Doppler effect applies to *all* types of waves. With electromagnetic waves, we are generally not aware of the effect, because the wave speed $(3 \times 10^8 \, \text{m s}^{-1})$ is so much greater than typical speeds of objects. However, even small changes in frequency can quite easily be detected using suitable equipment – police radar speed traps measure the Doppler shift in radio waves reflected from moving vehicles.

Study note

By convention, a positive value of Δf corresponds to an increase in wavelength and hence to a decrease in frequency, which occurs when the source and receiver are moving apart; while a negative Δf corresponds to a decrease in wavelength and an increase in frequency.

Study note

As you will see if you study the unit *Reach for the Stars*, the light from some galaxies is noticeably shifted in frequency due to their movement away from us.

The Doppler effect in medicine

In a medical examination, blood flow can be measured using the change in frequency due to the Doppler effect when ultrasound is reflected from red blood cells. The technique can be used to measure the flow of blood through an artery for instance, or the walls of the heart or a valve within the heart. Blockages in blood vessels and thickening of their walls can be diagnosed very easily. Foetal heart monitoring is another common use of Doppler ultrasound. The Doppler shift from a single transducer can be converted into an audible signal and the technique amounts to a sensitive stethoscope. Using a phased ultrasound array, speed can be measured at many points simultaneously. These measurements are often displayed as colour-coded images in which the different colours represent different speeds.

Laser Doppler imaging is also used. Red light from a helium–neon laser is reflected from red blood cells. The frequency of the light is changed by the movement of the cells, just as the frequency of ultrasound is. This technique produces an image that is colour-coded to represent the amount of reflection (which is proportional to the number of blood cells) and the velocity of the cells. Each pixel (little square) on the computer images in Figure 64 corresponds to about $2 \, \text{mm}^2$ of tissue, an area less than $1.5 \, \text{mm}$ across.

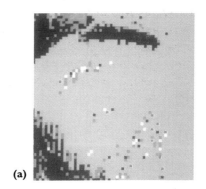

(a)

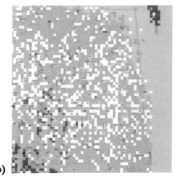

(b)

Figure 64 *Laser Doppler image of a transplanted liver (a) before and (b) after clamps were removed from blood vessels. The bottom image shows perfusion of blood into the liver*

Modifications to the simple Doppler expression

When waves from a stationary transmitter–receiver are reflected from a moving target back towards their source, they are Doppler-shifted twice. Suppose the target is approaching the source; it encounters waves at a higher frequency than those emitted, and the reflected signal has this higher frequency. But the reflected signal comes from something that is moving towards the transmitter–receiver, so the frequency of waves entering the receiver is greater than the frequency of waves leaving the target. The overall change in frequency is thus *double* that given by equation (16). This applies to Doppler ultrasound and laser imaging, and also to radar speed traps.

The transducer cannot be introduced into the blood vessel itself, so the ultrasound beam will be at an angle to the flow (Figure 65). The Doppler shift depends on the component of the blood velocity parallel to the ultrasound beam. As you saw in the unit *Higher, Faster, Stronger*, if the angle between two directions is θ, then the component of velocity along the ultrasound beam is given by $u \cos \theta$.

Modifying equation (16) to take account of the double Doppler shift and the angle, we get

$$\Delta f = \frac{2u f_{em} \cos \theta}{v} \tag{18}$$

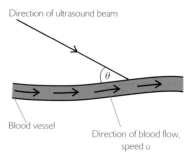

Figure 65 *Blood flow is usually at an angle to the ultrasound beam*

QUESTIONS

45 Calculate the shift in frequency when a vehicle travelling at $20\,\mathrm{m\,s^{-1}}$ is producing a siren note of 3 kHz and approaching a listener. (The speed of sound in air is $330\,\mathrm{m\,s^{-1}}$.)

46 A radar speed trap emits a 10 GHz signal and records a Doppler shift of 2500 Hz for an approaching car. Was the car exceeding the speed limit of 70 mph (about $30\,\mathrm{m\,s^{-1}}$)? (Radar signals travel in air at $3.0 \times 10^{8}\,\mathrm{m\,s^{-1}}$. 1 GHz (gigahertz) $= 1 \times 10^{9}$ Hz.)

47 Ultrasound with a frequency of 6.0 MHz was used to measure the speed of blood in a blood vessel. It displayed a velocity of $5.0\,\mathrm{mm\,s^{-1}}$. What Doppler shift did it detect if the angle between the ultrasound and the blood flow was estimated to be 60°? (Assume that the speed of the ultrasound was $1500\,\mathrm{m\,s^{-1}}$.)

Further investigations

Use the *Multimedia Sound* CD-ROM to record and analyse sounds from moving objects. You could study the sounds produced by road vehicles such as cars and motorbikes, and relate your results to their speeds.

4.4 Summing up part 4

In this part of the unit, you have extended your knowledge of waves – the way they behave at boundaries between materials, and the Doppler effect.

ACTIVITY 23 **Sound advice**

Look back through your work on this part of the unit and make sure you know the meaning of all the terms printed in bold.

Then look back at Activity 31 in *The Sound of Music*. Add two new rows to the bottom of your table, one on the Doppler effect, and one on reflection/transmission at a boundary. (You could also add a column on the right to show the properties of electron waves from part 2, but you might not be able to complete all the rows for this.)

---

5 Recovery

5.1 Getting better

This unit has touched on several areas of physics, and has built on much of the work that you have done in earlier units. In part 2 you developed your knowledge of physical properties of materials, on both a large and a small scale, in part 3 you extended your knowledge of light and lenses, and in part 4 you learned more about waves. Use the following activities to remind yourself of the work that you have done.

ACTIVITY 24 **Getting better**

Look back through your work on other units in this course, and look for links with this unit. Annotate your notes to show where similar ideas come up in different situations, and extend them where you think it is relevant (for example, you could add some notes on stress and strain in the relevant sections of *Higher, Faster, Stronger* and *Good Enough to Eat*).

ACTIVITY 25 **Bedside manners**

Imagine that you are talking to someone who is to have either a hip replacement, cataract surgery or an ultrasound examination for a suspected heart problem, and they are a bit unsure about what is involved. Decide how you could help to inform and reassure them. Either talk to another student who is playing the role of the patient, or make a tape-recording that the patient could play on their own. Think carefully about what information would be helpful, how you could explain it in an appropriate way – and also think about what **not** to include.

5.2 *Questions on the whole unit*

QUESTIONS

48 When new materials are developed, their physical properties are recorded so that users can decide whether a material is suitable for a particular purpose. The graphs in Figure 66 show the performances of two materials, X and Y.

(**a**) Up to point A, the graph for material X is a straight line from the origin. Up to point B, the material returns to its original condition if the stress is removed. Beyond point C, the material continues to stretch while a constant stress is applied. What are the names of points A, B and C?

(**b**) Which of materials X and Y is the stiffer? Explain your answer.

(**c**) The pictures in Figure 67 are electron diffraction pictures of rubber. One shows it in an unstretched state. The other in a stretched state. Which is which?

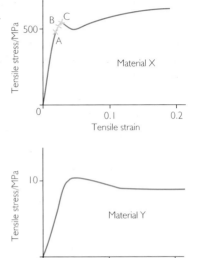

Figure 66 *Graphs for question 48(a,b)*

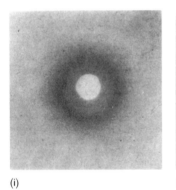

(i)

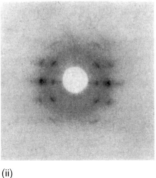

(ii)

Figure 67 *Electron diffraction pictures for question 48(c)*

49 If a video tape becomes stretched when in use, the playback will be affected. There needs to be some 'give' in the tape to prevent snapping, but not so much that the magnetic tape information gets badly distorted. A certain manufacturer requires that a tape of thickness 0.02 mm and width 1.3 cm is not to undergo a strain of more than 3.0×10^{-3} when a force of 1 N is applied to it.

When choosing material for the tape, what is the smallest allowable value for its Young modulus?

50 Some cameras, such as the Polaroid 690 SLR, have ultrasonic transmitters and receivers linked to their lens focusing systems. A moment before the picture is taken a burst of ultrasound is transmitted. An in-built computer measures the time for the 'echo' to return and adjusts the lens to produce a sharp image on the film.

(**a**) The lens system of the 690 SLR can be considered as a simple converging lens of power +8.62 D. At what distance from its optical centre would this lens produce a sharp image of a *very distant* object?

(**b**) The camera is now pointed at a much closer object. The burst of ultrasound takes 0.010 s to return. (Speed of ultrasound in air, $v = 330\,\mathrm{m\,s^{-1}}$.)

   (**i**) How far away from the camera is this object?

   (**ii**) How far must the lens be from the film in order to produce a sharp image of this object?

(**c**) On its own, the 690 SLR camera can photograph objects no closer than 26 cm, but, with an additional 'close-up' lens attached to the front of the camera, objects as close as 11 cm can be photographed clearly. What type of lens would need to be used as the 'close-up' lens?

51 Table 5 shows the measurements a student made when determining the focal length of a lens. Figure 68 shows a graph of her results.

u/m	v/m	u^{-1}/m^{-1}	v^{-1}/m^{-1}
0.21	0.16	4.8	6.3
0.30	0.13	3.3	7.7
0.38	0.12	2.6	8.4
0.48	0.11	2.1	9.1

Table 5 *Data for question 51*

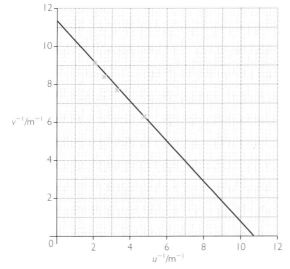

Figure 68 *Graph for question 51*

(**a**) What was the focal length of the lens, together with any experimental uncertainty?

(**b**) Suggest three ways in which the student could have reduced the experimental uncertainty in her final result.

5.3 *Achievements*

Now you have studied this unit you should be able to:

- explain the meaning of, use and calculate *tensile/compressive stress, tensile/compressive strain, strength, breaking stress, stiffness* and *Young modulus* (2.2)*;

- draw force–extension, force–compression, and tensile/compressive stress–strain graphs and identify the *limit of proportionality, elastic limit* and *yield point* (2.2);

- calculate the elastic strain energy ΔE_{el} in a deformed material sample, using the expression $\Delta E_{el} = F\Delta x/2$ where applicable, and from the area under its force–extension graph (2.2);

- use electron diffraction images to deduce ordered structure, or lack of it (2.3);

- understand the need for a wave model when explaining electron diffraction (2.3);

- recall that polymers consist of long chain molecules in varying states of order and disorder (2.2, 2.3);

- recognise and use the equation $1/v + 1/u = 1/f$ for a thin lens (with the 'real is positive' sign convention) (3.2);

- recall that, in general, waves are transmitted and reflected at an interface between media (3.3, 4.2);

- explain how different media affect the transmission/reflection of waves travelling from one medium to another (3.3, 4.2);

- explain how a pulse–echo technique can provide details of the position and/or speed of an object (4.2, 4.3);

- explain qualitatively how the movement of a source of sound or light relative to an observer/detector gives rise to a shift in frequency (Doppler effect) (4.3).

*Numbers indicate the section(s) that relate to each achievement.

Answers

1   A shell.

2   You might include: supports the body's weight; provides levers for movement; anchors the muscles; protects internal organs.

3   It would be very brittle (the fibres help it to become tough).

4   A hinge joint can move only in one plane, whereas a ball and socket joint can rotate and move in any plane.

5   Taking bone from another part of the body exposes the patient to two operations, leading to increased risk (and increased cost). Taking bone from another person may lead to infection.

6   Organic fibres (mainly collagen).

7   (a) Elastic, tough and durable.
       (b) Stiff, tough, hard and durable.
       (c) Stiff, tough, hard and durable.

8   You need to estimate your weight and the area of your bones. If mass $= 60\,$kg, then
$F = $ weight $= mg \approx 600\,$N. If diameter of leg bone $= 6\,$cm, then area of one
bone $\approx \pi r^2 \approx 30\,\text{cm}^2 = 30 \times 10^{-6}\,\text{m}^2$. When standing on both feet, total area $A = 60 \times 10^{-6}\,\text{m}^2$. So
$$\sigma = \frac{F}{A} \approx \frac{600\,\text{N}}{(60 \times 10^{-6}\,\text{m}^2)} = 10^7\,\text{Pa} = 10\,\text{MPa}.$$
Bones are commonly subject to much larger stresses, e.g. when moving, or simply when standing on one leg.

9   (a) Using $v^2 = u^2 + 2as$, with $u = 0$, $a = 9.8\,\text{m s}^{-2}$,
       $s = 1.5\,$m (taking downwards as positive)
$$v^2 = 29.4\,\text{m}^2\,\text{s}^{-2}, \ v = 5.42\,\text{m s}^{-1}.$$
       (b) Magnitude of deceleration $a = \dfrac{\Delta v}{\Delta t} = 54.2\,\text{m s}^{-2}$.

       (c) Magnitude of force $F = ma = 70\,\text{kg} \times 54.2\,\text{m s}^{-2}$
$$= 3.80 \times 10^3\,\text{N}$$

       (d) Total cross-sectional area $A = 60\,\text{cm}^2$
$$= 60 \times 10^{-4}\,\text{m}^2$$
       Stress $\sigma = \dfrac{F}{A} = \dfrac{3.80 \times 10^3\,\text{N}}{60 \times 10^{-4}\,\text{m}^2}$
$$= 6.3 \times 10^5\,\text{Pa}$$

10   Strain $= 2.5\,\text{mm}/400\,\text{mm} = 6.3 \times 10^{-3} = 0.63\%$. (Notice that you get the same answer if you express both lengths in cm, or both in m – it does not matter which units you use, provided you use the same for both lengths.)

11   Expressed as a decimal, strain $= \dfrac{0.15}{100} = 1.5 \times 10^{-3}$.
From equation (3),
$$x = \varepsilon \ell = 1.5 \times 10^{-3} \times 50\,\text{cm}$$
$$= 7.5 \times 10^{-2}\,\text{cm} = 0.75\,\text{mm}.$$
If the original length were ten times longer, then the extension, too, would be ten times as great, i.e. 7.5 mm.

12   (a) $A = 0.5 \times 10^{-6}\,\text{m}^2$

       (b) $\sigma = \dfrac{F}{A} = \dfrac{75\,\text{N}}{0.5 \times 10^{-6}\,\text{m}^2} = 1.5 \times 10^8\,\text{Pa}$

       (c) $\varepsilon = \dfrac{6.0 \times 10^{-3}\,\text{m}}{8.0\,\text{m}} = 7.5 \times 10^{-4}$

       (d) $E = \dfrac{\sigma}{\varepsilon} = \dfrac{1.5 \times 10^8\,\text{Pa}}{7.5 \times 10^{-4}} = 2.0 \times 10^{11}\,\text{Pa}$

       (e) Steel has a much greater Young modulus than bone, so it would take most of the stress in a replacement joint and the natural bone would waste away.

       (f) Total area of cross-section of 100 strands,
$$A = 100 \times 0.5 \times 10^{-6}\,\text{m}^{-2} = 5 \times 10^{-5}\,\text{m}^2.$$
       Weight of ten people,
$$F = mg = 850\,\text{kg} \times 9.8\,\text{N kg}^{-1} = 8.33 \times 10^3\,\text{N}$$
       Stress due to weight of people,
$$\sigma = \frac{8.33 \times 10^3\,\text{N}}{5 \times 10^{-5}\,\text{m}^2} = 1.67 \times 10^8\,\text{Pa}$$
       Strain $\varepsilon = \dfrac{\sigma}{E} = \dfrac{1.67 \times 10^8\,\text{Pa}}{2.0 \times 10^{11}\,\text{Pa}} = 8.33 \times 10^{-4}$
       Extension $= \varepsilon \ell = 8.33 \times 10^{-4} \times 90\,\text{m}$
$$= 7.5 \times 10^{-2}\,\text{m}$$

13   (a) See Table 6 and Figure 69

Tension /10^3 N	Extension /10^{-3} m	Stress	Strain
0.00	0.00	0.00	0.00
35.0	0.10	2.69	1.53
38.0	0.20	2.92	3.08
36.5	0.40	2.81	6.15
36.0	0.70	2.77	10.8
37.0	1.00	2.85	15.4
40.0	1.40	3.08	21.5
45.0	2.10	3.46	32.3
50.0	3.10	3.85	47.7
55.0	5.10	4.23	78.5
57.5	7.20	4.42	111
60.0	9.10	4.62	154
60.0	13.1	4.62	202
57.5	14.7	4.42	226
55.0	15.2	4.23	234
52.5	15.8 (broke)	4.04	243

Table 6   *The answer to question 13(a)*

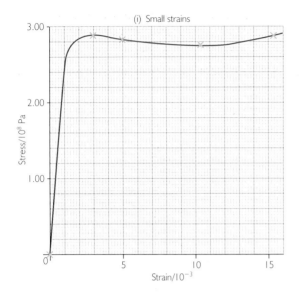

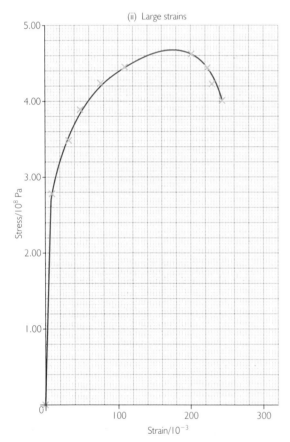

Figure 69 *The answer to question 13(a)*

(b) (i) Yield stress: about 2.6×10^8 Pa – where the graph in Figure 69(i) starts to curve and the sample extends with no additional stress.

(ii) Ultimate tensile stress: about 4.7×10^8 Pa – from Figure 69(ii).

(iii) Breaking strain $= 243 \times 10^{-3} = 0.243 \approx 24\%$.

14 Area of string,
$$A = \pi(0.2 \times 10^{-3}\,\text{m})^2 = 1.26 \times 10^{-7}\,\text{m}^2$$
Strain produced by 8 turns,
$$\varepsilon = \frac{8 \times 4.0\,\text{mm}}{840\,\text{mm}} = 3.8 \times 10^{-2}$$
Stress, $\sigma = \varepsilon E = 3.8 \times 10^{-2} \times 3.0 \times 10^9$ Pa
$$= 1.14 \times 10^8\,\text{Pa}$$
tension $= \sigma A = 1.14 \times 10^8\,\text{Pa} \times 1.26 \times 10^{-7}\,\text{m}^2$
$$= 14.4\,\text{N}.$$
The Young modulus of the material must be high, and it must be able to achieve quite large strains without breaking (which means that its breaking stress must be high).

15 The material would need to have a large Young modulus (large E) and be capable of undergoing large strains (large ε) without failing.

16 (a) See Figure 70. Each large square represents an energy density of $1 \times 10^7\,\text{J}\,\text{m}^{-3}$, and each small square represents $4 \times 10^5\,\text{J}\,\text{m}^{-3}$. From counting the squares, the area under the curve thus represents about $10.5 \times 10^7\,\text{J}\,\text{m}^{-3}$.

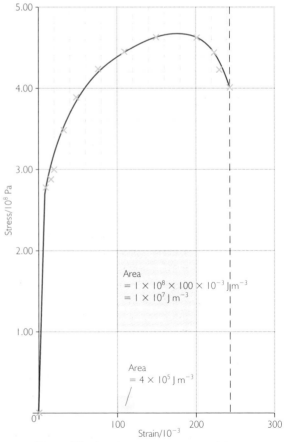

Figure 70 *See the answer to question 16*

(b) If we assume that all the stored elastic energy becomes kinetic energy when the wire breaks, and that all parts of the wire move at the same speed, and deal with a volume V of the wire, then we can write (ρ is the density)

$$\text{mass } m = \rho V$$
$$E_{el} = UV$$
$$\text{kinetic energy } E_k = \tfrac{1}{2}(\rho V)v^2 = UV$$
$$\text{and so} \quad \tfrac{1}{2}\rho v^2 = U$$
$$v^2 = \frac{2U}{\rho}$$
$$= \frac{2 \times 10.5 \times 10^7\,\text{J m}^{-3}}{8 \times 10^3\,\text{kg m}^{-3}}$$

Note that the units of v^2 are J kg^{-1} and that $1\,\text{J kg}^{-1} = 1\,\text{m}^2\,\text{s}^{-2}$. So

$$v = 1.6 \times 10^2\,\text{m s}^{-1}$$

This answer shows that the wire will move very fast when it breaks. As the kinetic energy will not in practice be evenly distributed, the moving end of the wire will in fact move at several hundred metres per second.

Maths reference

Derived units

See Maths note 2.3

17   The potential difference is equal to the energy transferred to each coulomb ($1\,\text{V} = 1\,\text{J C}^{-1}$). Assuming this is manifested only as kinetic energy of electrons, we can write

$$\tfrac{1}{2}mv^2 = eV$$
$$v^2 = \frac{2eV}{m} = \frac{2 \times 1.6 \times 10^{-19}\,\text{C} \times 100\,\text{J C}^{-1}}{9.1 \times 10^{-31}\,\text{kg}}$$
$$= 3.52 \times 10^{13}\,\text{m}^2\,\text{s}^{-2}$$

Units of v^2 are J kg^{-1}, which is equivalent to $\text{m}^2\,\text{s}^{-2}$. So $v = 5.93 \times 10^6\,\text{m s}^{-1}$

$$\lambda = \frac{h}{mv} = \frac{6.6 \times 10^{-34}\,\text{J s}}{9.1 \times 10^{-31}\,\text{kg} \times 5.93 \times 10^6\,\text{m s}^{-1}}$$
$$= 1.2 \times 10^{-10}\,\text{m}.$$

Again notice the units of λ: $\text{J s kg}^{-1}\,\text{m}^{-1}$ s, which is equivalent to m.

18 (a) The graph for a metal would be much steeper (as its Young modulus would typically be a thousand times greater) and it would not reach such a large strain (polymers can be strained by several hundred per cent, while metals break at strains of a few per cent.) The graph for the metal might curve over as it yielded (as in Figure 69b).

(b) The area represents the difference between energy transferred to the sample on stretching, and the energy recovered as it is unloaded; it represents the energy dissipated due to heating.

(c) For point A your sketches should resemble Figures 24(a) and 23(a), and for point C they should resemble Figures 24(b) and 23(b).

19   Four (on entering and leaving the cornea; entering and leaving the lens).

20   You want the ciliary muscles to be relaxed. This corresponds to a stretched lens, which is the condition for looking into the distance.

21   It increases. (If you are not sure, compare some fat and thin lenses. Thin lenses have a long focal length.)

22   Your diagram should resemble Figure 71, i.e. the image is diminished, erect, and between F and the lens.

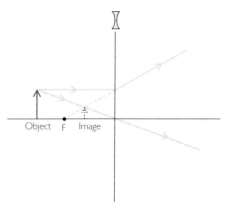

Figure 71   *The answer to question 22*

23   $u = 10\,\text{cm}$, $f = -10\,\text{cm}$
Rearranging the lens formula gives

$$\frac{1}{v} = \frac{1}{f} - \frac{1}{u}$$
$$\frac{1}{v} = \frac{-1}{10\,\text{cm}} - \frac{1}{10\,\text{cm}}$$
$$\frac{1}{v} = \frac{-2}{10\,\text{cm}} = \frac{-1}{5\,\text{cm}}$$
$$v = -5\,\text{cm}$$

So the image is 5 cm from the lens – and it is virtual.

24   $u = 6\,\text{cm}$, $v = -2\,\text{cm}$
Substituting in the thin lens formula gives

$$\frac{1}{f} = \frac{1}{6\,\text{cm}} - \frac{1}{2\,\text{cm}} = \frac{-1}{3\,\text{cm}}$$

So the lens's focal length is 3 cm – and it is a diverging lens.

25 (a) See Figure 72

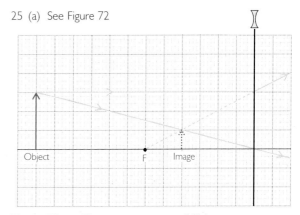

Figure 72   *The answer to question 25(a)*

(b) $u = 12\,cm$, $f = -6\,cm$

$$\frac{1}{v} = \frac{-1}{6\,cm} - \frac{1}{12\,cm} = \frac{-1}{4\,cm}$$

$$v = -4\,cm$$

So the image is 4 cm from the lens – and it is virtual.

26 From Activity 14, the combined power P of three lenses in contact is given by

$$P = P_1 + P_2 + P_3$$

where P_1, P_2 and P_3 are the individual powers of the three lenses.

Required power = $1.0 + 0.5 + 0.25 = 1.75\,D$

$$f = \frac{1}{P} = \frac{1}{1.75\,D} = 0.57\,m$$

27 (a) Adding the powers gives 4.0 D.
   (b) Combined power = $+0.5\,D + (-2.0\,D) = -1.5\,D$.
   (c) Powers are $+10\,D$ and $+4\,D$,
       so combined power = $+14\,D$.

28 (a) Combined power = $+16\,D$,
       so focal length = $\frac{1}{16}\,m = 6.25\,cm$.
   (b) Combined power = $-20\,D$,
       so focal length = $-\frac{1}{20}\,m = -5\,cm$.
   (c) $\frac{1}{f} = \frac{1}{10\,cm} + \frac{1}{5\,cm} = \frac{3}{10\,cm}$
       So $f = \frac{10\,cm}{3} = 3.3\,cm$.

   (Note that it is easier to combine the powers first, and then work out the focal length.)

29 (a) Focal length = 20.0 cm (because rays are parallel from a distant object, and the parallel rays focused at 20.0 cm.)
       Power = $\frac{1}{0.20\,m} = +5.0\,D$.
   (b) Combined power = $+5.0\,D + (-1.0\,D) = +4.0\,D$
       Combined focal length = $\frac{1}{4.0}\,m = 25\,cm$. So the image should be formed at 25 cm from the lenses, which is what the student found.
   (c) Image distance without diverging lens = 10 cm.
       Combined power of
       lenses = $+10\,D + (-1.0\,D) = 9.0\,D$
       So the image will be formed at $\frac{1}{9.0}\,m = 11.1\,cm$ from the lenses.
   (d) The image moved further in the first case, i.e. when the diverging lens was added to the longer focal length (weaker) converging lens.

30 In your list you should include: stiffness, strength, hardness, refractive index and transmittance.

31 (a) Ray 3 is the incident ray; rays 1 and 2 are the reflected rays.
   (b) Their amplitudes must be equal.
   (c) The two waves must be exactly out of step; i.e. there must be a phase difference of 180° between them.

(d) The thickness is one-quarter of the wavelength of light inside the coating material. So this gives the wavelength as 100 nm × 4 = 400 nm. However, the wavelength in air will be longer than this, by a factor equal to the refractive index: Wavelength = 400 nm × 1.4 = 560 nm. The light must strike the surface at right angles; otherwise, the distance it travels through the material will be more than 200 nm.

(e) From part (d) above, you can see that a coating of thickness 100 nm will only result in perfect cancelling for light whose wavelength is 560 nm. Light whose wavelength is greater or less than this will not experience perfect cancelling when it falls normally (at right angles) on the coating. At different angles, the rays of light travel different distances through the coating. At any particular angle, only one wavelength will be perfectly cancelled. A suitable thickness for an effective coating will correspond to a wavelength near the middle of the visible range.

32 (a) 380 nm to 750 nm; note that these are only rough values, and different individuals can see over slightly different wavelength ranges.
   (b) Standard crown glass transmits more ultraviolet. The rose-tinted crown glass would be better for manufacturing spectacle lenses, since it offers more protection against the effects of ultraviolet.
   (c) Photogray allows through all wavelengths in the visible range to roughly equal extents.
   (d) This blue glass lets through a lot of ultraviolet, as well as a lot of visible light. Also, because it lets through short wavelengths (blue) more than longer wavelengths, it will make the world look blue.

33 As a ray of light passes from water into a cornea, it is entering a material with a slightly *higher* refractive index, so it will bend slightly *away from* the normal. We rely on our corneas to bend rays towards the normal, so helping to focus them on the retina. (Recall that the lens plays only a small part in the focusing of the image.) So we can't see clearly under water.

34 If someone is suffering from short sight, parallel rays from a distant object are focused in front of the retina. To focus them further back, the front of the eye must be less curved. To achieve this, more cells must be removed from the centre of the cornea (Figure 73).

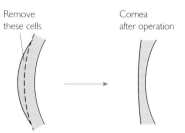

Remove these cells   Cornea after operation

Figure 73 *Diagram for the answer to question 34*

35 By the age of 45, the near point has moved to about 40 cm (see Figure 33). To achieve this, a book must be held at arm's length.

36 The range over which they can focus gets more and more limited, so they need one pair of spectacles for close-up, and one for distance viewing. The problem would not be solved by a single pair of contact lenses, but they could wear contact lenses for distance viewing and have spectacles for close-up, to wear in addition to the contact lenses.

37 Your eyeball is too short, because the rays focus beyond the retina.

38 The implanted lens cannot be adjusted for viewing at different distances. It is suitable for middle-distance viewing, so spectacles are needed to extend the range over which the user can see clearly.

39 (a) Lens 2 is a converging lens – it gives a magnified view of the grid.
(b) Lens 3 has the greater power – it reduces the grid more than lens 1.
(c) Lens 1; since it has a lower power than lens 3, its focal length must be greater.

40 (a) Using the lens formula (equation 10) gives
$$\frac{1}{f} = \frac{1}{0.025\,m} + \frac{1}{0.50\,m} = 42\,m^{-1}$$
$$f = \frac{1}{42}\,m = 0.024\,m = 2.4\,cm.$$

(b) From part (a), the power of the patient's unaided eye is +42 D. Now we can follow the same procedure to calculate the power required when they have a lens to help them focus on an object at 20 cm:
$$\frac{1}{f} = \frac{1}{0.025\,m} + \frac{1}{0.20\,m} = 45\,m^{-1}.$$

So the new power is 45 D, and the lens must have a power of +3 D to achieve this.

41 The problem which elderly people have is that they can only focus over a limited range of distances. They cannot focus clearly on nearby objects or on objects in the distance.
(a) The lower part.

(b) A converging lens is needed to increase the power of the eye, so that the reader can see the book at a closer distance.
(c) Diverging.

42 Using the wave equation,
$$\lambda = \frac{v}{f} = \frac{1500\,m\,s^{-1}}{10 \times 10\,Hz} = 1.5 \times 10\,m = 0.15\,mm.$$

43 Speed in soft tissue is $1500\,m\,s^{-1}$. Distance $s = 10\,cm$ (there and back), $s = vt$, so
$$t = \frac{s}{v} = \frac{0.1\,m}{1500\,m\,s^{-1}} = 0.067\,ms.$$

The interval between pulses must be less than 0.067 ms, so the frequency of pulses must be given by
$$f > \frac{1}{0.067\,ms}\ \text{i.e.}\ f > 15\,kHz.$$

(The frequency of pulses is the no. of pulses per second – *not* the same as the wave frequency.)

44 For muscle, speed = $1600\,m\,s^{-1}$.
$$s = vt = 1600\,m\,s^{-1} \times 20 \times 10^{-6}\,s$$
$$= 3.2 \times 10^{-2}\,m = 3.2\,cm.$$

This is twice the thickness of the heart wall, as it is the difference in the times for each pulse to travel there and back, so at the point where it is measured, the wall is 1.6 cm thick.

45 From equation (16), $\frac{\Delta f}{f_{em}} \approx \frac{u}{v}$, so
$$\Delta f \approx \frac{3000\,Hz \times 20\,m\,s^{-1}}{330\,m\,s^{-1}} = 182\,Hz$$

46 Using equation (18), with $\theta = 0$, $\cos\theta = 1$:
$$\frac{\Delta f}{f_{em}} \approx \frac{2u}{v},$$
and so speed of car,
$$u = \frac{v\Delta f}{2f_{em}} = 3.0 \times 10^8\,m\,s^{-1} \times \frac{2500\,Hz}{2 \times 10^{10}\,Hz}$$
$$= 37.5\,m\,s^{-1}$$
so it *is* exceeding the speed limit.

47 From equation (18), with $u = 5.0 \times 10^{-3}\,m\,s^{-1}$, $\theta = 60°$ and $f_{em} = 6.0\,MHz = 6.0 \times 10^6\,Hz$:
$$\Delta f = 2 \times 5.0 \times 10^{-3}\,m\,s^{-1} \times \frac{6.0 \times 10^6\,Hz\cos 60°}{1500\,m\,s^{-1}}$$
$$= 20\,Hz$$

Maths Notes

0 Signs and symbols

0.1 Equations and comparisons

In physics, we are often interested in whether two quantities are exactly equal, or almost equal, or whether one is greater than the other. Table 1 lists the signs used for expressing such relationships.

Symbol	Meaning	Notes
$=$	is equal to	
$\equiv$	is exactly the same as	used to emphasise the point that two expressions are two ways of writing exactly the same thing (as opposed to two different things being the same size)
$\neq$	is not equal to	
$\approx$	is approximately equal to	
$\sim$	is the same order of magnitude as	
$<$	is less than	the smaller quantity is written at the narrow end of the symbol
$>$	is greater than	
$\leqslant$	is less than or equal to	
$\geqslant$	is greater than or equal to	
$<<$	is much less than	
$>>$	is much greater than	

Table I   *Signs for equations and comparisons*

Maths reference

Order of magnitude
See Maths note 7.4

0.2 The delta symbol

The symbol Δ (the capital Greek letter delta) is used to mean 'a small amount of' or 'a change in'. Notice that Δ does *not* represent a number, so resist the temptation to cancel Δ if it appears on the top and bottom of an expression.

For example, the symbol Δt represents a time interval and is often used when describing rates of flow or rates of change. For example, if an amount of charge ΔQ flows past a point in a time interval Δt, then the current I can be written

$$I = \frac{\Delta Q}{\Delta t}$$

The delta symbol is also used to denote an experimental uncertainty. For example, if a distance x is measured as 23 mm but could be out by 1 mm in either direction, then the uncertainty in the measurement is $\Delta x = 1$ mm. The measurement is written as $x \pm \Delta x$, i.e. 23 mm $\pm$ 1 mm.

1 *Index notation*

An **index** (plural **indices**) or **power** is the superscript number which, when a positive whole number, means squared, cubed, etc. For example

$5^2 = 5 \times 5 = 25$

$7^3 = 7 \times 7 \times 7 = 147$

$0.6^4 = 0.6 \times 0.6 \times 0.6 \times 0.6 = 0.1296$

1.1 *Index notation and powers of 10*

Table 2 shows 'powers of 10'. The number in any row is found by dividing the number in the row above by 10.

100 000 =	$10 \times 10 \times 10 \times 10 \times 10 =$	10^5
10 000 =	$10 \times 10 \times 10 \times 10 =$	10^4
1 000 =	$10 \times 10 \times 10 =$	10^3
100 =	$10 \times 10 =$	10^2
10 =	$10 =$	10^1
1 =	$1 =$	10^0
0.1 =	$\dfrac{1}{10} =$	10^{-1}
0.01 =	$\dfrac{1}{10 \times 10} = \dfrac{1}{10^2} =$	10^{-2}
0.001 =	$\dfrac{1}{10 \times 10 \times 10} = \dfrac{1}{10^3} =$	10^{-3}

Table 2 *Positive and negative powers of 10*

Extending the pattern gives a meaning to zero and negative indices. If you replace all the 10s in Table 2 by any other number that you choose, you should be able to convince yourself that

$$x^0 = 1 \qquad \text{for } any \text{ value of } x.$$

Maths reference

Units and physical quantities
See Maths note 2.1

1.2 *Standard form*

To represent very large and very small numbers, we generally use **standard form**, also called **scientific notation**.

A number written in standard form consists of a number with a single digit (not zero) before the decimal point, multiplied by a power of 10.

Large numbers

5 620 000 (five million six hundred and twenty thousand) becomes 5.62×10^6

407 300 (four hundred and seven thousand, three hundred) becomes 4.073×10^5.

Small numbers

$0.5680 = 5.680 \times 0.1 = 5.68 \times 10^{-1}$

$0.000\,702\,3 = 7.023 \times 0.0001 = 7.023 \times 10^{-4}$

1.3 Combining powers

Powers of the same number

When multiplying two numbers expressed as 'powers' of the same number, the powers add:

$$10^2 \times 10^3 = (10 \times 10) \times (10 \times 10 \times 10) = 10^5$$

i.e. $\quad 10^2 \times 10^3 = 10^{(2+3)}$

$$6^2 \times 6^2 = (6 \times 6) \times (6 \times 6) = 6^4$$

When dividing, the powers subtract

$$10^6 \div 10^2 = (10 \times 10 \times 10 \times 10 \times 10 \times 10) \div (10 \times 10) = 10^4$$

i.e. $\quad 10^6 \div 10^2 = 10^{(6-2)}$

The rules still work when negative powers are involved:

$$10^5 \times 10^{-2} = 10^5 \times \left(\frac{1}{10^2}\right) = 10^5 \div 10^2 = 10^3$$

i.e. $\quad 10^5 \times 10^{-2} = 10^{(5-2)}$

$$x^4 \times x^{-3} = x^{(4-3)} = x$$

$$4^3 \div 4^{-2} = 4^3 \div \left(\frac{1}{4^2}\right) = 4^3 \times 4^2 = 4^5$$

i.e. $\quad 4^3 \div 4^{-2} = 4^{(3--2)} = 4^{(3+2)}$

Maths reference

Reciprocals
See Maths note 3.3

Powers of different numbers

When dealing with a mixture of numbers of different type, collect together all numbers of the same type and combine their powers by adding or subtracting:

$$2 \times 10^4 \times 3 \times 10^5 = (2 \times 3) \times (10^4 \times 10^5) = 6 \times 10^9$$

$$1.38 \times 10^{-23} \times 2.3 \times 10^3 = 1.38 \times 2.3 \times 10^{(-23+3)}$$
$$= 3.174 \times 10^{-20}$$

$$3y^2 \times 7y^5 = 21y^7$$

$$5z^2 \times 3z^{-2} = 15z^0 = 15$$

1.4 *Manipulating powers on a calculator*

Powers of 10

Think of the EXP or EE key as 'times 10 to the power of'.

To enter 7.54×10^9: enter 7.54, press EXP and enter 9. (Notice that you do *not* type in 10 – if you do, you will multiply your number by 10, making it 10 times too big.)

Your calculator might use its own shorthand to display this number as 7.54 09, or 7.54^9, or 7.54 EE 9 (or similar). But you should always *write* it as 7.54×10^9.

Negative powers of 10

To enter a negative index, use the ± or +/− key (*not* the 'minus' key, because that will subtract the next number from the one you have just entered).

To enter 1.38×10^{-23}: enter 1.38, press EXP, enter 23 and press ±.

Squares, etc.

To square a number, use the x^2 key. For example, to work out 1.3^2, enter 1.3 and press x^2 to get 1.69.

Pressing x^2 again squares the answer, i.e. calculates your original number to the power of 4. Pressing x^2 three times altogether gives you your original number to the power of 8, and so on – each time you press x^2, you double the power.

Other powers

Use the y^x key to raise one number to the power of a second number. y is the first number you enter, and x the second.

To calculate 2.5^3: enter 2.5, press y^x, enter 3, press =.

Other negative powers

As with powers of 10, use the ± or +/− key to enter negative numbers.

To calculate 2.5^{-3}: enter 2.5, press y^x, enter 3, press ±, press =.

1.5 *Powers that are not whole numbers*

The square root of a number x can be written as $x^{\frac{1}{2}}$ or $x^{1/2}$:

$$x^{\frac{1}{2}} \times x^{\frac{1}{2}} = x^{\left(\frac{1}{2} + \frac{1}{2}\right)} = x^1 = x$$

so $x^{\frac{1}{2}} = \sqrt{x}$.

Similarly, $x^{\frac{1}{3}} = \sqrt[3]{x}$ (the cube root of x); $x^{\frac{1}{4}} = \sqrt[4]{x}$ and so on.

Other fractional powers can also be interpreted in terms of roots, for example:

$$x^{\frac{3}{2}} = \sqrt{(x^3)} \text{ (the square root of } x\text{-cubed)}$$

$$= (\sqrt{x})^3 \text{ (the cube of the square root of } x)$$

and

$$x^{-\frac{1}{2}} = \frac{1}{x^{\frac{1}{2}}} = \frac{1}{\sqrt{x}}$$

Fractional powers can also be written using decimal numbers, for example:

$$x^{\frac{1}{2}} = x^{0.5}$$
$$x^{\frac{3}{2}} = x^{1.5}$$

Powers that are neither simple fractions nor whole numbers are less easy to interpret, but they still exist and can be calculated (e.g. using the y^x key of a calculator. For example:

$$10^{0.333} = 2.153$$
$$10^{0.6021} = 4000$$
$$5.6^{\pi} = 224.1$$
$$9.34^{-0.83} = 0.1565$$

(All these answers are given to four significant figures.)

Maths reference

Significant figures
See Maths note 7.2

2 *Units*

The SI system of units (Système Internationale d'Unités) has been established by international agreement. In your study of physics you will use mainly SI units. The basic SI units are listed in Table 3. Notice that, when a unit is named after a person, the unit symbol has a capital but the *name* of the unit does not.

Quantity	SI unit	Notes
mass	kilogram, kg	
time	second, s	
length	metre, m	
electric current	ampere, A	used to define the unit of charge, the coulomb
temperature	kelvin, K	
luminous intensity	candela, cd	not used in this course, but included here for completeness
amount of substance	mole, mol	

Table 3   *The basic SI units*

2.1 *Units and physical quantities; graphs and tables*

A physical quantity consists of a number and a unit. Without the unit, the quantity is incomplete. When a symbol represents a physical quantity, it represents the *complete* quantity – units and all. For example, suppose v represents speed, and a particular speed is found to be $5 \, \text{m s}^{-1}$. You should write

$$v = 5 \, \text{m s}^{-1}$$

(*not* just $v = 5$ and *not* $v \, (\text{m s}^{-1}) = 5$).

Units can be manipulated just like numbers and other symbols. When labelling axes of graphs, and when listing physical quantities in tables, it is conventional to divide each quantity by its unit to get a pure number.

For example, you can divide both sides of the expression for v above by m s^{-1} and write

$$v/(\text{m s}^{-1}) = 5$$

If you were plotting values of v on a graph, or listing them in a table, you should label the graph axis, or the table column, as $v/\text{m s}^{-1}$.

Large and small numbers

Suppose you were dealing with speeds that were all several million metres per second:

$$v = 2 \times 10^6 \text{ m s}^{-1}, \qquad v = 7 \times 10^6 \text{ m s}^{-1}, \text{ etc.}$$

To make the numbers more manageable, you could use the same rule as above to write $v/(10^6 \text{ m s}^{-1}) = 2$, etc., and label you graph and table as shown in Figure 1.

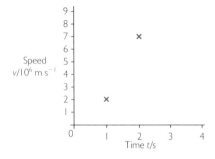

Figure 1   *Labelling graphs and tables*

2.2   *Manipulating units; index notation and units*

In calculations, the units should be manipulated as well as the numbers. This can help you keep track of what you are doing as well as being correct – so it is a good habit to get into.

Indices can be used with units and with algebraic symbols. For example,

$$4^{-1} = \frac{1}{4} = 0.25, \qquad x^{-2} = \frac{1}{x^2}$$

Units such as coulombs per second, or joules per coulomb, can be written either as C/s and J/C or using index notation: C s^{-1} and J C^{-1}. Similarly, metres per second, in calculations of unit of speed, can be written as m/s or m s^{-1}. Using the index notation helps prevent table headings and graph labels having too many oblique strokes. For example,

$$70 \text{ m} \div 20 \text{ s} = 3.5 \text{ m s}^{-1}$$

When multiplying numbers, units or symbols, collect together all those of the same type and add their indices. For example:

$$2 \text{ C s}^{-1} \times 4 \text{ s} = 8 \text{ C}$$

$$10 \text{ m s}^{-1} \div 5 \text{ s} = 2 \text{ m s}^{-2}$$

2.3   *Derived units*

Table 4 shows how SI units are combined to give units of various quantities. Some common combinations are given 'shorthand' names.

Maths reference

Index notation and powers of 10
See *Maths note 1.1*

Units and physical quantities; graphs and tables
See *Maths note 2.1*

Quantity	Unit name	Symbol	Equivalent
speed			$m\,s^{-1}$
acceleration			$m\,s^{-2}$
force	newton	N	$1\,N = 1\,kg\,m\,s^{-2}$
gravitational field strength			$1\,N\,kg^{-1} = 1\,m\,s^{-2}$
energy, work	joule	J	$1\,J = 1\,N\,m = 1\,kg\,m^2\,s^{-2}$
power	watt	W	$1\,W = 1\,J\,s^{-1}$ $(= 1\,kg\,m^2\,s^{-3})$
frequency	hertz	Hz	$1\,Hz = 1\,s^{-1}$
electric charge	coulomb	C	$1\,C = 1\,A\,s$ $1\,A = 1\,C\,s^{-1}$
potential difference, emf	volt	V	$1\,V = 1\,J\,C^{-1}$ $(= 1\,kg\,m^2\,C^{-1}\,s^{-2})$
electrical resistance	ohm	W	$1\,W = 1\,V\,A^{-1}$ $(= 1\,kg\,m^2\,C^{-2}\,s^{-1})$

Table 4 *Some common derived SI units*

Study note

In writing units, the coulomb is often treated as as if it were the basic unit rather than the ampere.

2.4 SI prefixes

When dealing with quantities that are large or small, we often use prefixes as an alternative to standard form. For example, a distance of 1.3×10^4 m could be written as 13 km, and a distance of 0.0037 m could be written as 3.7 mm. The official SI prefixes go up and down in steps of 10^3. Table 5 lists the SI prefixes that you are likely to encounter in your study of physics.

Prefix	Symbol	Equivalent in powers of 10
tera	T	10^{12}
giga	G	10^9
mega	M	10^6
kilo	k	10^3
centi	c	10^{-2}
milli	m	10^{-3}
micro	μ	10^{-6}
nano	n	10^{-9}
pico	p	10^{-12}
femto	f	10^{-15}

Table 5 *SI prefixes*

Study note

The centimetre is not officially an SI unit [because 'centi' (10^{-2}) does not fit the pattern] but it is widely used

When dealing with conversions involving prefixes, it is wise to write down each step using appropriate powers of 10, *and include the units at each stage*. For example, suppose light of a certain colour has a wavelength of 468 nm and you want to use standard form to write the wavelength in metres:

$$468 \text{ nm} = 468 \times 10^{-9} \text{ m}$$
$$= 4.68 \times 10^2 \times 10^{-9} \text{ m}$$
$$= 4.68 \times 10^{-7} \text{ m}$$

Suppose the tension in a rope is 1.35×10^5 N and you want to express it in kN:

$$1 \text{ kN} = 10^3 \text{ N, so } 1 \text{ N} = \frac{1}{10^3} \text{ kN} = 10^{-3} \text{ kN}$$
$$1.35 \times 10^5 \text{ N} = 1.35 \times 10^5 \times 10^{-3} \text{ kN}$$
$$= 1.35 \times 10^2 \text{ kN}$$
$$= 135 \text{ kN}$$

Suppose an electric current is 4.56×10^{-4} A and you want to express it in μA:

$$1 \text{ } \mu\text{A} = 10^{-6} \text{ A, so } 1 \text{ A} = \frac{1}{10^{-6}} \text{ } \mu\text{A} = 10^6 \text{ } \mu\text{A}$$
$$4.56 \times 10^{-4} \text{ A} = 4.56 \times 10^{-4} \times 10^6 \text{ } \mu\text{A}$$
$$= 4.56 \times 10^2 \text{ } \mu\text{A}$$
$$= 456 \text{ } \mu\text{A}$$

2.5 Dimensions

The **dimensions** of a quantity show how it is related to the basic quantities listed in Table 3. Symbols M, L and T are used to represent the dimensions of mass, length and time.

For example, volume is calculated from length × breadth × height so has dimension of length^3 or L^3; speed is found from distance ÷ time so has dimensions of L/T or LT^{-1}. The dimensions of force are those of mass × acceleration: MLT^{-2}.

Square brackets are used to denote the dimensions of a quantity. For example

$$[\text{velocity}] = LT^{-1}$$

$$[\text{force}] = [\text{mass}] \times [\text{acceleration}] = MLT^{-2}$$

Dimensions are more fundamental than units. You might, for example, choose to express a speed in miles per hour rather than SI units of m s^{-1}, but the dimensions are still LT^{-1}, i.e. length (miles) ÷ time (hours).

Any equation must be dimensionally consistent, that is, the dimensions of the left-hand side must be the same as those of the right-hand side. This can help you check whether a particular equation is correct, and can also enable you to derive relationships between quantities.

3 *Arithmetic and algebra*

3.1 *Fractions, decimals and percentages*

A fraction is really a division sum, e.g.

$$\frac{4}{5} = 4 \div 5; \qquad \frac{7}{3} = 7 \div 3.$$

You can express a fraction as a decimal number by doing the division on a calculator.

When fractions are multiplied together, you can often simplify the arithmetic by using the fact that the multiplication and division can be carried out in any order, e.g.

$$\frac{7}{5} \times \frac{3}{14} = \frac{7 \times 3}{5 \times 14}$$

and cancelling any common factors, e.g.

$$\frac{7 \times 3}{5 \times 14} = \frac{3}{5 \times 2} = \frac{3}{10} = 0.3.$$

You can think of the **percentage** sign, %, as being made up of a 1, 0, 0 to remind you that it is a fraction of 100 parts. To calculate a percentage from a number expressed as a fraction or a decimal, you multiply by 100:

$$\frac{1}{2} = 0.5 \text{ and } 100 \times 0.5 = 50 \text{ so } \frac{1}{2} = 50\% \text{ (or } 50/100)$$

$$\frac{1}{4} = 0.25 \text{ and } 100 \times 0.25 = 25 \text{ so } \frac{1}{4} = 25\% \text{ (or } 25/100)$$

$$\frac{7}{8} = 0.875 \text{ and } 100 \times 0.875 = 87.5 \text{ so } \frac{7}{8} = 87.5\%$$

For example, if a solar array produces an output power of 600 W from an input power of 4 kW (4000 W), its efficiency is

$$\frac{600 \text{ W}}{4000 \text{ W}} = 0.15 = 15\%.$$

To find a percentage of a quantity, you *multiply* the quantity by the percentage expressed as an ordinary fraction or decimal number. For example, to find 15% of 60 multiply 60 by 15/100 (or by 0.15)

$$\frac{15}{100} \times 60 = \frac{90}{10} = 9$$

or

$$0.15 \times 60 = 9.$$

3.2 Brackets and common factors

To evaluate an expression such as

$$6(2 + 3 - 4 + 5), \qquad \frac{12 + 8}{4} \qquad \text{or} \qquad I(R_1 + R_2 + R_3)$$

you usually first deal with the additions and subtractions inside the bracket and then multiply or divide the result by the number or symbol outside. Alternatively you can carry out several separate multiplications or divisions on each number or symbol inside the bracket in turn, then do the additions or subtractions. For example

either $\quad 6(2 + 3 - 4 + 5) = 6 \times 6 = 36$

or $\quad 6(2 + 3 - 4 + 5) = 12 + 18 - 24 + 30 = 36$

either $\quad \dfrac{12 + 8}{4} = \dfrac{20}{4} = 5$

or $\quad \dfrac{12 + 8}{4} = \dfrac{12}{4} + \dfrac{8}{4} = 3 + 2 = 5$

A calculation that involves several multiplications or divisions using the same number and then adding or subtracting the results can be simplified if it is rewritten using brackets with the **common factor** outside. For example

$$25 + 30 + 35 = 5(5 + 6 + 7)$$

$$3x + 3y + 3z = 3(x + y + z)$$

$$IR_1 + IR_2 + IR_3 = I(R_1 + R_2 + R_3)$$

$$\frac{7}{2} + \frac{3}{2} + \frac{6}{2} = \frac{(7 + 3 + 6)}{2}$$

$$\frac{a}{x} + \frac{b}{x} + \frac{c}{x} = \frac{a + b + c}{x}$$

3.3 Reciprocals

The value obtained by dividing 1 by a number is called the **reciprocal** of the number (reciprocals can be found using the $1/x$ key of a calculator). Finding the reciprocal of a reciprocal gets you back to the original number. For example:

$$\frac{1}{2} = 0.5, \qquad \frac{1}{0.5} = 2.$$

For a lens:

$$\text{power } P = \frac{1}{f}, \qquad \text{focal length } f = \frac{1}{P}.$$

Reciprocals are sometimes written using a negative index:

$$x^{-1} = \frac{1}{x}.$$

To find the reciprocal of a fraction, simply turn it the other way up. For example:

$$\frac{1}{\frac{1}{2}} = \frac{2}{1} = 2$$

$$\frac{1}{\frac{2}{3}} = \frac{3}{2} = 1\frac{1}{2}$$

$$\left(\frac{3}{7}\right)^{-1} = \frac{7}{3}$$

This is not just an arbitrary rule. It makes sense if you think in terms of division sums. Consider the second example above. Question: 'How many times does $\frac{2}{3}$ go into 1?' Answer: 'one-and-a-half times.'

Adding and subtracting

One place where you need to add and subtract reciprocals is in calculations of resistors in parallel. To find the net resistance R of several resistors connected in parallel, you must first find the reciprocal of each resistor, then add the reciprocals together (to get $1/R$), then find the reciprocal of $1/R$ to get R.

For example, if $R_1 = 2.0\ \Omega$, $R_2 = 5.0\ \Omega$, $R_3 = 1.0\ \Omega$, then

$$\frac{1}{R_1} = \frac{1}{2}\ \Omega^{-1} = 0.50\ \Omega^{-1} \text{ (notice the unit of } 1/R)$$

$$\frac{1}{R_2} = 0.20\ \Omega^{-1},$$

$$\frac{1}{R_3} = 1.00\ \Omega^{-1}$$

(notice that $1/1 = 1$ – the number stays the same but the unit still changes). So

$$1/R = (0.50 + 0.20 + 1.00)\ \Omega^{-1} = 1.70\ \Omega^{-1}$$

$$R = \frac{1}{1.70}\ \Omega = 0.59\ \Omega$$

Notice that adding the reciprocals of two numbers is *not* the same as adding the two numbers and then finding the reciprocal of their sum.

Multiplying and dividing

Multiplying by the reciprocal of a number is the same as dividing by that number. For example

$$7 \times \frac{1}{2} = 7 \div 2 = 3.50$$

Dividing by the reciprocal of a number is the same as multiplying by that number. For example

$$4 \div \frac{1}{3} = 4 \times 3 = 12$$

$$9 \div \frac{3}{4} = 9 \times \frac{4}{3} = \frac{9 \times 4}{3} = 12$$

For a wave,

$$f = \frac{v}{\lambda}, \qquad \text{time period } T = \frac{1}{f} = \frac{1}{(v/\lambda)} = \frac{\lambda}{v}$$

We can simplify divisions involving fractions. For example:

$$\frac{3}{4} \div \frac{5}{4} = \frac{3}{4} \times \frac{4}{5} = \frac{3 \times 4}{4 \times 5} = \frac{3}{5} = 0.6.$$

3.4 Algebra and elimination

If we have two different relationships that both involve some of the same things, we can combine them to produce a new equation. This allows us to avoid measuring, or calculating, something that is not already known – we can eliminate it (remove it) from the equations. For example, we can take an expression for electrical power

$$P = IV$$

and use the resistance equation

$$V = IR$$

to write IR instead of V:

$$P = I \times IR = I^2R$$

This enables us to relate P directly to I and R without needing to know or calculate V. Similarly, if we want to eliminate I:

$$P = \frac{V}{R} \times V = \frac{V^2}{R}$$

3.5 Adding and subtracting fractions

You can of course add and subtract fractions on a calculator – you carry out several division sums and add or subtract the results. But for simple fractions it can often be quicker to do the sums 'by hand'.

The trick is to write the fractions so that they have the same denominator (the number underneath the fraction). Sometimes it is quite easy to spot how to do this. For example:

$$\frac{3}{4} + \frac{5}{6} = \frac{3 \times 3}{3 \times 4} + \frac{2 \times 5}{2 \times 6}$$

$$= \frac{9}{12} + \frac{10}{12} = \frac{9 + 10}{12} = \frac{19}{12}$$

Otherwise, make a common denominator by multiplying the original denominators together:

$$\frac{2}{17} + \frac{4}{3} = \frac{2 \times 3}{17 \times 3} + \frac{4 \times 17}{3 \times 17}$$

$$= \frac{6}{51} + \frac{68}{51} = \frac{6 + 68}{51} = \frac{74}{51}$$

Another example:

$$\frac{1}{2} + \frac{1}{3} = \frac{3}{6} + \frac{2}{6} = \frac{5}{6}$$

4 Solving equations

It may sound obvious, but the main thing to understand about equations is that the '=' sign means that the two things on either side are *equal* to one another. So whatever you do to one side, you must also do to the other, otherwise they would no longer be equal. (Beware of getting into the bad habit of writing '=' when you really mean 'and so the next step is...'.)

One way to think of an equation is as a 'recipe' for calculating. For example, $F = ma$ tells you how to calculate the net force F if you know the acceleration a that it gives to a mass m. In this example, F is the **subject** of the equation – it is written on its own (usually on the left).

4.1 Rearranging an equation

Quite often, the quantity we want to calculate is wrapped up in the right-hand side of an equation, and we need to make it the subject. When doing this, it helps if you try to understand what you are doing rather than blindly trying to apply a set of rules. It is also wise to write down each step, justifying each one to yourself as you do so. This might sound time-consuming, but it isn't really because it helps you to keep track of what you are doing and, if you do make a slip, it is quite easy to go back and check.

Look at the part of the equation that contains the quantity that you want to know. Think what you need to do to get that quantity on its own, and do the same thing(s) to both sides.

For example, suppose you want to know the acceleration that a force F gives to a mass m:

$$F = ma$$

To get a on its own, you need to divide the right-hand side by m ($ma \div m = a$), so do the same to the left-hand side:

$$\frac{F}{m} = a, \qquad \text{or} \qquad a = \frac{F}{m}.$$

Another example: suppose you want to calculate internal resistance r from

$$V = \mathcal{E} - Ir$$

It is a good idea first to arrange that the thing you are interested in has a positive sign. You can do this by adding Ir to both sides:

$$V + Ir = \mathcal{E}$$

then to get r on its own you subtract V from both sides:

$$Ir = \mathcal{E} - V$$

and then divide by I

$$r = \frac{\mathcal{E} - V}{I} \qquad \text{or} \qquad r = (\mathcal{E} - V)/I$$

(Notice that you have to divide the *whole* of the right-hand side by I – hence the brackets.)

Maths reference

Brackets and common factors
See Maths note 3.2

4.2 Simultaneous equations

Simultaneous equations arise if we have two (or more) different ways of writing a relationship between quantities. If we have two unknown quantities, then they can both be found if we have two simultaneous equations. For three unknown quantities, we'd need three separate equations, and so on.

The trick in solving simultaneous equations is to carry out some algebra and arithmetic to get an expression that involves just *one* of the unknown things, and then use that value to calculate the other one.

For example, the equation $\mathcal{E} = V + Ir$ involves two things that can be measured (V and I). If neither $\mathcal{E}$ nor r is known, then they cannot be found from a single pair of values of V and I. However, if you obtain two *different* pairs of readings (V_1 and I_1, and V_2 and I_2) for the same power supply (using two different external loads), then you can write down two simultaneous equations – two different equations that both describe a relationship between the two unknown things $\mathcal{E}$ and r. These equations let you find both $\mathcal{E}$ and r. So

$$\mathcal{E} = V_1 + I_1 r$$
$$\mathcal{E} = V_2 + I_2 r$$

Since the right-hand side of each equation is equal to $\mathcal{E}$, then they must also be equal to each other:

$$V_1 + I_1 r = V_2 + I_2 r$$

Subtracting V_1 from each side

$$I_1 r = V_2 - V_1 + I_2 r$$

Subtracting I_2r from both sides (and being careful with signs and with the subscripts 1 and 2)

$$I_1r - I_2r = V_2 - V_1$$

Now r is a common factor on the left-hand side, so

$$r(I_1 - I_2) = V_2 - V_1$$

Dividing both sides by $(I_1 - I_2)$ (and using brackets to keep the subtracted things together)

$$r = \frac{(V_2 - V_1)}{(I_1 - I_2)} \qquad \text{or} \qquad r = (V_2 - V_1)/(I_1 - I_2)$$

This value of r can then be used in one of the original equations to find $\mathcal{E}$.

For example: a power supply gives readings of $V_1 = 3$ V, $I_1 = 7$ A, and $V_2 = 8$ V, $I_2 = 2$ A. So

$$r = \frac{8\,\text{V} - 3\,\text{V}}{7\,\text{A} - 2\,\text{A}} = \frac{5\,\text{V}}{5\,\text{A}} = 1\,\Omega$$

and

$$\mathcal{E} = V_1 + I_1r = 3\,\text{V} + 7\,\text{A} \times 1\,\Omega = 3\,\text{V} + 7\,\text{V} = 10\,\text{V}$$

(you would find the same value using V_2 and I_2).

5 *Relationships and graphs*

Graphs are extremely useful in physics for giving us a pictorial representation of how one quantity is related to another. Trends in data are not always clear from a table of results, but become immediately evident when viewing a plot of the two quantities involved.

5.1 *Graphs and proportionality*

Many important relationships in physics involve the idea of direct proportion.

For example, if a conductor obeys Ohm's law, doubling the potential difference produces double the current, tripling the pd triples the current ... and so on. Mathematically, we say that the potential difference is **directly proportional** to the current. In symbols

$$V \propto I \qquad \text{or} \qquad V = kI$$

The symbol $\propto$ means 'is directly proportional to' and k is called a **constant of proportionality** and has a fixed value for a particular set of values of V and I. (The constant k in this example is the same thing as the electrical resistance R.)

If one quantity is directly proportional to another, then a graph of one plotted against the other is a straight line through the origin.

5.2 Linear relationships

The equation $V = \mathscr{E} - Ir$ is an example of a **linear relationship** between two variables, V and I in this case. A graph of V (on the vertical axis, the y-axis) against I (on the horizontal axis, the x-axis) gives a straight line. Linear relationships and graphs are often said to be of the type $y = mx + c$, where y stands for whatever is plotted on the y-axis and x for whatever is plotted on the x-axis, and m and c are constants (they remain fixed when x and y change). This type of graph has two properties that are often useful for doing calculations using experimental results. We can illustrate these with a graph of $y = 2x + 1$, i.e. $m = 2$, $c = 1$ (Figure 2).

On Figure 2, the line cuts the y-axis at $y = 1$ (using the equation, when $x = 0$, $y = c$). The line of such a graph always cuts the y-axis where $y = c$.

If y is directly proportional to x, then the line goes through the origin and $c = 0$.

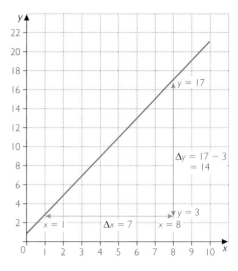

Figure 2 A graph of $y = 2x + 1$

5.3 Gradient of a linear graph

Figure 2 is a graph of the linear relationship $y = 2x + 1$.

The **gradient** (or slope) of the graph is defined as the rise of the graph (the increase in y, Δy) divided by the run (the corresponding increase in x, Δx) found by drawing a right angled triangle as shown in Figure 2. On Figure 2,

$$\Delta y = 14, \qquad \Delta x = 7,$$

$$\text{gradient} = \frac{\Delta y}{\Delta x} = 2.$$

Notice that Δy and Δx are numbers read from the graph scales, and are *not* lengths measured with a ruler, and that any similar triangle drawn on the graph will give the same value of the gradient.

The gradient of a linear graph of y against x is always equal to the value m in the relationship $y = mx + c$.

The graph in Figure 2 has a positive gradient. If m is negative, then the graph slopes down from left to right.

If two variables measured in an experiment are related by a linear equation, then plotting them on a graph enables you to find the values of the constants relating them. It is helpful if you arrange the relationship so that it looks as much like $y = mx + c$ as possible. For example, by subtracting Ir from both sides you can write $\mathscr{E} = V + Ir$ as

$$V = (-r)I + \mathscr{E}$$

which can be compared directly with

$$y = mx + c$$

If you plot measured values of V on the y-axis against corresponding values of I on the x-axis, the graph will be a straight line that cuts the y-axis at $\mathscr{E}$, and with a gradient $m = -r$.

Maths reference

Error bars and error boxes
See Maths note 7.5

5.4 *Inverse proportionality*

If one quantity is **inversely proportional** to another, then as one increases, the other will decrease. For example, the acceleration produced by a given net force is inversely proportional to the mass on which it acts: doubling the mass halves the acceleration, tripling the mass divides the acceleration by three and so on – and vice versa.

Such a relationship is written using reciprocals and the symbol for direct proportion:

$$a \propto \frac{1}{m} \qquad a = \frac{k}{m}$$

or

$$m \propto \frac{1}{a} \qquad m = \frac{k}{a}$$

Maths reference

Reciprocals
See Maths note 3.3

(In this case, the constant of proportionality is the same as the net force F.)

If one quantity is inversely proportional to the other (Table 6), the graph of one plotted against the other is curved as in Figure 3.

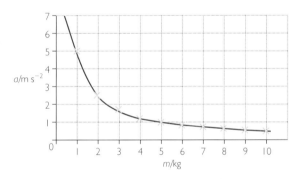

m/kg	$(1/m)$/kg^{-1}	a/m s^{-2}
1	1.000	5.00
2	0.500	2.50
3	0.333	1.67
4	0.250	1.25
5	0.200	1.00
6	0.167	0.83
7	0.143	0.71
8	0.125	0.63
9	0.111	0.55
10	0.100	0.50

Figure 3 *A graph showing how the acceleration a produced by a constant force F (= 5 N) depends on mass m (data from Table 6)*

Table 6 *Data for Figures 3 and 4*

But if one quantity is plotted against the *reciprocal* of the other, then the graph is a straight line through the origin, as shown in Figure 4.

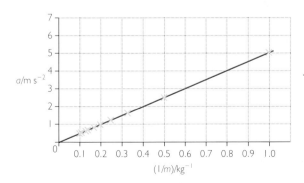

Figure 4 *The data from Figure 3 plotted as a against 1/m*

5.5 *Testing mathematical relationships*

Sometimes we are interested in finding a mathematical relationship between two measured quantities. This usually involves some educated guesswork, based on ideas about the underlying physics and/or from looking at the numbers. Plotting graphs provides a way of testing the guesses.

Direct proportion

For example, if both quantities increase together, you might guess that one is directly proportional to the other. Plot a graph of one against the other and see whether you can draw a straight line through all the error boxes.

Examples that give straight-line graphs include:

$s \propto t$ for motion at constant speed

$I \propto V$ for an ohmic conductor.

If the plot does not give a straight line, try something else. For example, motion from rest at constant acceleration is described by the equation

$$s = \tfrac{1}{2}at^2$$

$$s \propto t^2$$

A graph of distance s against time t is a curve, but a graph of s against t^2 is a straight line with gradient $a/2$ or $\tfrac{1}{2}a$.

Sometimes you need to use the square root of a quantity to get a straight line. For example, for a simple pendulum a plot of its period T against the square root of its length l gives a straight line:

$$T \propto \sqrt{\ell}$$

Maths reference

Experimental uncertainty
See Maths note 7.1

Error bars and error boxes
See Maths note 7.5

Inverse proportion

If one quantity increases as the other decreases, you might guess that you are looking at inverse proportionality, so try plotting a graph using the reciprocal of one quantity.

If this does not give a straight line, try plotting the square, or the square root, of the reciprocal.

For example, suppose you measure the frequency f of the note from a plucked string of mass per unit length μ. Frequency f decreases as you increase μ, but suppose you find that a graph of f against $1/\mu$ is not a straight line.

If a graph of f against $\dfrac{1}{\mu^2}$ is a straight line, then $f \propto \dfrac{1}{\mu^2}$

If you need to plot f against $\dfrac{1}{\sqrt{\mu}}$ to get a straight line, then $f \propto \dfrac{1}{\sqrt{\mu}}$

Maths reference

Reciprocals
See Maths note 3.3

Inverse proportionality
See Maths note 5.4

6 Trigonometry and angular measurements

6.1 Degrees and radians

A **radian**, or **rad** for short, is a unit for measuring angles commonly used in physics instead of degrees. Figure 5 shows how the size of an angle, in radians, is defined.

For a full circle, length of arc = length of circumference = $2\pi r$.

Size of angle $= \dfrac{2\pi r}{r} = 2\pi$ radians, i.e. approximately 6.28 rad.

Table 7 lists some useful conversions between radians and degrees.

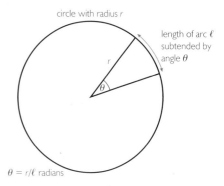

circle with radius r

length of arc ℓ subtended by angle θ

$\theta = r/\ell$ radians

Figure 5 *The size of an angle measured in radians*

Angle	Size in degrees	Size in radians
full circle	360°	2π rad = 6.28 rad
half circle	180°	π rad = 3.14 rad
	114.6°	2.0 rad
quarter circle	90°	$\pi/2$ rad = 1.57 rad
	60°	$\pi/3$ rad = 1.05 rad
	57.3°	1.0 rad
	45°	$\pi/4$ rad = 0.79 rad
	30°	$\pi/6$ rad = 0.52 rad
	28.6°	0.5 rad

Table 7 *Some conversions between radians and degrees*

Note that π is a *number* (approximately 3.14) that frequently, but not always, appears in angles measured in radians.

6.2 Sine, cosine and tangent of an angle

Figure 6 shows a right angled triangle. The sides of the triangle are related by Pythagoras's theorem:

$$c^2 = b^2 + a^2$$
$$c = \sqrt{(a^2 + b^2)}$$

(Care! You can't 'cancel' the squares inside the bracket.)

All similar triangles, i.e. those with the same angle θ, will have sides in the same proportion to one another. The ratios of the sides depend only on the angle θ.

The sine, cosine and tangent of the angle θ are known as **trigonometric ratios**.

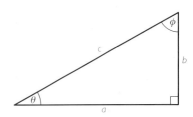

Figure 6 *A right angled triangle*

- Sine of angle θ, $\sin \theta = \dfrac{\text{opposite side}}{\text{hypotenuse}} = \dfrac{b}{c}$

- Cosine of θ, $\cos \theta = \dfrac{\text{adjacent side}}{\text{hypotenuse}} = \dfrac{a}{c}$

- Tangent of θ, $\tan \theta = \dfrac{\text{opposite side}}{\text{adjacent side}} = \dfrac{b}{a}$

We can combine these to give another useful relationship. Since

$$\frac{b}{a} = \frac{b}{c} \div \frac{a}{c} \quad (c \text{ cancels}),$$

we can write

$$\tan \theta = \frac{\sin \theta}{\cos \theta}$$

Also

$$\sin \phi = \frac{a}{c} = \cos \theta \qquad \text{and} \qquad \cos \phi = \frac{b}{c} = \sin \theta$$

i.e. if two angles add up to 90°, then the cosine of one is equal to the sine of the other.

Using Pythagoras's theorem leads to another useful result. Dividing $c^2 = a^2 + b^2$ by c^2:

$$1 = \frac{a^2}{c^2} + \frac{b^2}{c^2} = \left(\frac{a}{c}\right)^2 + \left(\frac{b}{c}\right)^2$$

$$1 = (\cos \theta)^2 + (\sin \theta)^2,$$

which is true for any angle and is usually written as

$$\cos^2 \theta + \sin^2 \theta = 1$$

6.3 Graphs of trigonometric functions

For angles greater than 90°, Figure 7 shows how sin, cos and tan are defined. For some angles, negative numbers are involved. Figure 8 shows how the sin, cos and tan vary with angle θ. Note that we have labelled the axis in degrees and in radians.

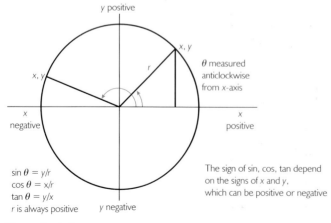

$\sin \theta = y/r$
$\cos \theta = x/r$
$\tan \theta = y/x$
r is always positive

The sign of sin, cos, tan depend on the signs of x and y, which can be positive or negative

Figure 7 *Defining sin, cos and tan for angles greater than 90°*

Maths reference

Degrees and radians
See Maths note 6.1

(a) sin θ

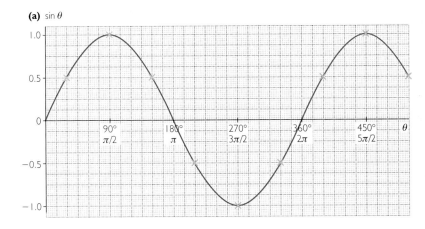

(b) cos θ

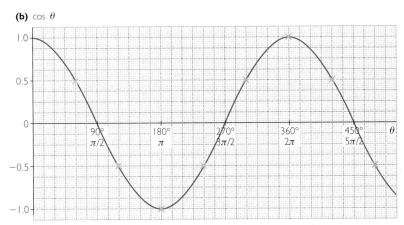

(c) tan θ

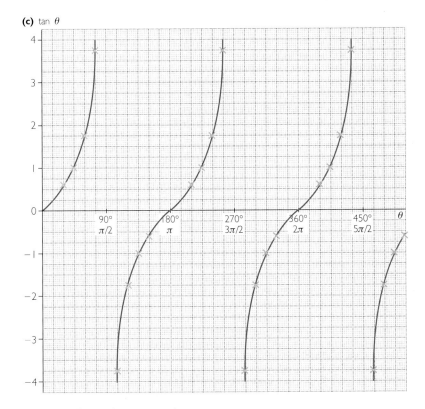

Figure 8 *Graphs of trigonometric functions*

Notice that sin θ and cos θ are always between $+1$ and -1, but tan θ is infinite for some angles (notice the different scale).

Also notice some useful values, e.g. sin $30° =$ cos $60° = 0.5$. Look at the values of sin θ and cos θ when θ is a multiple of $90°$.

6.4 Inverse sin, etc.

The angle whose sin is x is written $\sin^{-1} x$. We can write the relationships from Figure 6 as

$$\theta = \sin^{-1} \frac{b}{c}$$

$$\theta = \cos^{-1} \frac{a}{c}$$

$$\theta = \tan^{-1} \frac{b}{a}$$

$$\phi = \sin^{-1} \frac{a}{c}$$

Beware! The index -1 here does *not* indicate a reciprocal:

$$\sin^{-1} x \text{ is } not \text{ the same as } \frac{1}{\sin x}$$

6.5 Trigonometry on a calculator

You can find the sine, cosine and tangent of an angle on a calculator. For example, to find sin $30°$, type 30 and press sin.

Many scientific calculators can be switched between 'degree' and 'radian' modes. The display will indicate which one you are in.

If you switch your calculator to 'radian' mode, you can find sin, etc., of angles in radians without having to convert to degrees. Check that you know how to do this.

With you calculator in radian mode, type π, $\div$, 2 (you may need to press $=$ as well) and then press sin or cos. You should get sin $(\pi/2) = 1$, cos $(\pi/2) = 0$. If you have your calculator in degree mode by mistake, you will find the sin or cos of $1.57°$ ($3.14° \div 2$).

Try finding the sin, cos and tan of some angles in degrees and in radians. Check that you get the same values as shown in Figure 8.

If you know the sin, cos or tan of an angle and wish to determine the size of the angle, use the 'inv' key.

For example, to find the angle whose sin is 0.5, type 0.5, press inv and then press sin. You should get 30 if you have your calculator in degree mode. If you do this with your calculator in radian mode, you will get 0.5236 ($\approx \pi/6$).

6.6 The small angle approximations

There are some useful approximations involving the trigonometric ratios of small angles. These become evident when we express the sine and tangent of an angle θ in terms of the right angled triangles shown in Figure 9.

From the triangle OAC

$$\sin \theta = \frac{AC}{OC} = \frac{AC}{r}$$

and

$$\cos \theta = \frac{OA}{OC} = \frac{OA}{r}$$

From the triangle OBD

$$\tan \theta = \frac{BD}{OB} = \frac{BD}{r}$$

and

$$\cos \theta = \frac{OB}{OD} = \frac{r}{OD}$$

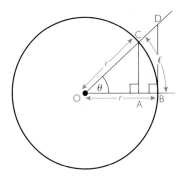

Figure 9   *The sine and tangent of an angle*

Figure 9 shows that $\tan \theta$ is always greater than $\sin \theta$ because BD is greater than AC.

As θ is made smaller, the lines AC and BD become closer together and more equal in length, and the lines OA and OD become closer to r, so *for small angles*:

$$\sin \theta \approx \tan \theta$$

and

$$\cos \theta \approx 1$$

With your calculator in degree mode, try finding the sin, cos and tan of the angles listed in Table 7, and some smaller angles. Notice that the approximations get better as the angles get smaller.

Small angles in radians

Comparison with Figure 5 shows that the size of θ *measured in radians* lies between $\sin \theta$ and $\tan \theta$ (the arc length ℓ is longer than AC and shorter than OD):

$$\sin \theta < \theta < \tan \theta$$

When θ is small,

$$AC \approx \ell \approx BD$$

and so *for small angles measured in radians* we have some additional approximations:

$$\sin \theta \approx \theta$$

and

$$\tan \theta \approx \theta$$

Switch your calculator into radian mode, and again try finding the sin, cos and tan of various angles. Notice that the approximation gets better at small angles.

7 Size and precision

7.1 Precision in measurements; experimental uncertainty

In any measurement, there is a limit to the precision of your result. Sometimes this **experimental uncertainty** arises because you get different answers when you repeat the measurement. For example, if you time an athlete running 100 metres, the same athlete will probably record different times on different occasions. The uncertainty in the measurements is indicated by the 'scatter' in the results.

For example, suppose a certain athlete records times of 12.5 s, 12.1 s, 12.6 s, 12.5 s and 12.3 s. The average time is $t = 12.4$ s. The difference between the average and the biggest or smallest value indicates the uncertainty Δt – in this case, $\Delta t \approx 0.3$ s.

Sometimes the uncertainty arises because it is difficult to judge exactly what to measure. For example, if you are measuring the distance from a lens to a clear image it produces on a screen, it might be hard to judge exactly where to put the screen to get the sharpest image. If you measure a distance $v = 24.5$ cm, but are unsure of the sharpest position by 0.5 cm in each direction, then the uncertainty would be $\Delta v \approx 0.5$ cm.

Even if there is no problem deciding exactly what to measure, and you get the same answer each time you repeat the measurement, there is still an uncertainty because the measurement is limited by the instrument you are using. For example, if you use a digital ammeter to measure a current I, and you get 0.357 A each time, you can only be sure that the current is closer to 0.357 A than it is to either 0.356 A or 0.358 A – it could lie anywhere between 0.3565 A and 0.3575 A. So the uncertainty is $\Delta I \approx 0.0005$ A.

Some books refer to **experimental error** rather than uncertainty. Don't be misled into thinking that they mean a mistake. However carefully and correctly you carry out a measurement, there will always be an uncertainty.

Experimental uncertainties apply to *all* measured quantities – including those you look up in a data book, though these values have usually been measured with much greater precision than you can achieve in a school or college laboratory.

7.2 Calculations with uncertainties; significant figures

If you carry out a calculation using a measured value, there will always be an uncertainty in your answer. You can use the uncertainties in the measurements to work out the uncertainty in the calculated value.

For example, suppose you measure a current of $I = 0.24$ A $\pm$ 0.01 A and a corresponding pd of $V = 0.67$ V $\pm$ 0.02 V.

On a calculator, the resistance found using the 'best' values is

$$R_{best} = \frac{V}{I} = \frac{0.67\,V}{0.24\,A} = 2.791\,6667\,\Omega$$

But, using the largest possible V (0.39 V) and the smallest possible I (0.23 A), the calculated resistance could be as large as

$$R_{max} = \frac{0.69\,V}{0.23\,A} = 3\,\Omega$$

Or, using the smallest V and the largest I, it could be as small as

$$R_{min} = \frac{0.65\,V}{0.25\,A} = 2.6\,\Omega$$

There are several things to notice! First, there are quite large differences between the three values. Second, the first value extends to the full length of the calculator display, whereas the others do not.

The large differences show that you cannot *possibly* say that the resistance is precisely 2.791 6667 Ω. This value is close to 2.8 Ω, and the other two differ by 0.2 Ω in either direction, i.e. the uncertainty in R is $\Delta R \approx 0.2\,\Omega$. The resistance can therefore be written as

$$R = 2.8\,\Omega \pm 0.2\,\Omega.$$

The second figure in this answer (the 8 after the decimal point) is uncertain, and so any further figures are meaningless.

Another way of putting this is to say that the answer has (only) two **significant figures** – the one before the decimal point and the first one after it. The rest of the figures in the original 'best' answer are meaningless. They are *not* significant.

7.3 *A useful rule of thumb*

In a calculation, the answer cannot be known any more precisely than the values used to calculate it. As a useful rule of thumb, the final answer has no more **significant figures** than the *least* precise value used in the calculation. (The example in Maths note 7.2 illustrates this.)

Suppose you did a calculation to find the frequency f of light whose wavelength is 468 nm (4.68×10^{-7} m). The speed of light is known very precisely: $2.997\,925 \times 10^{8}$ m s^{-1}.

Using speed $\div$ wavelength

$$f = \frac{2.997\,925 \times 10^{8}\,m\,s^{-1}}{4.68 \times 10^{-7}\,m}$$

$$= 6.4058 \times 10^{14}\,Hz$$

However, we only knew the wavelength to three significant figures, so we cannot quote the frequency this precisely. We must stick to the three significant figures and write

$$f = 6.41 \times 10^{14}\,Hz$$

There was in fact no point in using the very precise value for the speed of light. Values listed in data books are often rounded to, say, three significant figures if they are likely to be used only in calculations requiring this precision or less.

7.4 Significant figures and orders of magnitude

The speed of light to seven significant figures is $2.997\,925 \times 10^8$ m s^{-1}; the significant figures are 2997925.

Zeros in front of a number are not significant. The speed of light could be written (rather oddly) as $002.997\,925 \times 10^8$ m s^{-1} or $0.000\,299\,7925 \times 10^{12}$ m s^{-1} without making any difference to its value.

However, zeros at the end of a number are (or at least can be!) significant. If you wrote the speed of light as 299 792 500 m s^{-1}, that would imply that you knew that the last two figures were definitely zeros and not some other numbers. If they are, in fact, not known, it is better to use standard form so that the meaningless zeros can be dropped.

To five significant figures, the speed of light would be 2.9979×10^8 m s^{-1}. To three significant figures, it would be 3.00×10^8 m s^{-1}. Here the zeros *are* significant and should be written down, because 2.997... rounds to 3.00.

To one significant figure the speed of light would be 3×10^8 m s^{-1}.

If a value is rounded to just the nearest power of 10, then we say we are giving just the **order of magnitude**. Two values are said to have the same order of magnitude if one is between 1 and 10 times the other. For example, the wavelengths of red and blue light (about 400 nm and 700 nm) are within the same order of magnitude. But the wavelengths of infrared radiation range from about 10^{-6} m to about 10^{-3} m – they cover three orders of magnitude.

7.5 Error bars and error boxes

When plotting a graph of experimental data, you should take account of the uncertainties. Rather than representing each measurement by a point, you should draw an **error bar** to represent the range of possible values. Then use the vertical and horizontal error bars to draw an **error box** around each plotted point. Once you have plotted the error boxes, you can then draw a trend line on your graph. It might be possible to draw a straight line passing through all the boxes, even if you could not draw one through all the points.

8 Logarithms

8.1 Logs and powers of 10

If a number can be written as *just* a 'power of 10', then the power is the **logarithm** of that number; strictly speaking, it is the **logarithm** to base 10, or **common logarithm**, of the number, but it is often simply called the **log**.

Table 8 lists some examples using whole-number powers.

Number x	$\log_{10}(x)$
$100\,000 = 10^5$	5
$10\,000 = 10^4$	4
$1000 = 10^3$	3
$100 = 10^2$	2
$10 = 10^1$	1
$1 = 10^0$	0
$0.1 = 10^{-1}$	-1
$0.001 = 10^{-2}$	-2

Table 8   *Some numbers and their common logarithms*

In fact *any positive number* can be expressed as a power of 10, using powers that are not whole numbers. Most whole numbers have logs that are not themselves whole numbers or simple fractions. For example:

$$10^{0.6021} = 4.000$$

so

$$\log_{10}(4.000) = 0.6021$$

All numbers between 1 and 10 have logs that lie between 0 and 1. For example:

$$10^{0.333} = 2.153$$

so

$$\log_{10}(2.513) = 0.333$$

Similarly, all numbers between 10 and 100 have logs that lie between 1 and 2; all numbers between 100 and 1000 have logs between 2 and 3, and so on.

All numbers less than 1 have negative logs. For example:

$$\log_{10}(0.5) = -0.3010$$
$$\log_{10}(0.1) = -1.000$$

Maths reference

Powers that are not whole numbers

See Maths note 1.5

8.2 *Logs on a calculator*

To find the common log of a number using a calculator, type in the number and then press the key marked log or lg.

This process can be reversed to find the **antilog** of a number. Type in the log whose number you want to find, then press the keys marked INV and log (or lg). By doing this, you can show that 4.000 is the antilog of 0.6021, and 2.513 is the antilog of 0.333.

Notice that using the INV and log keys to find the antilog of a number x gives exactly the same result as using the y^x key to find 10^x.

Index

Abbé refractometer 258
acceleration 6
    due to gravity 6, 14
    force and 13–16
    from gradient of velocity–time graph 7–8, 10
    non-uniform 9–10, 12
    uniform 6, 11–12
acceleration zone 33–4
accommodation of the eye 300–2
acoustic impedance 322
acoustic lenses 320, 321–2
adding fractions 350–1
adding reciprocals 349
air columns (pipes) 135–7, 145–7
algebra 347–51
alloys 202
alpha (α) radiation 211–12
amorphous polymers 293
amplitude 123
anaerobic power 36–7
analogue storage-and-retrieval systems 150
angular measurements 357–61
antilogs 365
antinodes 134
antiphase 124–5
anti-reflection coating 310–11
Archimedes' principle 237–8
arithmetic 347–51
artificial skin 290–1
Asch, Henry van 40
astigmatism 303, 308
atomic line spectra 165–6
atomic vibrations 99
Austin, Nick 186

background count 213
background radiation 212–13
ball-and-socket joints 277, 278
band theory 209–11
Bardeen, John 100
batteries
    and temperature 91, 92–4
    see also solar cells
beta (β) radiation 211–12
binary code 151
biomechanics 4
blinds 102
    sun-catching venetian blinds
        108–9
blood flow 327, 328
bones 203, 276–90
    bone and joint replacement
        277–80, 285–6
    materials for substitutes 279–90
boundaries
    behaviour of light 155–7, 162–3,
        257–9

behaviour of ultrasound 321–3
Boyle, Robert 208
brackets 348
Brattain, Walter 100
breaking stress 281–2
Brinell hardness number (BHN) 250–1
brittleness 253, 255, 280
Bubka, Sergei 43
bungee jumping 15, 16, 39–43
buoyancy force 237–8, 239
bus (circuit) 75–6

calculators
    logs 365
    manipulating powers 342
    trigonometry 360
calibration 239
Cassini-Huygens mission 92, 93
cataracts 297–8
chain molecules 287, 293–5
charge 73
    conservation 73, 110
charge-coupled device (CCD) imager 214
Chernobyl accident 222
Chladni figures 255
chocolate 232–4
    flowing 234–5
circulating liquids, cooling with 102–7
closed tubes 135–7, 145–7
coatings
    anti-reflection 310–11
    on CDs 155–7
coefficient of viscosity 237
coherent waves 132, 152
    laser light 154, 166–7
coloured light 163–4
combining vectors
    displacement 19–20
    force 20–2
common factors 348
communications satellites 67
compact disc (CD) player 148–70
compact discs (CDs)
    coating 155–7
    metallic layer 150–1
    storage of information 148–51
comparisons 339
complex sounds 142–7
compliance 25
components of vectors *see* resolving
        vectors into perpendicular
        components
compression 281–3
    testing 252–3
compressions and rarefactions 127, 128
compressive strain 283
compressive stress 281

computer-aided tomography (CAT) scans 198, 200
computer models 49–50
conduction 101
conduction band 209–10
conductivity 188
conductors 190–1
conservation 109–11
    charge 73, 110
    energy 30, 41, 110
    mass 110
consistometer 236
constant of proportionality 353
constructive superposition 133, 153–4
contact lenses 298–9
continuous casting process 107
convection 101
converging (convex) lenses 158–62, 303, 307
    eye 299–300
    ray diagrams 160–1, 304–5
cooling 101–7
    by circulating liquids 102–7
coplanar forces 22
Coppergate Helmet 199–201
coral 279–80
corrosion products 199, 202
cosines 357–61
cosmic radiation 212
coupling gel, ultrasound 317, 323
critical angle 162–3, 258–9
critical control points (CCPs) 264
crossed Polaroids 259, 261
crystals 205, 291
current 73
current-voltage graphs 78–9
Curtis, Jeremy 66
cushioning 27
cycles 123
    see also oscillations

dating artefacts 207–22
Davisson, Clinton 292
de Broglie, Louis 291–2
de Broglie wavelength 292
decimals 347
defect levels 210–11
degrees 357
delta symbol (Δ) 339–40
dendrochronology 207
density 322–3
derived units 344–5
Dermagraft 291
design specifications 74–6
designing electrical systems 85–6, 87
destructive superposition 133, 153–4
dextrorotatory materials 261
diaphragm meter 244–5
diffraction
    electron 291, 292–3
    grating 164
    patterns 291
    X-ray 201–6, 291
digital information storage-and-retrieval 150–1
dimensions 346
direct proportionality 353–4
    linear relationships 354
    testing 356
direction 5–6

displacement 5
    area under a velocity–time graph 10–13
    combining displacement vectors 19–20
    projectile motion 47–50
    speed skiing 33–4
displacement–distance graphs 129, 131–2
displacement–time graphs 7, 9–10
    oscillations 123–4
    travelling waves 130, 132
distance 5
    see also displacement; displacement–distance graphs; pressure–distance graphs
diverging lenses 159, 303–7
dividing reciprocals 349–50
Doppler effect 325–8
    in medicine 327–8
Dreschler, Heiki 45
drop tests 26
ductility 253, 280
durability 280

echoes, ultrasound 319–25
eclipses, satellites and 70–1
Edwards, Jonathan 4
efficiency 31
    and power in an electric circuit 85
Einstein, Albert 216
elastic energy 29, 41–3, 289–90
elastic limit 253, 284–5
elasticity 25, 253, 280
electric circuits 73–4, 77–81
    power 82–6
    series and parallel 73, 74, 79–80, 188
    see also resistance; solar cells; spacecraft power systems
electric fields 245, 260
electromagnetic spectrum 197
electromagnetic waves 260–1
electronic materials 99–100
electrons
    change in resistance with temperature 99
    diffraction 291, 292–3
    energy levels in atoms 165
        thermoluminescence 208–11
    free and conduction 191
    operation of a solar cell 72
    photoelectric effect 215, 216–20
    thermionic emission 292
    wave nature 291–3
electronvolt 219
electo-rheological effect 245
electroscope 215
elimination, algebra and 350
emf 74
    internal resistance 81
    see also potential difference; voltage
empirical models 96
energy 29–30
    conservation 30, 41, 110
    elastic 29, 41–3, 289–90
    electric circuits 74, 192
    kinetic see kinetic energy
    photoelectric effect 217–18
    potential 29, 32–3
    radiant energy flux 87–90
energy density 290
energy levels 165
    thermoluminescence 208–11

'energy return' shoes 27–33
    calculating energy return 31–2
energy transfer 25–6
    and control on a spacecraft 87–109
    and temperature change 104–7
    thermal energy transfer processes 101
    work 30–1
enrobing process 234–5
equations 339
    rearranging 351–2
    simultaneous 352–3
    solving 351–3
equilibrium 18–19, 21–2
equilibrium position 123
equipotential 195
error bars 78–9, 364
error boxes 78–9, 364
experimental uncertainty 78–9, 362–3, 364
extension
    stress and strain 281–3
    and tension in a rope 25–6
    see also force–extension graphs
eye 297–316
    contact lenses 298–9
    focusing and sight 299–303
    laser treatment 314–15
    lens implants 297–8
    prescribing lenses 302, 307–9
    structure 297

falling ball viscometer 236–9
Fanshawe, Andy 18
far point 301
fast twitch (FT) muscle fibres 36–7
fibreglass poles 43
fibrils 294–5
flow 234–47
    controlling 245
    laminar/streamlined and turbulence 240–1
    measuring flow rates 241–5
flowmeters 241–5
fluoroscopy 198
focal length 158, 304, 307
    measuring 309
focal point 158, 304
food
    physics in the food industry 232–3
    quality and safety 263–4
forbidden gap 210
force–extension graphs 41–2, 284–5
    elastic energy as area under 42, 289
    testing in the food industry 252–4
forced convection 101
forces
    and acceleration 13–16
    biomechanics 4
    on a bungee jumper 15, 16, 41
    combining force vectors 20–2
    on a falling ball 237–9
    pairs of 15–16
    resolving force vectors 23–5
    tension in a rope 25–6
forgeries, detecting 222
fractional powers 342–3
fractions 347
    adding and subtracting 350–1
free fall 6, 14

frequency
    Doppler effect 326–7, 328
    sound 123, 319
        resonant frequencies 136–7, 140–2, 144–7
    threshold frequency in photoelectric
        effect 216, 217–18, 218–19
fundamental frequency
    pipes 136–7
    stringed instruments 140–2

gamma (γ) radiation 211–12
geostationary satellites 70–1
Germer, Lester 292
glass 309–10
gradient
    linear graphs 354
    tangents and 9–10
graphite 292
graphs 343–4
    direct proportionality 353, 354, 356
    inverse proportionality 355, 356
    motion 7–13
    relationships and 353–6
    see also under individual types
gravitational field
    acceleration due to gravity 6, 14
    weight and 14–15
gravitational potential energy 29, 32–3
gray 213

Hackett, A.J. 40
HAPEX 286
hardness 250–1, 280
harmonic motion 123–6
harmonics 144–7
Hazard and Critical Control Points (HACCP) system 264
heart
    replacement valves 317
    ultrasound imaging of 316–18, 323–5
heat pipes 102–3
heating
    and cooling 101–7
    sources of for spacecraft 92
    thermal energy transfer processes 101
hinge joints 277, 278
hip replacements 285–6
Hooke's law 26, 42, 282–3
    and the Young modulus 284–6
hot thermistor flowmeter 245
hot wire flowmeter 245
hydrogen 165
hypermetropia/hyperopia (long sight) 302, 307

images
    locating position of 159–62, 304–6
    real 159
    ultrasound imaging of heart 316–18, 323–5
        moving images 324–5
    virtual 159, 305
impedance matching 84, 85
    see also internal resistance
index notation 340–3
    combining powers 341
    manipulation on a calculator 342
    powers of 10 340, 342, 364–5
    powers that are not whole numbers 342–3
    and units 344
information storage-and-retrieval systems 150–1

infrared (IR) radiation 312
Instron Universal Testing Machine 254
insulators 190–1
intensity of solar radiation 87–90
interatomic spacing 204–5
interference 153–4
    X-ray diffraction 204–5
International Space Station (ISS) 67–8, 71
internal resistance 81
    measuring power in a circuit 84, 85
inverse dynamics 4, 13–14
inverse proportionality 355, 356
inverse sine/cosine/tangent 360
ionising radiation 211–12, 222

jelly laser 167
joints 276, 277, 278
    replacement 277–80, 285–6
jumping 45–8

kinetic energy 29, 32–3
    photoelectric effect 217–18

lactic acid 37
laevorotatory materials 261
lamella formation 294–5
laminar flow 240–1
lasers
    Doppler imaging 327
    light from 153–4, 166–8
    treatment for eyes 314–15
    types of 168
lattice vibrations 99
launch angle 48–9
lens formula 159–60, 306–7
lenses
    acoustic 320, 321–2
    contact lenses 298–9
    converging see converging (convex) lenses
    diverging 159, 303–7
    human eye 299–302
        lens implants 297–8
    materials for 309–11
    power of a lens 158, 307–9
    prescribing 307–9
    ray diagrams 160–2, 304–5
    'real is positive' sign convention 159, 306
    tinted 312–13
    underwater 313
Lewis, Carl 45
light
    coloured 163–4
    detection
        faint light 214–16, 220
        with a photodiode 168
    focused beam 157–62
    laser light 153–4, 166–8
    optical properties of materials 310–11
    optical scanning 151–4
    particle (photon) model 164–6, 216–18
    photoelectric effect 215, 216–20
    polarimetry 259–62
    refraction see refraction
    refractometry 257–9
    splitting a beam 162–3
    thermoluminescence see thermoluminescence
    wave model 164
    wave-particle duality 166

    see also lenses
light-gate flowmeter 242–3
limit of proportionality 26, 284
line spectra 165–6
line spread test 236
linear relationships 354
liquid circulation, cooling by 102–7
logarithmic scale 190
logarithms (logs) 364–5
    antilogs 365
    on a calculator 365
    and powers of 10 364–5
long jump 45
long-playing records (LPs) 149
long sight (hypermetropia/hyperopia) 302, 307
longitudinal waves 126–7, 260–1
    graphs 131–2, 319
    sound 128

magnetic fields 260
magnification 161
malleability 253
mass, conservation of 110
mass flow rate 241
materials
    analysis with X-ray diffraction 201–6
    for lenses 309–11
    mechanical properties 280–90
    polymers 290–1, 293–5
    to replace bone 279–90
    small-scale structure 204–5, 291–5
    testing 248–56
    ultrasound speed in different materials 321–3
maximum power transfer in a circuit 81–6
mechanical properties 280–90
    materials for lenses 309–10
    materials testing 248–56
metallic layer of a CD 150–1
metals 199, 202
Mir space station 87, 88
modelling 95–7
    light 164–6
    model making and model fitting 96–7
    resistance 95, 97–9
Mohs scale of hardness 250
molecular chains 287, 293–5
monochromatic light 154, 163, 166–8
motion 4–17
    describing 4–7
    graphs 7–13
    Newton's laws 13–14, 15–16
    projectiles 45, 46–50
    see also acceleration; displacement; speed; velocity
moving images, ultrasound 324–5
Multimedia Motion 9
multiplying reciprocals 349–50
multi-probe resistance surveying 193
muscle fibre 36–7
musical notes 135–42, 145–7
    stringed instruments 138–42, 145–7
    wind instruments 135–7, 145–7
myopia (short sight) 302, 307

NASA Spacelink page 69, 70
near point 301
negative powers 341, 342

negative lenses *see* diverging lenses
Newton's laws of motion
  first law 13–14
  second law 13–14
  third law 15–16
nodes 134
non-uniform acceleration 9–10, 12
normal 155
Norman invasion, site of 186
nuts 232–3

Ohm's law 77–9
open circuit 82
open tubes 135–7, 145–7
optical properties 310–11
optical scanning 150, 151–4
optically active materials 261
orders of magnitude 364
oscillations 123–6
  see also sound
overtones 144–7
Owens, Jesse 45

pacemaker 317
packaging 264–5
pairs of forces 15–16
parabolic trajectory 47
parallel circuits 73, 74, 80, 188
particle model of light 164–6, 216–18
path difference 153–4
penetration, radiation 212
percentages 347
periodic oscillations 123–6
period 123, 142–4
phase 124–6
  phase change on reflection 138
photodiode 168
photoelectric effect 215, 216–20
photomultiplier 214–16, 220
photons
  particle model of light 164–6, 216–18
  photoelectric effect 215, 216–18
  wave–particle duality 166
photorefractive keratectomy (PRK) 314–15
photosensitive materials 215, 217, 218
photovoltaic cells *see* solar cells
physical quantities 343–4
piezoelectric crystals 320, 324
pigments 202
pipes (air columns) 135–7, 145–7
pitch *see* frequency
Planck's constant 164
plastic behaviour 253, 280
plastic lenses 309–10
polarimetry 259–62
polarisation 259–61
  rotating the plane of 261–2
pole vaulting 43–4
polymers 286–7, 290–1, 295
  small-scale structure 293–5
positive lenses *see* converging (convex) lenses
potential 194–5
potential difference 74, 191–5
  potential and 194–5
  stopping potential 218–19
  terminal potential difference 77, 81, 81–2

see also emf; voltage
potential divider 192
potential energy 29, 32–3
powder photos 205
power 35–8
  in electric circuits 81–6
  measuring 36–7
  spacecraft power demands 88–9
power of a lens 158, 307–9
power supply for a spacecraft *see* spacecraft power systems
powers of 10 340, 342, 364–5
  see also index notation
precision 362–4
prefixes, SI 345–6
presbyopia 301
pressure–distance graphs 131–2
pressure–time graphs 132
principal focus 158, 304
prisms 163, 164
projectile motion 45, 46–50
  range of a projectile 48, 49–50
proportionality
  constant of 353
  direct 353–4, 356
  inverse 355, 356
  limit of 26, 284
Pulfrich refractometer 258
pulse-echo technique 323–5
pumping iron 35–8

quadrature 124–5
quality, food 263–4
quantities, physical 343–4

radians 357
  small angles in 361
radiation 101
  solar radiation energy flux 87–90
radiation dose 213–14, 222
radiators, space 105–7
radioactivity 211–14
  types and sources of radiation 211–13
radiocarbon dating 207
radiography *see* X-rays
radioisotope thermoelectric generators (RTGs) 69
range of a projectile 48, 49–50
rarefactions and compressions 127, 128
ray diagrams 160–2, 304–6
real images 159
'real is positive' sign convention 159, 306
rearranging equations 351–2
reciprocals 348–50
Recoil trainer 28
Redwood viscometer 236
reflection
  anti-reflection coating 310–11
  standing waves on a string 138
  superposition of waves reflected from a CD 152–4
  total internal reflection 162–3
  ultrasound echoes 319–25
refraction 155–7, 257–9, 313
  light entering the eye 300
  and reflection at a boundary 162–3
  Snell's law 155–6
refractive index 156, 157, 257–9, 311, 313
refractometry 257–9

regenerative fuel cells 69
relationships 353–6
  direct proportion 353–4, 356
  inverse proportion 355, 356
  linear 354
  testing 356
replacement heart valves 317
replacement joints 277–80, 285–6
resistance 77–81, 184–96
  internal 81, 84, 85
  Ohm's law 77–9
  resistors in series and parallel 79–80, 188
  and temperature 94–9
resistive surveying 184–6
  multi-probe 193
resistive tomography 193–4
resistivity 186–91
resolving vectors into perpendicular components
  forces 23–5
  projectile motion 45–53
  speed skiing 33–4
resonant frequencies
  fundamental 136–7, 140–2
  harmonics and overtones 144–7
resultant vector 19–20
  zero resultant 20
rock climbing 18–27
Rockwell hardness test 251
ropes 25–6
rubber 293
running 4–17

safety, food 263–4
sampling 148
satellites 66–71
  studying with 67–8
scalars 5
scale drawings 19–22
scientific modelling see modelling
scientific notation 340–1
semiconductor lasers 168
semiconductors 99–100, 190–1
sensory profile 248–9
series circuits 73, 74, 79–80, 188
short circuit 82
short sight (myopia) 302, 307
SI units 343–6
significant figures 362–4
signs 339–40
  'real is positive' sign convention 159, 306
simultaneous equations 352-3
sines 357–61
sinusoidal waveforms 123–6
size 362–4
skeleton 277
  see also bones; joints
slow twitch (ST) muscle fibres 36
ski jumping 46–8
skiing, speed 33–4
small angle approximations 360–1
small-scale structure 204–5, 291–5
small time intervals 8–10
smoothness 280
Snell's law of refraction 155–6
solar cells 66–7, 69, 70–1, 72–6

alignment with the Sun 87–90
  impedance 84
  joining 76
  size of solar array 88–90
  and temperature 91, 92–4
  see also spacecraft power systems
solar radiation flux 87–90
sonometer 140–1
sound 122–48, 319
  complex sounds 142–7
  musical notes 135–42
  oscillations 123–6
  synthetic sounds 122, 147–8
  waves 128, 319
  see also ultrasound
sound box 139–40
sound spectrum 143–4
space blanket 67
space engineering 66–7
space radiators 105–7
Space Shuttle 102–3
spacecraft power systems 71–87
  design specifications 74–6
  designing 85–6, 87
  elements of 68–71
  maximising power 81–6
  size of solar array 88–90
  see also solar cells
spacesuits 103, 104
spare part surgery 274, 276
  bone and joint replacement 277–80, 285–6
  for the heart 317
  lens implants 297–8
specific heat capacity 104–5
spectra, line 165–6
spectrum analyser
  light 164
  sound 143–4
speech 142–4
speed 5
  of sound in different materials 320–3
  waves 130
    standing wave on a string 140–1
  see also velocity
speed skiing 33–4
spider diagram 249
sprinting 15
standard form 340–1
standards (specifications) 74–6
standing waves 134–5
  musical notes 135–42, 144–7
star diagram 249
stiffness 25–6, 252–3, 280, 285–6
Stokes' law 237
stopping potential 218–19
strain 281–3
  see also stress–strain graphs
streamlined flow 240–1
strength 25, 253, 281
stress 281–3
stress–strain graphs 284–5, 288
  energy density from area under 289–90
stringed instruments 138–42, 145–7
strobe lighting 129
subtracting fractions 350–1
subtracting reciprocals 349
sugar concentration 257–63
sun-catching venetian blinds 108–9

superposition
    in a CD player 153–4
    optical scanning 152–4
    and standing waves 132–5
symbols 339–40
synovial joints 277, 278
synthetic sounds 122, 147–8

tables 343–4
tangents
    of angles 357–61
    of curves and gradients 9–10
tasters 248–9
temperature 203
    changes in spacecraft 91–100
    control 101–4
    energy and temperature change 104–7
    resistance and 94–9
        temperature coefficient of resistance 97
tensile strain 283
tensile stress 281
tensile testing 252–4
tension, and extension 25–6
terminal potential difference 77, 81–2
    internal resistance 81
terminal velocity 238
testing, materials 248–56
thermal energy transfer see heating
thermal flowmeter 245
thermal treatments 202
thermionic emission 292
thermistors 97
thermoluminescence (TL) 207–11
    dating 213–14
        accuracy 221–2
    measuring the light 214–20
    other uses 222
thixotropy 241
Thomson, George 292
three-point bend test 254
threshold frequency 216, 217–18
    measuring 218–19
throwing 45, 48–50
time
    period (of a cycle) 123, 142–4
    small time intervals 8–10
tomography 193, 200
    computer-aided (CAT) scans 198, 200
    resistive 193–4
total internal reflection (TIR) 162–3
toughness 253, 280
trajectory, parabolic 47
transistor 99–100
transmittance curves 312–13
transverse waves 126–7
    graphs 128–30
    polarisation of electromagnetic waves 260–1
travelling waves 126–32
triangle of forces 21
trigonometry 357–61
    calculators and 360
    graphs of trigonometric functions 358–60
    inverse functions 360
    small angle approximations 360–1
    trigonometric ratios 357–8
turbulence 240–1
Tyrolean traverse 18, 23–4

UHMWPE (ultra-high-molecular-
        weight polyethylene) 286, 287, 289
ultimate compressive/tensile stress 281–2
ultrasound 316–28
    Doppler effect 325–8
    echoes 319–25
    imaging of the heart 316–18, 323–5
    medical investigations using 323–5
    transducers 320, 324
ultraviolet (UV) radiation 312
uncertainty, experimental 78–9, 362–3, 364
uniform acceleration 6, 11–12
units 343–6
    derived 344–5
    dimensions 346
    manipulating 344
    SI prefixes 345–6
UoSAT satellites 67
upthrust 237–8, 239

valence band 210
vector polygon 20
vectors 5
    combining 19–22
    resolving into perpendicular components
        23–5, 33–4, 45–53
velocity 5
    from gradient of displacement–time graph 7, 9-10
    independence of vertical and
        horizontal components 45–53
    terminal 238
    see also speed
velocity–time graphs 7–8
    acceleration from gradient 7–8, 10
    displacement from area under 11–13
venetian blinds, sun-catching 108–9
virtual images 159, 305
viscometers 235, 236, 239
viscosity 235–40
viscous drag force 237, 238, 239
viscous drag viscometer 239
voltage 74
    space equipment power supply
        design specifications 74–6
    see also emf; potential difference
voltage–current graphs 78–9
volume flow rate 241
Von Laue's experiment 204–5

wafers, testing 254–5
water cooling systems 102–7
water waves 127
wave equation 130, 320
wave model of light 164
wave–particle duality 166
waveforms 123–6
wavelength 129
    de Broglie 292
    and diffraction 204–5
    Doppler effect 327
    and images by reflection 321
    refraction and 157
    ultrasound 319, 320–1
waves 170–1
    coherent 132, 152, 154, 166–7
    diffraction see diffraction

Doppler effect 325–8
electromagnetic 260–1
electron 291–3
interference 153–4, 204–5
longitudinal *see* longitudinal waves
polarised 260–1
sound 128, 319
standing 134–42, 144–7
superposition 132–5, 152–4
transverse *see* transverse waves
travelling 126–32
ultrasound 319–25
water 127

weight 14–15
weight training 35–8
Wenner, Frank 193
wind instruments 135–7, 145–7
work 30–2
work function 217–18

X-rays 197–206, 318
   diffraction 201–6, 291

yield point (elastic limit) 253, 284–5
Young modulus 284–6, 288, 293